Industrial Applications
of Rare Earth Elements

Industrial Applications of Rare Earth Elements

Karl A. Gschneidner, Jr., EDITOR,
Iowa State University

Based on a symposium

sponsored by the Division of

Industrial and Engineering Chemistry

at the Second Chemical Congress

of the North American Continent

(180th ACS National Meeting),

Las Vegas, Nevada,

August 25–26, 1980.

ACS SYMPOSIUM SERIES 164

AMERICAN CHEMICAL SOCIETY
WASHINGTON, D. C.   1981

Library of Congress CIP Data

Industrial applications of rare earth elements.
  (ACS symposium series 164; ISSN 0097-6156)

  Includes bibliographies and index.

  1. Rare earth metals—Congresses.
  I. Gschneidner, Karl A. II. American Chemical Society. Division of Industrial and Engineering Chemistry. III. Chemical Congress of the North American
Continent (2nd: 1981: Las Vegas, Nevada). IV Series.

TA480.R3I5   621.1'89291   81–10875
ISBN 0–8412–0641–4   AACR2
                    ACSMC8 164 1-297 1981

ACS Symposium Series

M. Joan Comstock, *Series Editor*

FOREWORD

The ACS SYMPOSIUM SERIES was founded in 1974 to provide a medium for publishing symposia quickly in book form. The format of the Series parallels that of the continuing ADVANCES IN CHEMISTRY SERIES except that in order to save time the papers are not typeset but are reproduced as they are submitted by the authors in camera-ready form. Papers are reviewed under the supervision of the Editors with the assistance of the Series Advisory Board and are selected to maintain the integrity of the symposia; however, verbatim reproductions of previously published papers are not accepted. Both reviews and reports of research are acceptable since symposia may embrace both types of presentation.

CONTENTS

PREFACE

For the last twenty years conferences concerning rare earth materials have been held in the U.S.A. every 18 to 24 months. In general these conferences have dealt with the science of these materials, and only one or two sessions ($\sim 10\%$ of the papers) were concerned with industrial and commercial aspects. This is also true for rare earth conferences held in other countries with one exception—the 1972 NATO Conference on Analysis and Applications of Rare Earth Materials, in which about half of the papers dealt with their uses. The rapid and continued growth of rare earth markets in the last two decades—10 to 15% per year—suggested that an exclusive conference would be of considerable interest not only to the worldwide rare earth community but also to many scientists, engineers, and technical business managers in other industries and technologies that may have an interest in, or possible future applications involving the rare earths. The symposium that formed the basis of this volume was devoted exclusively to industrial applications and commercial aspects of the rare earths.

The industrial applications of the rare earths can be divided into two categories—uses that involve the mixed rare earths in proportion to their occurrence in their ores or in concentrates (not exceeding 90% of any one rare earth element), and uses that involve the separated individual rare earth elements ($> 90\%$ pure). Of the total volume of rare earths consumed about 95% is in the form of mixed rare earths or concentrates, but in monetary terms the contribution by both categories is about equal.

The mixed rare earths are used as additives to improve the properties of steel and ductile iron by removing the tramp elements and modifying the morphology of the metal product. The other major use is the addition of rare earths to zeolite cracking catalysts to improve the efficiency of gasoline refining processes. Other miscellaneous uses of the mixed elements are: lighter flints, alloy additives to nonferrous metals, carbon arc-cores for lighting, and glass polishing materials. Chemical concentrates, which contain up to approximately 90% of one rare earth element, are primarily used in the glass and ceramic markets, for example, CeO_2 as polishing compounds and for decolorizing glass, La_2O_3 in glasses to increase the index of refraction (e.g., camera lenses), CeO_2, Nd_2O_3, and Pr_6O_{11} for coloring glasses and ceramic tiles, and in temperature compensated capacitors.

The individual separated rare earth elements (chemical purities ranging from 95% to 99.999%) are used in advanced technological applications. These so-called exciting and glamorous uses include: phosphors for cathode ray tubes, color television, fluorescent lighting, and x-ray intensifying screens; magnetic bubble devices for computer data storage; microwave devices; the strongest known permanent magnets; hydrogen storage materials; oxygen and carbon sensors; electrooptical devices and lasers; control rods and burnable poisons for nuclear reactors; glass additives as decolorizing agents and also to impart color; simulated diamonds; and as alloying agents to improve the properties of high temperature oxidation/corrosion resistant alloys.

The book is divided into three sections based on the nature of the rare earth application: metallurgical uses of the mixed rare earths; mixed rare earths in nonmetals; and individual rare earth element uses. The first section contains three chapters including an overview of the rare earth industry as developed from a historical perspective. The second section contains four chapters that deal with the use in the glass, glass polishing, and catalyst industries. The last section contains nine chapters covering a wide range of topics, including an overview of the industrial methods of separating the rare earth elements, three chapters on phosphors, and five chapters on a variety of applications.

The authors of the chapters were asked to include the following information whenever possible: the description of the use or application; the scientific basis for the use; market size—current and future; competitive advantage of the rare earths; and competition from other markets. Naturally some chapters for various reasons did not discuss all of these points.

The editor would like to acknowledge several friends in the rare earth industry for suggesting topics and potential authors. These are: G. A. Barlow (Union Molycorp), J. G. Cannon (Union Molycorp), I. S. Hirschhorn (Ronson Metals Corporation), W. A. Otis (Ronson Metals Corporation), and O. A. Wunderlich (Davison Specialty Chemical Company, W. R. Grace and Company). The efforts of the four Session Chairmen, I. S. Hirschhorn (Ronson Metals Corporation), J. R. Long (Aldrich Chemical Company, Incorporated), M. Tecotzky (United States Radium Corporation), and J. W. Cunningham (Research Chemicals, NUCOR Corporation), who kept the symposium running smoothly and on schedule were appreciated by the speakers and attendees. Particular thanks go to J. E. McEvoy (Councilor), W. N. Smith (Program Chairman), and R. A. Stowe (Program Secretary) of the Division of Industrial and Engineering Chemistry of the American Chemical Society who helped the editor in organizing this symposium. The editor appreciates the assistance of the sixteen unnamed persons who refereed the papers published in this volume.

An acknowledgment is also due to the ACS Books Department for their guidance in getting this volume ready for publication—with special thanks to S. B. Roethel (Acquisitions Editor) and her secretary, A. Drexler. Finally the kind and wonderful assistance of the editor's staff and colleagues (C. J. Catus and B. L. Evans [Rare-Earth Information Center], and O. D. McMasters [Ames Laboratory]), and especially that of his secretary, L. M. McVicker, is deeply appreciated.

KARL A. GSCHNEIDNER, JR.
Iowa State University
Ames, Iowa 50011

March 5, 1981

MIXED RARE EARTH USES—METALS

History of Rare Earth Applications, Rare Earth Market Today

Overview

E. GREINACHER

Th. Goldschmidt AG, Goldschmidtstrasse 100, 4300 Essen 1, West Germany

About 25 000 tons of RE Metals - calculated as oxide - are currently consumed in the world per year. This quantity is divided among a dazzling variety of applications. In order to bring a certain systemization into this variety, these applications and possible applications have been reviewed from 3 different aspects: from a historic development, from the special properties of the rare earths and from the degree of separation of the individual elements or group of elements of the rare earth metal series.

The individual applications will be present in more detail in the following papers by experts in the fields involved.

History of the Applications of Rare Earth Elements

The history of the rare earth elements begins in 1788 in Sweden. I would like to divide the time between that year and the present day into 4 periods of application of the rare earths.
First Period:
1788 - 1891 is the preliminary period in which the rare earth elements were scientifically examined but were not yet technically used.
Second Period:
1891 - 1930 is the period of first industrial usage of the mixed or simply separated rare earth elements.
Third period:
1930 - 1960 is the start of the wide usage of the properties of the rare earth elements, wherein the period from 1940 - 1960 is distinguished by the systematic discovery of properties, of methods of separation and of usage of the rare earth elements as the by-product of the various atomic research programs in the industrial countries, foremost among which were in the USA and England.

0097-6156/81/0164-0003$05.00/0

Fourth period:
From 1960 to the present is the time of qualitatively and
quantitatively rapidly rising applications of the rare earth
elements which are now abundantly available in every desired
quality, although not always at a low price.

Preliminary Period. In 1788 the mine foreman GEYER in
Ytterby, Sweden found a black mineral which was then called
Ytterbite and later Gadolinite. In 1794 it was studied by
Professor Gadolin at the University in Abo, later named Turku,
Finland. He found for the first time a new kind of "earth"
which he called the "rare earths".

At that time the metallic oxides were generally called,
"earth" for example: bitter earths (magnesia), zirconium earths
(zirconia) and beryllium earths (beryllia).

In 1803 Klaproth and independently Berzelius found at an
abandoned iron ore mine at Bastnas, likewise in Sweden, a mineral which received the name Bastnasite. In this mineral the
researchers found new earths which they named "ochroite earths"
because upon heating of the mineral a yellow substance resulted.
They gave the assumed metal the name cerium after the small
planet Ceres.

In 1839 Mosander began for the first time systematically to
analyze the mixed rare earths. This work of separation of the
rare earth elements was carried forward by a number of scientists
and achieved particularly useful results through the work of
Bunsen and Kirchhoff, who introduced spectroscopy as a useful
control instrument for the separation of the rare earth elements.
Up to the year 1891 a great many learned men with famous names
busied themselves with the rare earth elements and reported
interesting work. Nevertheless, no applications or industrial
usage came out of these efforts.

In this early period of general industrial development and
of the beginning growth of our large cities, there arose a
primary technical problem, whose scale we can hardly imagine
today. This was the certain, reliable, rapid and cheap production
of light.

There was a search for the possibility of utilizing the
night hours above all during the winter. This problem is today
so fully solved that except for a couple of specialists we no
longer give it many thought.

The three major (and up to the year 1930 only) uses for the
rare earth elements were related either directly or indirectly
to light. Two of these important inventions stem from the great
Austrian scientist, inventor and entrepreneur, Carl Auer von
Welsbach. His greatness can be gauged by his basic contributions
to both of the major developments in the production of light.
He discovered a useful gas lamp and made a significant contribution to the development of the electric incandescent lamp.
A photograph of von Welsbach is shown in Figure 1 and a sketch
of his laboratory in figure 2 (1).

Technisches Museum

Figure 1. Carl Auer von Welsbach (1)

The problem of production of light had been investigated above all in England for 60 years. This preliminary work provided a clear objective but no technically useful path thereto until the invention of Auer von Welsbach. It was required to bring a hot gas flame to luminosity and to radiate as much visible light as possible. The solution was already available: a solid of suitable composition with maximum surface area had to be brought to radiation in the hot zone of the flame. The large surface area was necessary in order to radiate as much light as possible with good thermal efficiency.

Auer von Welsbach had already reported in 1885 a patent for a lanthanum-zirconium incandescent element and also produced them. This incandescent mantle had two properties:

It consisted of a solid body (La_2O_3 + ZrO_2) which thanks to its composition was stimulated by the heat of the flame (Bunsenflame) to give off a high radiation of light in the visble range.

The method of production was simple: A cotton sock was saturated with a salt solution of such composition that upon ignition a mixture of oxides yielding optimum radiation with large surface area was formed in the hottest zone of the flame, see figure 3.

The incandescent mantle was however not accepted by consumers because it was too brittle and produced a "cold" blue-green light.

Period of First Industrial Usage. By improvement of this first discovery there arose the first industrial consumption of rare earths and the hour of birth of the rare earth industry in the year 1891, when Auer von Welsbach reported his patents for the Auer incandescent mantle which is composed of 99 % thorium oxide and 1 % cerium oxide. This light was superior for decades to electric light. It was cheaper so that until the year 1935 approximately 5 billion incandescent mantles had been produced and consumed in the world.

Even today this method of light production remains superior to electric lighting systems in remote areas or in signal devices for railroads. For example, in front of my house in Essen, Germany, there are open street lanterns with gas-heated Auer-incandescent mantles which provide a pleasant light on our quiet street.

The carbon filament lamp which was developed in parallel at the beginning of this century was always several times as expensive in use as an Auer incandescent mantle. As a result, this first use of the rare earth elements achieved great economic success and thanks to his capabilities Auer von Welsbach played a major role in this worldwide achievement. He was in the position to survive the extraordinarily complicated and obstinately pursued patent battles.

Der Erfinder des „Gasglühlichtes" in seinem Laboratorium.

Technisches Museum

Figure 2. *The laboratory of von Welsbach in which he invented the incandescent gas lamp, see insert in upper left (1)*

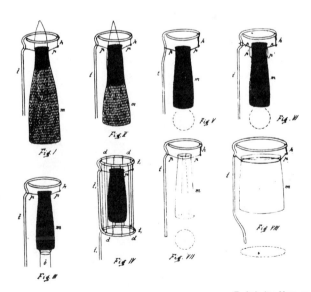

Technisches Museum

Figure 3. *The preparation of an incandescent gas mantle (1)*

Gadolinite and bastnasite from Sweden served at first as
raw material for the rare earth elements and thorium. Later it
was necessary to seek new raw materials and the so-called
"Carolina sand" was found in the USA, a monazite which occurred
there in certain gold-panning areas. Finally a nearly
inexhaustible reserve of monazite was discovered in Brazil which
guaranteed raw material supplies far into the future.

Again, we take a short look into the origin of this discovery. Auer von Welsbach had accumulated so much thorium
in the processing of rare earths for production of lanthanum-
zirconium incandescent mantles - the predecessor of Auer
incandescent mantles - that he had to look for a use for them.
He established that thorium oxide provided an interesting light
radiation at elevated temperatures and that this light radiation
became poorer as the thorium oxide became purer. He further
established that cerium was the main impurity and it was not
difficult from this to come to the optimum dosage of thorium
oxide with cerium oxide.

So it was at the beginning of the industrial applications
of the rare earth elements the need of the rare earth industry
to utilize valuable residual fractions. Up to the present day,
this remains a problem to be solved by research departments,
applications technicians, inventors and developers of the rare
earth industry.

Two situations lead to the next use of rare earths by Auer
von Welsbach:

the large quantities of rare earth elements which were left
over from the production of Auer incandescent mantles had accumulated in large waste piles, and

the necessity to find a simple ignition system for Auer
lamps.

In ignition, electric incandescent lamps were far superior
to the Auerlights. But this situation was ameliorated in 1903
when von Welsbach was granted a patent for a pyrophoric metal
alloy ("flintstone") composed of 70 % mischmetal and 30 % iron.
This patent was also strenuously litigated but victoriously
defended.

After the discovery of pyrophoric alloys, the so-called
Auer-metals, the main problem was to produce mischmetal from
the large dumps resulting from the production of Auer
incandescent mantles. To do this Auer von Welsbach founded in
1907 the Treibacher Chemische Werke in the rooms of an iron works.
In 1908, for the first time, he succeeded in producing pore-free
mischmetal by fused salt electrolysis. 800 kilos of mischmetal-
iron flints were brought on to the market in 1908. The imagin-
ation of the inventor was tremendous. Among other things, he
proposed to use flints for ignition in gasoline engines, an idea
which one perhaps should think through again today in view of

the efforts to make our engines and cars lighter. A fascinating idea, instead of the quite complicated electrical ignition mechanisms, one inserts every 10 000 miles a set of flints into the engine for ignition. Unfortunately, an estimate shows that this would be too expensive.

At this point I would like to present a brief biography of the founder of the rare earth industry:

Auer von Welsbach was born in Vienna in 1858. His father was a creative inventor and expert in the field of printing. Early in his life he left his children such a large inheritance that his son Karl was able to pursue his studies of chemistry in 1878 in Vienna with Professor Lieben and in 1880 with Bunsen in Heidelberg without material worries. In the laboratory of Bunsen he was first introduced into the chemistry of the rare earth elements. Until his death in 1929 he remained true to this field of work. The intensive involvement in spectroscopy with Bunsen also made him familiar with the problems of radiant light which without doubt was important for his later invention of Auer-Light and with that the use of the rare earth elements. Further, he had an insight into the work of winning the rare earth metals from their salts through Bunsen, Hillebrand and Norton who succeeded for the first time in 1875 to produce rare earth metals by electrolysis which later was further developed in Munich by Muthmann. The concepts "pyrophor" and "pyrophoricity" originate from Auer von Welsbach.

The third major invention for the use of the rare earth elements was the addition of rare earth fluoride as a wick in arc light carbons which, at that time, were used for a wide range of lighting purposes and later also for cinema production and for search lights. This use of rare earth compounds is based on the intensive arc light developed by Beck in Germany in 1910.

In the 22 years between 1908 and 1930 about 1 100 - 1 400 tons of flints were produced as the most important rare earth product. This required the consumption of about 1 300 - 1 800 tons of rare earth oxides in the form of rare earth chloride. If one adds to this the other applications, the consumption was probably between 2 000 - 3 000 tons of oxides. On the other hand, at the same time, about 7 500 tons of thorium nitrate were needed for Auer incandescent mantles. If one assumes that monazite contains 6 % thorium oxide and 60 % rare earth elements, then 30 000 tons of rare earth oxides were produced during this period of which only about 10 % was consumed.

Period of Wide Technical Application. In the time between 1930 and 1940 work was done on various applications for the rare earth elements. Particularly successful was the production of sunglasses ("Neophan"), polishing media from rare earth oxides to replace iron oxide, decolorization of glass using cerium oxide, pure cerium oxide as opacifier in ceramic glazes, use of cerium

oxalate in"peremesin" to combat seasickness and nausea during
pregnancy, and neodymium in "Thrombodym" to combat thromboses.

All of these applications however had only relatively small
use during this transition period as compared to the large
quantities of rare earths which continually became available,
as for example, from use of ThO_2 as a catalyst in plants for
production of gasoline by the Fischer-Tropsch Process. After
a few years ThO_2 was replaced in this application by MgO.

This disequilibrium was greatly increased in the fifties
at first in the USA and England, later in other countries as
major programs for use of atomic energy were carried out. The
large stockpile purchases of thorium by the atomic states as
feed material for atomic breeder reactors left behind at the
end of the fifties - beginning of the sixties, huge quantities
of rare earth by-products. This disequilibrium was again
eliminated by the middle of the sixties following termination
of the stockpile programs. Since then, thorium is accumulating
in large inventory stocks at all monazite processors until
perhaps in the near future a new use for this material will be
found.

The large atomic programs provided a great advantage for
the rare earth industry. The rare earth elements which occurred
abundantly in the fission products of atomic reactors were
intensively scientifically examined at great expense and their
separation from each other was pursued so that by the end of the
fifties a large volume scientific research results and properties of the rare earth metals were known. In particular I
mention Prof. Spedding and the rare earth center he established
in Ames/Iowa. Building on this stable scientific foundation,
which in the following years further widened, there developed
between 1960 and the present day a wide usage of the rare earth
elements with an exponentially increased consumption. However,
until today, the coupled production remains the fate and the
task of the rare earth industry: if one rare earth element is
needed then automatically all the others become available.

So at the beginning of the sixties there was a market for
lanthanum in the optical glass industry, for cerium in polishing
media and for praseodyminium/neodymium (so-called "didymium")
in the glass industry for coloring and decolorization but no one
wanted to have samarium and europium. At Goldschmidt, for
example, there had at that time accumulated large stocks of
these materials in the form of concentrates and high purity with
a book value of zero. This changed suddenly when in 1965
europium was used in the USA as a red phosphor in color TV; however even then the samarium oxide continued to remain behind.
These stocks were first reduced by the development of magnet
materials in recent years.

A balance between the various applications must be
achieved in order that the costs for each application should not

rise excessively. This will also apply to the future; however, it is indicated that with the great broadening of the use of the rare earths the balance has become easier to achieve. Most importantly, there are today enough uses for mixtures of the rare earth elements. So, for example, it makes little difference in catalytic cracking that samarium and europium have been previously extracted. This provides a certain elasticity in the use of the rare earth elements as for example with samarium and europium.

The Special Properties of the Rare Earth Elements with Reference to their Use

In order to bring about a systemization among the variety of uses I have broken down the uses of the rare earth elements into five groups of properties: chemical, metallurgical, optical, magnetic and nuclear.

Chemical Properties. In the uses of chemical properties the high affinity of the rare earth metals for oxygen is primarily involved. This leads to their application as flints, wherein their highly exothermic reaction with oxygen in air is used. On the same properties rests their application as getter metals, wherein residual oxygen, as for example in amplifier tubes, is bound up.

The chemical-ceramic properties of the rare earth elements result from their high affinity for oxygen yielding highly stable oxides which can be used in high temperature materials; likewise the high melting points of sulfides are of interest. The use of the rare earth elements in this field is however limited because of their sensitivity toward CO_2 and water vapor.

Yttrium oxide has become increasingly important in the stabilization of ZrO_2 in the cubic phase. This ZrO_2 is used as a high temperature material. Because at high temperatures it becomes conductive, the Y_2O_3-stabilized ZrO_2 serves also as an electrode, for example in the high temperature electrolysis of water, where in addition yttrium-lanthanum oxide serves as the solid electrolyte. ZrO_2/Y_2O_3 has a similar function as an electrode in the so-called Lambda-Sensors, which are used to determine the oxygen content in exhaust gases of automobiles.

Chemical properties are also used in the largest field of application for the rare earth elements: as catalysts. Most important are the cracking catalysts for the petroleum industry. The rare earth elements are combined into molecular sieves (Y-Zeolite) and serve in fluid bed or fixed bed reactors to increase the yield of gasoline. In addition thereto, there are the combustion catalysts for automobiles and for air pollution control.

The chemical properties are at least in part responsible
for the use of rare earths in polishing media. According to
various researches, this involves, in the polishing process,
extensive chemical reactions on the surfaces of the glass which
work to remove the material with mechanical abrasion perhaps
also playing a role. Therefore, one must use different polishing
materials for each material (for example metal or glass) and
even for individual kinds of glass. The rare earth oxides, especially cerium oxide, have outstandingly justified their use
for the polishing of glass surfaces.

The rare earth elements are physiologically inert and
therefore present no danger to the environment. The two pharma-
ceutical applications which go back to the thirties are based
primarily on the anions or corresponding salts rather than on
the effect of the rare earth metals: ceriumoxalate as treatment
for seasickness and Nd-isonikotinate as treatment for thromboses.

Metallurgical Properties. Here the rare earth elements
operate as scavengers for oxygen and sulfur and other deleterious elements as well as being boundary surface active substances. This is especially true in the two most economically
important fields of applications: the production of nodular
graphite castings through spheroidization of graphitic components, and the treatment of steel for sulfide inclusion shape
control. In both cases great effects are achieved with small
additions.

On the other hand, the use of rare earth metals for the
fixing of oxygen and sulfur in light metals for production of
conductive copper and conductive aluminum has remained insignificant. However, the use of rare earth elements as magnesium
hardeners remains important. Here the rare earth metals serve by
precipitation of intermetallic compounds of high thermal
stability.

Optical Properties. The optical properties of the rare
earth elements are of great importance in their application.
Due to the atomic structure of the 4 f-shell there are narrow
and sharp absorption and/or emission lines in the visible range
which may be used in various ways. In addition the oxides and/or
oxide systems in glasses provide a high index of refraction with
low dispersion.

The first applications of the rare earth elements, as
already mentioned, were in the optical field, namely the Auer
incandescent mantles and the arc light carbons. In 1964/65 as a
result of the work of Levine and Palilla the use of the truly
rare and therefore expensive europium together with yttrium made
a major leap forward for the rare earth industry as red phosphors
in color TV screens. Due to the strong and sharp emission line
of europium at 610 Å, without a yellow component, which is

perceived by the eye as a wonderfully saturated red color tone, it was possible to achieve in color TV an evenly colored picture.

Gd_2O_3 plays an important role in x-ray intensifiers. A foil with rare earth oxides is placed on the x-ray film and is excited by x-rays to emit in the visible range. In this way the film is exposed with a minimum of radiation dosage.

The coloring of glass with rare earth elements, for example with neodymium or praseodymium, is also based on their selective absorption in the visible range. In the decolorizing of glass, the oxidation effect of 4-valent cerium is combined with the absorption of small quantities of neodymium/praseodymium. Accordingly, cerium concentrates which always contain some praseodymium and neodymium are added to glass melts. One achieves a chemical decolorization of iron by oxidation to the 3-valent stage with physical decolorization by the selective absorption of didymium through optical compensation. Therefore, a combination of chemical and optical properties is utilized.

The most important application of praseodymium is the production of very beautiful high temperature resistant lemon-yellow pigments for the ceramic industry. The praseodymium is built into the zirconium silicate lattice and thereby yields full optical splendor.

In the application of lanthanum oxide in glass use is made of the high index of refraction and the lack of color of this oxide. So today optical glasses with up to 40 % lanthanum oxide are made which are corrosion resistant.

Rare earth elements serve as activators in laser glasses. Well-known is the neodymium laser.

Magnetic Properties. The rare earth elements show as a result of their atomic structure interesting magnetic properties which have led to various applications.

Important is the use of light rare earth elements for production of hard magnetic materials. Most prominent are alloys of samarium with cobalt in the atomic ratio 1 : 5 or 2 : 17. It may also be assumed that in further development of these materials on a larger scale that praseodymium, neodymium, lanthanum and also individual heavy rare earth elements will be used to achieve particular effects. Interesting is the development of magnetic bubble memories based on gadolinium-gallium-garnets. They serve for storage of information because of their large storage density. The use of gadolinium metal as a heat pump is a further magnetic application in which the Curie Point, which lies at room temperature for this material, can be very well utilized.

Nuclear Properties. In connection with the major research programs for use of nuclear energy around 1960 there resulted interesting aspects for the rare earth elements, particularly the high capture cross-sections for thermal neutrons of Eu, Sm, Gd and Dy. Gadolinium and dysprosium were used as so-called burnable poisons to achieve a uniform neutron-flux during the lifetime of a fuel element. Europium shows exceptional properties insofar as a high capture cross-section of the natural isotopes is combined with an uninterrupted series of five isotopes, all of which arise upon capture of a neutron and all of which have a high capture cross-section. Therefore, the capacity of such a neutron absorber is extraordinarily great and there was an attempt to equip American atomic submarines with europium-bearing control rods. At the time this was not feasible because of an insufficient supply of europium. On the other hand, yttrium metal was brought into use as a tubing material for molten salt reactors because it has a low capture cross-section for thermal neutrons.

Cerium and yttrium hydrides were successfully tried as neutron moderators because of their temperature stability.

Applications According to Degree of Separation

For particular applications the rare earth elements are used in various purities according to whether the general properties of the rare earth elements or specific properties of individual elements are needed. The rare earth industry distinguishes in general three grades of purity: the group of unseparated rare earth elements in the composition which occurs naturally in ores; concentrates producible by simple chemical precipitation reactions which in general contain 60 - 90 % of the individual element desired; and the pure rare earth elements which contain between 98 and 99.999 % of a rare earth oxide.

The price for the products rises over several degrees of magnitude in the corresponding series.

In the large scale application of rare earth elements as in the steel industry, in catalysts and in the polishing of glass, in general, the naturally occurring mixtures or concentrates are utilized. While with phosphors and electronic applications pure products with much higher prices are used. Therefore, the application of the rare earth elements requires careful consideration and close cooperation between producers and users so that the optimum between desired effects, purity and production costs can be found for each specific application.

Allow me to cite three examples:

First example - In the production of red phosphors for color TV where each screen requires about 5 - 10 g yttrium oxide and 500 - 1 000 mg europium oxide, high requirements are placed on the purity and with reference to specific rare earth elements or non-rare earth elements. As a result, the prices are expressed in $/g.

Second example - In the production of samariumcobalt permanent magnets impurities have practically only a dilution effect. One can therefore use instead of a 99.9 % pure samarium metal a significantly cheaper 90 %, perhaps even 80 % pure metal with the balance other rare earths. In any case, it is necessary in this instance that the composition of the other rare earth elements be held constant, which is not always quite so simple.

Third example - Although ceric oxide really represents the active element in polishing media, most of the polishing plants are satisfied with about 50 % pure ceric oxide, which is available in the natural mixture of the light rare earth elements as they are extracted either from bastnasite or monazite, in order to keep the cost of the product low.

Substitution of the Application

In the development of the rare earth industry, substitution of the rare earth elements by other cheaper processes or other substances has - and also in the future will play - an important role. The rare earth elements were never a cheap material although they occur abundantly in nature. As we have heard, the cost of the rare earth elements rises rapidly if a specific rare earth element is required in high purity. Therefore, there arose always the tendency for users of rare earth elements to look around for a cheaper solution for an established field of application. A danger which the rare earth industry often has learned to fear and which has led to a characteristic rise and fall of economic success for rare earth enterprises. Examples of such rises and falls resulting from substitution are given below.

Through Processes:
- replacement of Auer-incandescent gas mantles by incandescent lamps.
- Replacement of rare earth elements for sulfide inclusion shape control by extreme steel desulfurization with the aid of calcium.
- Replacement of rare earth bearing arc light carbons by high pressure - argon - arc lights, particularly in cinema projectors and in searchlights.

Through Other Substances:
- Use of magnesium instead of mischmetal for production of nodular graphite castings.
- Use of hafnium instead of europium in atomic submarines for neutron absorption.
- Replacement of ceric oxide by tin oxide or zirconium oxide as opacifiers for enamels.
- Use of titanium-iron alloy for hydrogen storage instead of $LaNi_5$.

In general, however, one can say that where the optical properties, the chemical properties and the magnetic properties are used, substitution is not to be feared, while in the use of metallurgical and nuclear properties there is always the danger that a more economic solution of the problem can squeeze out the rare earth elements.

Therefore, it appears to me that the following fields of work are not threatened by substitution: polishing media, flints, catalysts, phosphors, magnets, optical glass components, coloring and decolorization of glass, pigment formers and x-ray intensifiers.

Market Survey

World demand for the rare earth elements is established in the range of 25 000 tons per year - calculated as rare earth oxides.

These materials are available through production of bastnasite at the Mountain Pass Mine in California, of monazite from Australia, India and Brazil, and of monazite as a by-product from the production of tin ores, rutile and various heavy mineral sands.

From new information about the huge reserves in the People's Republic of China, a ten-fold increase in this demand could be satisfied over a period of several years. Of particular interest is the fact that the large occurrence in the autonomous region of Inner Mongolia as a by-product of an existing hematite and magnetite mine is fully accessible through an infrastructure and railroad lines. The problem in the processing of the ores can be comprehended and solved. The future supply of ore presents in terms of quantity no problem for the rare earth industry. Another question naturally is the development of prices which, with respect to ore, is still characterized by a single dominant supplier.

The consumption of the rare earth elements is divided into four groups of application (2). One can see from this information that 98 % of the rare earth elements, with respect to quantity, are consumed in the following fields of application: metallurgy, chemicals/catalysts, glass and polishing media. If one however looks at the value of the products then the picture is drastically altered, then phosphors are the most important field of application of the rare earth elements.

Table I. Major world markets for rare earths (2)
(% by weight on REO basis estimated)

	1975	1976	1977	1978	1979
Metallurgical	45	32	34	32	43
Chemical/catalysis	36	38	39	32	26
Glass/ceramics	17	28	26	35	31
Phosphors/electronics	2	2	1	1	< 1

It is interesting to note the rising importance of metallurgy - above all in steel - and of the glass-ceramic-industry,
while catalysts and chemicals are declining. I assume that this
will again change in the future since a partial substitution of
rare earth metal (mischmetal) is noticeable in metallurgy and
on the other hand an increased demand for rare earth containing
catalysts is awaited in Europe.

The demand for rare earth elements is also effected by the
general economy, particularly in steel, glass, phosphors and
electronics, while the demand for rare earth containing catalysts
seems quite independent of the economy. Because of the conversa-
tion of refinery production in Europe toward greater gasoline
fractions, an increased demand for rare earths is to be expected.
The production of pyrophoric alloys is determined more by the
habits of smokers and the results of their attempt to give up
the habit of smoking. Therefore flints are quite independent
of the state of the economy.

Acknowledgement

I wish to thank my friend Is Hirschhorn of Ronson Metals Corp.
for translating this paper from German into English.

Literature Cited

1. Sedlack, Franz "Auer von Welsbach", Blätter für Ge-
schichte der Technik, zweites Heft; Julius Springer:
Wien, 1934

2. Cannon, J. Eng. Mining Journal, 1980, 179 [3] 184-7

RECEIVED December 29, 1980.

The Role of the Rare Earth Elements in the Production of Nodular Iron

H. F. LINEBARGER and T. K. McCLUHAN

Union Carbide Corporation, Metals Division, P.O. Box 579, Niagara Falls, NY 14302

Before discussing, in any detail, the role of rare earths in the production of nodular iron, it is important to arrive at some basic understanding regarding the metallurgy of this material. It is also appropriate to discuss the rare earth materials being used commercially.

Both gray and nodular irons are examples of iron-carbon-silicon alloys. Gray iron is one of the oldest ferrous alloys cast. Evidence indicates that iron was founded in China over six centuries before Christ. Effective use of iron casting technology was a driving force behind the industrial revolution. On the other hand, nodular iron is one of the newest alloys to achieve utility as an engineering material in the metals casting industry and, in reality, is an outgrowth from gray iron. Gray irons nominally contain from two-to-four percent (by weight) carbon, and from one-to-four percent silicon. The composition of nodular iron is more restricted. Typical nodular irons contain from three-to-four percent carbon, and two-to-four percent silicon. Carbon and silicon are important elements in the iron because of their effects upon microstructure and the resulting physical properties of the castings.

To the continual consternation of foundrymen, the properties of all the cast irons are also significantly affected by the presence of minute concentrations of many elements other than carbon and silicon. For example, the presence of sulfur, in concentrations from 0.01% to 0.1%, substantially affects the graphite morphology in the solidified cast iron (1). The presence of rare earth elements or the presence of magnesium, in amounts from about 0.02% to 0.1% (by weight) in irons which have a low (~0.01%) sulfur concentration, can change the entire growth pattern of the graphite as will be described later. Certain of these minor elements are intentionally introduced, as when treating base irons with magnesium or rare earth elements to produce nodular iron. Other trace elements, such as sulfur, are at times introduced

0097-6156/81/0164-0019$06.00/0

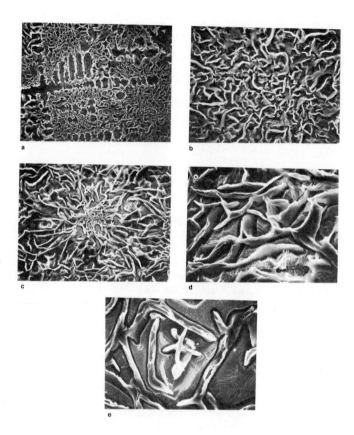

Figure 1.   Scanning electron micrographs of flake graphite etched in bromine and methanol: a, Type D graphite—175×;   b, Type D graphite—500×;   c, Type B graphite—175×;   d, Type B graphite—500×;   e, Type A graphite—500×. Graphite types are representative of a range of cooling rates: Type D graphite is typical of the most rapid cooling, then Type B, and then Type A.

intentionally or at other times are carried along in the raw materials used in producing the iron. For example, sulfur is a constituent of the coke used in cupola melting operations and there is some sulfur pickup from this source. Elements, such as chromium, phosphorus and titanium are picked up during the scrap remelting process.

Microstructures in cast irons are also dramatically influenced by cooling rates. If cooling is rapid, no graphite precipitates. Rather, the alloy solidifies in the metastable $Fe-Fe_3C$ state. In that state, the carbon is combined with iron as iron carbides. The fractured surface of carbidic cast iron is white. Such irons are hard and are not readily machined. Carbidic iron castings are used for some special applications, when abrasion resistance is important.

Graphite precipitates only if the liquid is allowed to solidify and cool as the thermodynamically stable iron-graphite system. In a so-called gray iron, the fractured surface is gray because the carbon has precipitated as graphite and the graphite is visible on the fracture. Depending upon the heat transfer, the graphite morphology is altered. Characteristic forms of graphite in gray iron are therefore a function of the cooling rate of the metal (see Figure 1).

From a practical standpoint, there is little a foundryman can do to control the cooling rate of iron in a given casting. He can, however, add nucleating agents to the iron which minimize the constitutional undercooling associated with the formation of the iron-carbide phase. This is accomplished by appropriate selection of nodulizing and inoculating alloys which promote very high degrees of nucleation. The degree of nucleation is measured by nodule counts in nodular iron or chill depth in gray iron.

In gray irons, the graphite grows upon the prism faces of the hexagonal crystal (see Figure 2). This growth is not uniform but, rather, is affected by mechanisms which result in the irregular structures observed in Figure 1. The graphite forms a nearly continuous network within the numerous eutectic or solidification cells. An oversimplification may be made: that gray iron is a steel matrix interrupted by large graphitic inclusions. When a sample of gray iron is polished and examined using a microscope, the two-dimensional cut through the graphite causes it to appear as isolated flakes (see Figure 3).

The morphology of the flake graphite, particularly the sharp edges, are thought to serve as internal notches in the material (2). Cracks can readily nucleate at the ends and edges of the graphite, and propagate through the graphite or along the iron-graphite interface. Gray irons fracture readily under stress. They are characterized by rather low tensile strengths (150-300 MNt/m^2) negligible ductility, and low impact strength (3). These materials are rather soft and readily machined. On the positive side, machinability is enhanced by the lubricating effect of the graphite. Yields (mass of casting divided by total mass of metal

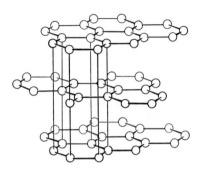

Figure 2. Hexagonal crystalline struc-
ture of graphite

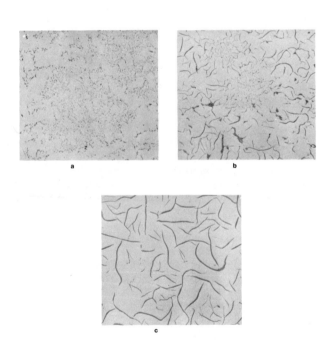

Figure 3.   Appearance of graphite (200×) in a polished specimen of gray iron:
a, Type D; b, Type B; c, Type A

in the mold) when producing gray iron are relatively high because
of eutectic graphite solidification. The melting point is relatively low compared to other ferrous alloys; which means that less
energy input is required during production than for some other
ferrous materials. In spite of the limitations of its physical
properties, gray iron is a useful engineering material. About 60%
of the total casting tonnage shipped in the United States is gray
iron (4).

Mechanical properties of gray irons can be intentionally
altered by the use of alloying elements, such as copper, tin,
manganese, nickel or chromium. Alloying affects the mechanical
properties of the matrix more so than the morphology of the graphite. However, the physical properties of the iron are primarily
affected by graphite morphology, whether nodule or flake; and,
secondarily, the matrix structure. This results in practical limitations upon the utility of alloying in the modification of physical properties.

It was known for some time that if the graphite morphology
could be altered, certain physical properties of the cast irons
could be improved. The malleable iron industry (specifically, the
black-heart malleable industry) had long made use of annealing
procedures applied to cast irons that had initially solidified as
the metastable $Fe-Fe_3C$ system (white iron). Heat treating procedures applied to these white iron castings caused the iron carbide to break down. The carbon diffused through the matrix and
was accreted at isolated sites. This graphite took the form of
spheroids rather than flakes. Irons produced in this manner had
higher tensile strengths than gray iron (typically 365–700 MNt/m^2)
and showed appreciable elongation (2% to 18%). The change in
graphite morphology, from flake to spheroidal, was the cause in
the improvements in these mechanical properties.

There were essentially two problems associated with malleable
irons. One was that the heat treatment procedures were costly.
Secondly, it was imperative that the iron solidify in the metastable state. That requirement made production of heavier, slow-
cooled sections impossible since they would likely contain free
graphite. However, the higher tensile strengths and ductility of
malleable irons were desired in some cases.

Therefore, the problem confronting the foundry industry was
to somehow produce spheroidal graphite without heat treatments or
constraints upon section thicknesses. It was from these chal-
lenges that nodular iron was developed and its use has grown. The
rare earths have assumed a crucial role in the process. One of
the workers attempting to produce as-cast iron containing nodules
was Henton Morrogh of the British Cast Iron Research Association.
Morrogh experimented with a variety of additions of alloying elements based upon three assumptions (5). He assumed that the nodulizing element need be an iron carbide stabilizing element, that
the element be capable of desulfurizing the iron, and that the
element readily dissolve in iron. His efforts resulted in the

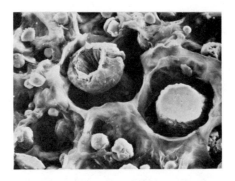

Figure 4.   Spheroids of graphite (250×); etched in bromine and methanol solution

Figure 5.   Appearance of polished nodular iron microsample (200×); etched in 2% nital. Matrix structure is pearlite.

discovery that additions of cerium would result in spheroidal
graphite structures in nickel-carbon and iron-nickel-carbon alloys. He continued these experiments and ultimately discovered
that spheroidal graphite could be routinely produced, in the laboratory, in irons having 0.02% cerium introduced as mischmetal.
The mischmetal was introduced into hypereutectic iron-carbon-
silicon alloys containing less than 0.06% sulfur in the base, or
untreated iron. Morrogh further restricted the phosphorus level
to less than 0.1% (6).

Morrogh announced his discovery in the United States at the
American Foundrymen's Society convention in Philadelphia in 1948
(7). Interestingly enough, during the discussion following his
presentation, T.H. Wickerdon of the International Nickel Company
announced that his company had been successful in producing nodular iron in a production environment. In their process, they had
used additions of magnesium. This magnesium was contained in a
nickel-magnesium alloy. Both hypo- and hyper-eutectic base irons
had been successfully treated using the nickel-magnesium alloy.
The nodular iron industry was born. However, there was much work
yet to be done.

The acceptance of nodular iron as an engineering material was
neither overwhelming nor immediate (8). The material remained
largely a laboratory curiosity for some time. Studies were under-
taken in order to explain the mechanisms of the graphite growth.
Even today, the phenomenon of producing spheroidal graphite has
not been unambiguously explained. It has been speculated that
this effect is the result of interrelated roles played by what can
be called the nodulizing elements (calcium, magnesium, the rare
earths). By the formation of oxides, sulfides or oxysulfides, the
sulfur and oxygen can be removed from the melt. As a result, the
graphite growth pattern is affected. It is now known that spheroidal graphite is characterized by growth upon the basal planes
of the graphite crystal rather than upon the prism faces as in
gray iron. Numerous fibers of graphite grow radially from a given
nucleation site. As a result, a spheroid of graphite is formed
(see Figures 4 and 5).

Other researchers have detected inclusions at the geometric
center of at least some of the spheroids of graphite in the nodular irons tested. In one reported study, using transmission electron microscopy, these inclusions were analyzed as being the oxides of the rare earth elements cerium and lanthanum, as well as
magnesium (9). Use of the electron microprobe allowed other
workers to identify sulfides of cerium, lanthanum and magnesium
(10) as well as calcium-magnesium sulfides (11) at the centers of
nodules (see Figures 6 and 7). It appears probable that such inclusions provide heterogeneous substrates on which at least some
of the graphite can readily nucleate.

The role of the nodulizing elements can, therefore, be speculated as two-fold. They cleanse the melt of elements such as
oxygen or sulfur which prohibit spheroidal graphite growth. The

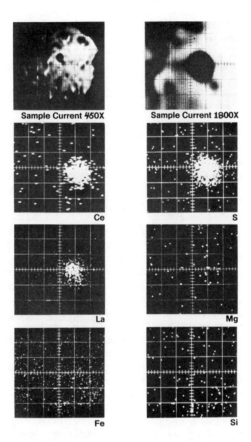

Cast Metals Research Journal

Figure 6. Photographs of CRT output from characteristic x-ray scans for the various elements listed using electron microprobe (10). Particle scanned was a graphite nodule. Scans verify presence of a heterogeneous inclusion in the nodule. Iron was treated with magnesium and a rare earth silicide. The element distribution pictures were taken at 1800×.

compounds thus formed provide heterogeneous substrates for graphite nucleation.

The spheroids of graphite no longer serve as internal notches in the matrix. Consequently, the material is not as easily fractured as gray iron. The tensile strengths, yield strengths, and percentages of elongation in castings containing spheroidal graphite are dramatically increased over those properties in gray iron. For example, nodular irons have tensile strengths from 300-400 MNt/m^2 and percentages of elongation from 6% to 18% in the as-cast condition. These quantities are on the order of those observed in malleable irons. These physical properties can be further modified by alloying or heat treating procedures, just as in gray iron. The machinability of nodular iron castings in generally not as good as for gray iron castings. Yields are somewhat lower because of altered solidification (around 50% as compared to 60% to 70% for gray iron). The good physical properties of nodular iron coupled with its good founding qualities, have established nodular iron's place as an engineering material.

As a final introductory point, it should be noted that there is some confusion within the foundry industry, and its literature, regarding the specific rare earths being employed. Early work in this field was conducted using mischmetal. However, in many instances, only the cerium level was reported in these tests. The presence of the other rare earths was ignored. Even today, the elements most often mentioned are the first four lanthanides: lanthanum, cerium, praseodymium and neodymium. That is not to say that the effects of the other elements in the series would not be similar to those of the first four or that they could not be utilized. Rather, their roles have not been studied individually. It should be kept in mind that commercially used rare earth sources contain small quantities of these other rare earths.

From this early availability and use of mischmetal grew a demand for bastnasite ore. In these alloys, about one-half of the present rare earths are cerium. In the mid-to-late sixties, a more economical source of cerium was introduced which was, in essence, a concentrate from which the lanthanum had been removed. This material allowed for the production of alloys whose rare earth concentration was about 90% cerium. These rare earth-bearing materials have the approximate analyses shown in Table I and are now used commercially, with the high cerium source predominating in the United States.

The various rare earths are used in the foundry industry as rare earth silicides, in which the rare earth content is about 30%. Other alloys are used in which the level of rare earths is about 10% (10% cerium, 2% other rare earths) with silicon and iron comprising the bulk of the remaining elements. In the magnesium-ferrosilicon alloys, the rare earths are present in amounts from about 0.1% to 1.0%. These alloys are used differently by the various consumers. However, the effects of the rare earth elements, introduced by whatever means, are the same.

TABLE I

Analyses of Rare Earth Sources

	Approximate Analyses, %	
	Mischmetal or Low Cerium Rare Earths	High Cerium Rare Earths
Cerium	50	90
Lanthanum	33	5
Neodymium	12	2
Praseodymium	4	1
Other Rare Earths	1	2

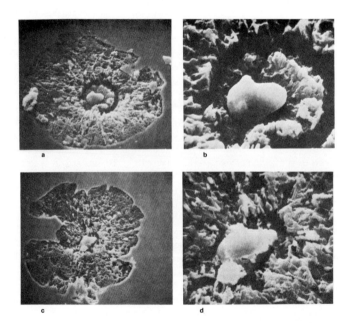

Transactions of the American Foundrymen's Society

Figure 7.   Photographs of CRT output of electron microprobe depicting hetero-geneous particle at the center of two graphite nodules (11). Particles were identified as calcium-magnesium sulfides: a, 1375✕; b, 5000✕; c, 1250✕; d, 5000✕.

The rare earths play three roles in the production of nodular iron. These roles are as a nodulizing element (or as the growth modifier) as a means of enhancing the nodule count (or nucleation) and, finally as controllers of deleterious elements. The use of the rare earths for each of these purposes will be described in detail in the following sections.

The Rare Earths as Nodulizers in the Production of Nodular Iron

The modern foundry process for producing nodular iron can be oversimplified by describing it as the treatment of a base iron (3% to 4% carbon, 1% to 2% silicon) having low (0.005% to 0.05%) sulfur levels and containing little (<0.05%) phosphorus. The treatment is carried out by means of the introduction of the appropriate nodulizer into this base iron. Inadequate addition of nodulizer results in incomplete spheroidization. Excessive concentrations of nodulizers promote the formation of unwanted iron carbides. The nodulizing elements include the rare earths, magnesium, yttrium and calcium. The latter two elements find little or no use today because of economical and technical problems.

The range of efficacy for a given nodulizer is quite restricted, being about 0.02% to 0.1% for either magnesium or the rare earth elements, in irons having 0.01% sulfur. Generally, the nodular iron treatment procedure requires the addition of a "post inoculant" as well. This final step is made in order to ensure that the matrix solidifies free of iron carbides and to provide for adequate nucleation and growth of the spheroidal graphite.

One of today's basic requirements for economical nodular iron production is a base (or untreated) iron having between 0.004% and 0.05% sulfur. In most practices, the sulfur level is held at approximately 0.01% in order to minimize the necessary addition of nodulizing elements. On the other hand, a minimal sulfur level is evidently required in order to facilitate adequate nucleation (12).

Base irons can be melted in electric furnaces or in cupolas. The sulfur levels in the irons melted in electric furnaces might typically be in the neighborhood of 0.05%. Use of a coke-fired cupola having a silica lining will result in the production of irons having sulfur levels of around 0.1%. A major portion of the total tonnage of cast iron production makes use of these acid-lined cupolas. There are not many basic slag cupolas in existence. Basic slag cupolas, which allow for the production of base irons having 0.01% sulfur levels at the cupola spout, are expensive to reline and are more difficult to control than acid-lined cupolas.

Since most base irons have sulfur levels higher than 0.01% sulfur, a desulfurization step that drives the sulfur level to about 0.01% is desirable. The rare earth elements could be used to desulfurize the iron. However, because of the valence state of the rare earths and their high mass weights, a considerable

mass input of rare earths would be required to remove the sulfur.
The cost of such a process would be formidable. Modern methods,
such as use of calcium-carbide desulfurization, allow for this
step to be done more economically than by the use of the rare
earths. Therefore, the rare earths are not used to desulfurize
the base iron.

The nodulizer is then introduced into this desulfurized base
iron. Magnesium or magnesium-bearing alloys are predominately
used as primary nodulizers in the industry today. It was partially an economic consideration that led to the use of these magnesium and magnesium-bearing alloys in commercial practice rather
than the rare earth elements. Quite simply, in the early days of
nodular iron production, the sulfur levels of the iron were high;
and since efficient, cost effective, means of desulfurization were
unavailable, it was too expensive to make nodular iron using rare
earths. Magnesium became an economically feasible alternative.
Generally, the magnesium residual required to produce spheroidal
graphite will vary with the section thickness of the casting. In
nodular iron pipe with very thin sections, residuals may be as low
as 0.02%. In heavy section castings, the residual magnesium may
be as high as 0.1%.

The use of magnesium as a primary nodulizer is not without
problems, however, as elemental magnesium vaporizes (at 1 atm
pressure) at 1103°C, which is lower than the temperature of the
molten metal ($\approx$1500°C) into which the magnesium is introduced.
Even though the use of alloys introduces the magnesium as either
Mg_2Si, or as a NiMg phase, the dissolution of these phases ultimately results in nascent magnesium being present in the melt.
Therefore, the magnesium tends to vaporize if not under suitable
pressures. In addition, the magnesium sources presently used commercially (except some nickel-magnesium sources) are less dense
than the liquid base iron, so the material tends to float to the
surface of the bath where combustion takes place. Magnesium oxidation also takes place since there is dissolved oxygen in the
melt. Because of these factors, magnesium recoveries range from
30% to 50% in the industry when 5% magnesium-ferrosilicon alloys
are used and as low as 20% if magnesium-coke materials are
plunged.

In view of the poor magnesium recoveries (and the associated
pyrotechnics) and the present availability of desulfurized base
iron, efforts have been made to establish the rare earths as the
primary nodulizers (13). After all, Morrogh originally produced
nodular iron by the use of mischmetal. The rare earths are more
dense than the liquid base irons (ρ=6.6 gm/cm^3 for cerium (14),
whereas ρ ~ 6.2 gm/cm^3 for gray irons above the liquidus (15)).
They also are liquid at iron founding temperatures. As a result,
there is not a problem with pyrotechnics and alloy flotation can
be minimized. Recoveries of the rare earths in the iron have
been found to be high.

However, the efforts to use rare earths as primary nodulizers
have not met with commercial success because there is apparently

a need to have at least eutectic or preferably hypereutectic irons.   The rare earths are strong carbide stabilizers, and there is a propensity for the formation of carbides in hypoeutectic irons if the level of rare earths becomes too high for the particular section thickness of casting.   However, efforts to use the rare earths as primary nodulizers can be expected to continue.

Results of other experiments have reported the desirability of having several nodulizers in the treatment alloy (16).   In these tests, the rare earths, yttrium and magnesium, were used in combinations in producing nodular iron.   It was concluded that the recovery of individual nodulizing elements was improved if several nodulizers were added as a group.   In addition, the fade of the nodulizers, or their loss of potency over time, was reduced since less of a given element was initially added.   It was also demonstrated that nodular iron could be produced at lower total levels of contained nodulizing elements than possible when using a single element.   It was further reported that the best nodule shapes were obtained when some magnesium was used.   The result of the work led to a proprietary alloy being produced that contains about 3% magnesium and about 2% rare earth elements.   This alloy has the advantage of higher magnesium recovery (low pyrotechnics) than the 5% magnesium-ferrosilicon alloys and the effective utilization of the rare earths present.   The alloy has, however, had only limited acceptance.

These same researchers also explored the efficacy of the individual rare earths as nodulizers (17).   They concluded, by their ability to produce nodular iron having adequate physical properties without excessive iron carbides present, that cerium was the most effective of the four rare earth elements (lanthanum-neodymium) evaluated as nodulizers.   They reported that it required 1.5 times as much neodymiun or praseodymium and three times as much lanthanum as cerium to yield equivalent results. No causes were established for the variation in behavior of the rare earths.   Unfortunately, no further work exploring the properties of the individual rare earths as nodulizing elements has been reported since that time.

The Rare Earths as Nucleating Agents

It is intuitively obvious that there should be a relationship between nodule shape, size, and distribution, and the physical properties of the iron.   Work is being done in attempting to relate these morphological quantities to the physical properties.   Quantitative metallography has, for example, been used to reconcile impact resistance and graphite morphology (18). Overall, it can be stated that these efforts are still in their embryonic stage.   It is generally accepted, however, that the nodule count (nodules/mm^2) and propensity for formation of primary iron carbides are inversely related (see Figure 8 (19)). In nodular iron, the goal is a carbide-free matrix; hence, a

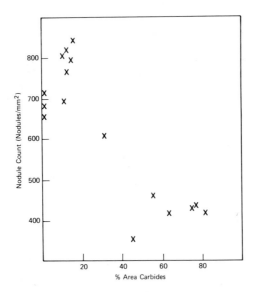

Figure 8.   The inverse relationship between nodule count and percentage area of carbides (19)

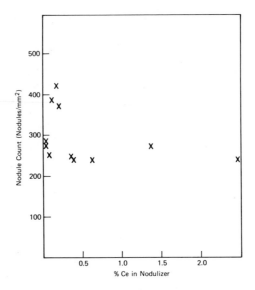

Figure 9.   The effect of cerium, introduced as mischmetal along with the treatment alloy, as a function of the cerium content of the alloy (21). Compositions of the irons were 3.4–3.7% C, 2.3–2.6% Si, 0.6% Mn, 0.01–0.02% S, 0.036–0.044% Mg.

high nodule count implies adequate nucleation and is considered desirable. It has been reported by several researchers that nodule counts are increased by additions of rare earths, along with magnesium, over those counts obtained by additions of magnesium alone (20). The improvement in percentage nodularity when rare earths were added is especially noticed when the magnesium residual is marginal.

Further, it was demonstrated that the introduction of cerium, as mischmetal, in proper amounts was effective in eliminating iron carbides which cause deterioration in physical properties (21). The elimination of iron carbides in thin sections by proper use of the rare earths represents a major contribution to the industry. Different researchers have agreed that there is an optimum percentage for this rare earths addition, which they reported as cerium only, from 0.01% to 0.02% cerium (from about 0.02% to 0.04% total rare earths) that provides this increase in nodule count and control of iron carbides when used in conjunction with magnesium nodulizers (see Figure 9).

As a result of this work, which demonstrated the desirability of adding the rare earth elements with the magnesium–ferrosilicon alloy, ferroalloys containing specified amounts of rare earth elements may be purchased. Most of these alloys in the United States use ceric hydrates as the rare earth sources, so they are adding essentially only cerium with the magnesium–ferrosilicon. However, another researcher claimed that increases in nodule count were more readily obtainable, in laboratory scale heats, if the ratio of lanthanum to cerium was higher than when the cerium-rich magnesium ferroalloys were used (22). As a result, alloys using refined bastnasite ores as the rare earth source are also available and find some industrial acceptance. Until further research is done to convince the user that one rare earth or group of rare earth elements demonstrates unambiguous advantages over another, both sources of rare earths will likely continue to be used. Fluctuations in consumption of the particular rare earths will reflect changes in marketplace participation enjoyed by the individual producers.

It should be recalled that the final step in the nodular iron treatment process is termed "post inoculation." The purpose of this procedure is to aid in the elimination of iron carbides and promote enhanced nucleation and proper growth of graphite spheroids. This is accomplished by the introduction of the element silicon (usually a ferrosilicon alloy) along with calcium and maybe some magnesium or rare earth. It has been demonstrated that the benefits of rare earth additions are not affected as a function of the time in the process that they are added (23). For example, the elimination of iron carbides by use of the rare earths is possible if the rare earths are introduced along with the primary nodulizer or with the post inoculant. In passing, it should be remarked that both the primary nodulizers and ferrosilicon inoculants contain about 1% calcium.

Research has demonstrated that some calcium addition is required
for proper graphite nucleation (24). This effect was observed
even if cerium was added during the treatment process.

The Rare Earths in Controlling Deleterious Elements

Thus far, the roles of the rare earths as nodulizers in
promoting and/or controlling nucleation and growth of graphite
and the associated phenomenon of control of carbides have been
discussed. Perhaps, however, the most important commercial use
of the rare earth elements has yet to be mentioned. This is the
role that the rare earth elements play in controlling the effects
of certain so-called deleterious elements that are present in
minute (around 0.001% to 0.05%, for example) concentrations in
the melt. Actually, the efficacy of the rare earths in controlling these subversive elements was largely responsible for the
success of the magnesium treatment process. That, in turn, made
the production of nodular iron an economic practicality, which
in turn led to the commercial success of the nodular iron industry (25).

The list of deleterious elements includes lead, bismuth,
antimony and titanium. Others have also suggested that teller-
ium, indium and thallium belong to that group (26, 27, 28). Generally, the first four elements mentioned are of most concern to
the foundryman.

These deleterious elements are usually carried along in the
pig iron or steel scrap melted by the foundry. (It might be
mentioned that foundries were "recycling" metals for centuries
before the practice became fashionable.) If the foundry were a
gray iron foundry, slight concentrations of some of these deleterious elements were not catastrophic. However, when it became
obvious that nodular iron would become a commercial success and
foundries converted some of their capacity to it, the adverse
effects of these elements were observed. For example, many
malleable iron foundries used bismuth and tellurium as carbide
stabilizers in their normal operations in order to avoid primary
graphitization (the precipitation of carbon as graphite upon
solidification rather than as Fe_3C) (29). Because many malleable iron foundries converted to the production of nodular iron,
possible sources for two deleterious elements were already in
the foundry. As another example, lead is a commonly used metal.
Some lead-containing materials may be inadvertently charged into
the melting furnace. Lead base paint used on castings may have
some effect, even though the lead is volatilized to some extent
at iron-founding temperatures. (Lead, it should be mentioned,
also adversely affects flake iron morphology. Concentrations of
a few parts per million result in Widmanstatten graphite.) The
presence of sufficient quantities of these deleterious elements
results in the degeneration of graphite spheroids to vermicular
or flake graphite. Subsequently, the physical properties of the

casting deteriorate. The tensile strengths and percentages of
elongation approach those quantities observed for gray iron. An
addition of rare earth elements can neutralize the effect of these
deleterious elements. For example, the graphite in a sample containing 0.012% lead is shown in Figure 10. After the addition of
0.017% cerium (as contained in mischmetal, so the total addition
of rare earth elements was about 0.03%), the sphericity of the
graphite was largely restored (see Figure 11) (30).

Similar deleterious effects of small concentrations (that is,
0.001% to 0.005%) have been well documented for bismuth and antimony. Similarly, these effects were overcome by additions of
small amounts of the rare earth elements. In the industry, it is
accepted that roughly 0.01% cerium (once again as mischmetal that
contains 50% cerium and approximately 50% lanthanum, neodymium
and praseodymium) will neutralize the effects of the deleterious
elements. The result is the production of high quality nodular
iron, while still allowing for the use of commercially available
steel scrap as a raw material.

The mechanism by which these deleterious elements are controlled is still a matter of speculation. Some researchers have
suggested that the rare earth elements combine with the deleterious elements to form innocuous insoluble intermetallic compounds
(31). However, such particles have been observed, using the
electron microprobe, only when concentrations of both the rare
earths and deleterious elements were well above those levels
usually found in commercial practice. Even then, the composition
of the particular phases was not determined. Further, the effective level of cerium at which the beneficial effects are observed
suggests that the mechanism may not be simply compound formation.

Certainly, from the thermodynamic studies reported by the
Rare Earth Information Center concerning the rare earth compounds
formed with bismuth, lead, and antimony, the formation of at
least some intermetallics would appear possible (32). On the
other hand, one might question if the amounts in a bath that also
contains roughly 0.01% sulfur and about 0.01% oxygen are sufficient to actually control the deleterious elements by forming
intermetallic compounds. Is it possible that the rare earth
elements are essentially used up in other chemical reactions?
Furthermore, it is known that arsenic can be alloyed with nodular
iron to form a pearlitic matrix. Levels of 0.2% arsenic and 0.3%
manganese have no effect upon graphite morphology even when cer-
ium-free alloys were used as nodulizers (33). Why doesn't arsenic behave like the other elements of that family in the
periodic table?

It is also interesting to note that the deleterious elements,
with the exception of titanium, are elements that can be used to
stabilize the iron-carbide phase. Titanium is also the only so-
called deleterious element that appears to be somewhat controllable by additions of more magnesium, instead of one of the rare
earths in common use (34). However, the use of rare earths

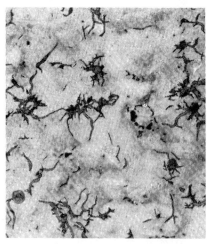

Figure 10. Flake graphite observed in a nodular iron containing 0.012% Pb (30). Etched in picric acid; 50×. Composition: 2.44% Si, 0.47% Mn, 0.010% S, 1.58% Ni, 0.113% Mg, 0.012% Pb.

Transactions of the
American Foundrymen's Society

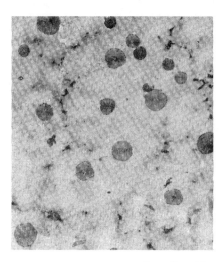

Figure 11. Restoration of spheroidal graphite in iron containing 0.013% Pb by addition of 0.017% Ce, as mischmetal (30). Etched in picric acid; 50×. Composition: 2.35% Si, 0.50% Mn, 0.010% S, 1.66% Ni, 0.079% Mg, 0.013% Pb.

Transactions of the
American Foundrymen's Society

controls titanium more efficiently. Titanium does not form intermetallic compounds with the rare earth elements either. Perhaps
the rare earths act as surface active elements on the growing
graphite or somehow affect the activity of carbon. Is it possible that some of the intermetallics, if they are formed at all,
affect graphite growth by formation of surfactant compounds? Is
there a difference in the chemical properties of the various intermetallics that would allow for the use of arsenic to stabilize
pearlite and the other elements in that family to be deleterious.
Obviously, there is considerable room for further research.

   Little research has been reported concerning the determina-
tion of which of the rare earths normally used in the industry
might be more potent in controlling these deleterious elements.
An early researcher reported that cerium appeared to be most
effective (35). Certainly, cerium is the most commonly used rare
earth, but primarily because of its abundance. However, since
that time, the problem of potency has not been addressed in detail.

   The effectiveness of the rare earths in overcoming the effects
of these deleterious elements, has resulted in some rare earths
being added to all proprietary magnesium-ferrosilicon alloys produced by major United States manufacturers. A foundry can speci-
fy a magnesium-ferrosilicon alloy containing a stated percentage
of rare earths (normally from 0.3% to 1.0%) because of the micro-
structural benefits to be obtained. However, even if a foundry
specifies the so-called "regular" grade of magnesium-ferrosilicon,
there are nominally 0.1% rare earths elements present. Typically,
a foundry might add from 1.5% to 2.0% of a 5% magnesium-ferrosilicon alloy via the primary nodulizer. In that case, enough
rare earth elements (0.015% to 0.12%) are unintentionally added
with the so-called "regular" magnesium-ferrosilicon to control
the deleterious elements found in their usual concentrations in
the treated iron.

   Today, a new variety of cast iron, called compacted graphite
iron, is gaining importance. It should be noted that this is an
intermediate form of graphite (vermicular) between flake and
spheroidal. It has the same appearance as the graphite in those
irons having deleterious elements present (see Figure 12). Such
Irons can be produced by deliberate undertreatment of the base
iron with magnesium and rare earths. Another method of producing
these irons has been to introduce enough titanium into the magnesium-ferrosilicon plus rare earth alloy to make the production
of completely spheroidal graphite irons improbable in most casting sections. It remains to be seen what role the rare earths
may ultimately play in the production of these compacted graphite
irons. They are being carefully scrutinized for use in compacted
graphite irons. If compacted graphite irons are ever used in
large quantities, the demand for rare earths could be appreciably
increased.

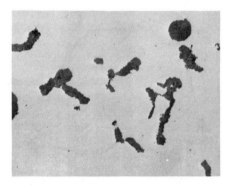

Figure 12.   Typical microstructure of compacted graphite iron (200×)

Future for the Rare Earth Elements

The rare earth elements have played a key part in the discovery and commercialization of nodular iron. The efficacy of these elements in controlling the effects of deleterious elements, in nucleation, and as nodulizers has assured their continued use.

The tonnages of the rare earths used are, of course, a function of the vitality of the nodular iron industry. That future looks promising indeed. In 1959, production of nodular iron castings was less than 170 thousand tons (36). By 1978, over 2.9 million tons of nodular iron castings were produced (37). That represents a seventeen fold increase over twenty years. (Assuming a typical 50% yield, in 1978, there would have been almost six million tons of hot metal treated.) The outlook for production is not completely optimistic; for the foundry industry, as a whole, is presently experiencing a painful period. In 1979, casting shipments of nodular iron were off about 10% compared to 1978, and this year appears even gloomier. Readjustments in the automotive industry, which represents about 50% of the nodular iron market, will undoubtedly have a negative impact on production statistics over both the short and long terms. Downturns in housing starts and, consequently, in the use of nodular iron pipe, will also have a negative impact, hopefully in the short term only. However, as new products are required and as other nations strive for a higher standard of living, the use of nodular iron and the concurrent need for the rare earth elements will continue to exist, and likely grow to some extent.

It is very difficult to estimate the amount of rare earths going into this market because of the wide variety of materials used and their different characteristics with respect to recoveries in their manufacture and use. For example, alloys containing from 0.1% to as high as 30% rare earths are used in the various stages in the production of nodular iron. Production processes of the nodulizing alloys themselves also vary widely with corresponding variations in the recoveries of rare earths, and these data are considered confidential by most producers. In addition, the fact that more than one source of rare earths is being employed makes it obvious that only a general estimate of demand can be made. Working from a normal production year, such as 1978, there are approximately 1.4 to 1.5 million pounds of rare earths in the nodular irons produced. This would translate to a ceric hydrate demand of three- to four-million pounds annually, a number which would be reduced somewhat depending upon the market demand for alloys using the lower cerium sources of rare earths.

As far as future research is concerned, one can anticipate a greater concern with the effects of the individual rare earth elements. Effects of cerium as opposed to lanthanum, or the other rare earths, may be more thoroughly researched. Perhaps the list of those elements specified by the foundry industry will eventually embrace those beyond neodymium. Nevertheless, much

research needs to be done before use of even the rare earths
commonplace in today's foundries is optimized.

LITERATURE CITED

1. Boyle, A. "The Structure of Cast Iron"; American Society
    for Metals: Cleveland, Ohio, 1947.

2. Ruff, G. F.; Doshi, B. K. Modern Casting, 1980, 70, (6), 51.

3. Flinn, R. A.; Trojan, P. K. "Engineering Materials and
    Their Applications"; Houghton Mifflin: Boston, Mass.,
    1975; p. 225.

4. Source was Bureau of the Census as quoted in Foundry Man-
    agement and Technology, June 1980, 108, 56, for the
    year 1978.

5. Morrogh, H.; Williams, W. J. Journal of the Iron and Steel
    Institute, March 1948, 158, 309.

6. Ibid., p. 309.

7. Morrogh, H. Transactions of the American Foundrymen's
    Society, 1948, 56, 72.

8. Karsay, S. I. "Ductile Iron Production Practices"; AFS
    Publication: Des Plaines, Ill., 1975, p. 4.

9. Francis, B. Metallurgical Transactions A, 1979, 10A, 21-31.

10. Warrick, R. J. AFS Cast Metals Research Journal, 1966, 2,
    (3), 97-108.

11. Lalich, M. J.; Hitchings, J. R. Transactions of the Ameri-
    can Foundrymen's Society, 1976, 84, 653-664.

12. Rice, M. A.; Malizio, A. B.; Brooks, H. F. Transactions of
    the American Foundrymen's Society, 1974, 82, 15-26.

13. Mickelson, R. L.; Merrill, T. W. Transactions of the
    American Foundrymen's Society, 1968, 76, 289-296.

14. Weast, R. C.; Astle, M. J., Ed. "Handbook of Chemistry and
    Physics - 60th Ed"; CRC Press: Boca Raton, Florida,
    1978; p. B221.

15. Lyman, T., Ed. "Metals Handbook - 8th Ed."; American
    Society for Metals: Novelty, Ohio, 1961, Vol. 1,
    p. 365.

16. Rice, Malizio, Brooks, op. cit., 15-26

17. Rice, Malizio, Brooks, op. cit., 15-26.

18. Capeletti, T. L.; Harnaday, J. R. Transactions of the American Foundrymen's Society, 1974, 82, 59-64.

19. Lalich, M. J. Transactions of the American Foundrymen's Society, 1974, 82, 441-448.

20. Amin, A. S.; Loper, C. R. Transactions of the American Foundrymen's Society, 1978, 86, 505-512.

21. McCluhan, T. K. Transactions of the American Foundrymen's Society, 1967, 75, 372-375.

22. Lalich, op. cit., 444.

23. Amin, Loper, op. cit., 512.

24. Linebarger, H. F. Unpublished research.

25. Clark, R. A. Private Communication.

26. Morrogh, H. Transactions of the American Foundrymen's Society, 1952, 60, 439-452.

27. Sawyer, J. F.; Wallace, J. F. Transactions of the American Foundrymen's Society, 1968, 76, 386-404.

28. Everest, A. B. as quoted in Morrogh, H. Transactions of the American Foundrymen's Society, 1952, 60, 451-452.

29. Ed. "Malleable Iron Castings"; Ann Arbor Press: Ann Arbor, Mich., 1960, p. 351.

30. Morrogh, op. cit., 442.

31. Bates, C. E. Effect of Neutralization of Trace Elements in Gray and Ductile Iron ; Ph.D. Thesis, Case Western Reserve University: Cleveland, Ohio, 1968.

32. Gschneidner, K. A., Jr.; Kippenhan, N.; McMasters, O. D. "Thermochemistry of the Rare Earths"; Rare-Earth Information Center, Iowa State University: Ames, Iowa, 1973, pp. 50-56.

33. Morrogh, op. cit., 447.

34. Lalich, M. J.; Loper, C. R.; Heine, R. W. Transactions of
     the American Foundrymen's Society, 1972, 80, 401–420.

35. Everest, A. B. as quoted in Morrogh, H. Transactions of
     the American Foundrymen's Society, 1952, 60, 451.

36. Source was Bureau of the Census as quoted in Foundry
     Management and Technology, Dec. 1960, 87, 83.

37. Source was Bureau of the Census as quoted in Foundry
     Management and Technology, June 1980, 108, 56.

RECEIVED February 18, 1981.

The Rare Earth Metals in Steel

L. A. LUYCKX

METSERV, Incorporated, 226 East Hazelcroft Aveune, New Castle, PA 16105

This is not a comprehensive review paper. My purpose is to concentrate on the leitmotiv of this symposium, namely on the large scale usage of the rare earth elements in industry. For research details and minor uses, the reader should refer to a set of reviews by Trombe (1), Savitskii (2), Spedding & Daane (3),- Kleber & Love (4), Leroy Eyring (5), Anderson & Spreadborough (6), Hirschhorn (7), Kippehan & Gschneidner (8), Reinhardt (9), Raman (10), and Waudby (11). References (7),(8) and (11) report on many industrial tests while references (2), (8) and (10) give interesting insights into the voluminous Russian literature on the subject.

The Rare Earth Alloys Used Today In Steelmaking.

Mischmetal.

This well known alloy produced by fused chloride electrolysis of the light lanthanide elements constitutes over 90% of the rare earth metals (REM's) consumed for steelmaking in the western world. It is estimated that approximately 3,000 metric tons of mischmetal, worth about $35 million, are added to liquid steel every year. Typical mischmetal for steelmaking contains 95 to 98% REM, 0.5 to 5% Fe to lower the melting point towards the eutectic and to make the casting of shapes easier, and from 0.1 to 1% of residual impurities, Mg, Al, Si, Ca, O, N, H, etc.

The relative concentrations of the four light lanthanide elements and of the "heavies" can vary significantly depending on the origin of the ores. Lanthanum content may vary from 17 to 30%, cerium from 45 to 58%, praseodymium from 4 to 8%, neodymium from 11 to 20% and the "heavies" including samarium, gadolinium and yttrium, from less than 0.1 to 2%. Although the effects of these individual elements on the properties of steel are far from identical, the cost of chemical separation prior to electrolysis can not be justified in terms of improved properties, at least for high tonnage carbon steels. In superalloys, lanthanum is specified.

0097-6156/81/0164-0043$09.00/0
© 1981 American Chemical Society

The price of mischmetal was of the order of $6.50 per lb during
most of the fifties then it drifted down to a low of $2.85 from
1967 to 1973 and rose back with inflation to $5.30 today (12).
    From the large scale steelmaking usage viewpoint, there is
plenty of ore and excess production capacity on a worldwide basis.
The main mischmetal producers of the western world are, (13,14):
-United States: Reactive Metals & Alloys Corporation and Ronson
Metals Corporation with a total capacity of 2,500 metric tons per
year (tpa) and working close to full capacity and 85 to 90% of the
output consumed by the steel mills.
-Europe: Treibacher Chemische Werke in Austria (1,000 tpa), Th.
Goldschmidt AG in West Germany (1,000 tpa), Ronson-British Flint
in the United Kingdom (150 tpa) and Rhone Poulenc-Pechiney in
France (250 tpa), most of these facilities working at much less
than 50% capacity because of substitution since the mid-seventies
in the steel industry.
-Brazil: Corona, Colibri and Fluminense with a combined capacity
of 1,000 tpa, also working below capacity, almost all of the output being exported.
-Japan: Santoku Metal Corporation (200 tpa) supplying a very limited steelmaking demand, is the only producer having converted entirely to the oxide-fluoride electrolysis process during 1979, while
increasing capacity (15).
The total mischmetal production capacity for the western world is
thus estimated at some 6,500 metric tons per year. It is currently
utilized at less than 50%, chiefly because of recent substitution
in the European steel industry. The U.S. mischmetal manufacturers
are now, in effect, producing over 50% of the free world's total.

    Physical Properties of Mischmetal. With regard to its use
in steelmaking, five physical properties of mischmetal are of importance. First, its total solubility in all liquid steels as
shown in Figure 1. The second property of importance is the low
vapor pressure shown by mischmetal at liquid steel temperatures.
In table I, (16), vapor pressures of the main elements of mischmetal are compared to common alloying elements for steelmaking.

Table I. Vapor Pressures of Alloying Elements in Steel @ 1,800°K.

Lanthanum	5.69×10^{-7}	at.
Cerium	6.82×10^{-7}	at.
Silicon	2.15×10^{-6}	at.
Praseodymium	1.49×10^{-5}	at.
Neodymium	1.39×10^{-4}	at.
Aluminum	8.08×10^{-4}	at.
Manganese	2.81×10^{-2}	at.
Calcium	1.29	at.
Magnesium	12.6	at.

A third property to be considered is the density of the alloy to
be introduced in the liquid steel. Table II, (17), compares the

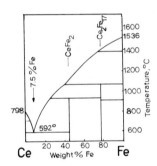

Figure 1. Cerium–iron phase diagram showing complete solubility in the liquid phase, zero solubility in the solid phases and one, single, low-melting point eutectic @ 92.5% Ce.

densities at room temperature of alloying elements to that of liquid carbon steel. It shows that mischmetal will have little buoyancy in liquid steel and compares favorably with most other additives.

Table II. <u>Compared Densities in Liquid Steel, grams/cm^3</u>.

Manganese	7.3
Liquid Steel	7.2
<u>Mischmetal</u>	6.7
Zirconium	6.5
Vanadium	6.0
REM Silicide, solid,	5.7
Titanium	4.5
REM silicide, crush,	3.5
Aluminum	2.7
Silicon	2.3
Magnesium	1.7
Calcium	1.5

The fourth property of concern is the melting point of the alloying additive as compared to the liquid steel bath. Here again mischmetal compares favorably with most other alloying metals used in steelmaking as shown in table III, (<u>16</u>):

Table III. <u>Compared Melting Points of Alloying Elements.</u>

	°C	°K	°F
Magnesium	649	922	1201
Aluminum	660	933	1220
<u>Cerium</u>	798	1071	1468
<u>Mischmetal</u> (4%Fe)	816	1089	1500
Calcium	839	1112	1541
<u>Lanthanum</u>	920	1193	1688
<u>Praseodymium</u>	931	1204	1708
<u>Neodymium</u>	1016	1289	1860
Manganese	1244	1517	2270
Silicon	1412	1685	2574
Low Carbon Steel	1520	1793	2768
Titanium	1670	1943	3038
Zirconium	1852	2125	3365
Chromium	1857	2130	3374
Molybdenum	2617	2890	4745

The fifth property is the negligible solubility of all rare earth elements in solid iron as shown also on the binary phase diagram of Figure 1.

The first four properties are very favorable to mischmetal as a steel additive. In fact their combination make mischmetal the most alloyable of all ferroalloys commonly introduced in liquid steel (<u>18</u>). While adding mischmetal to a liquid steel ingot, for example, after interruption of teeming at the hot top junction, Figure 2, no flare develops, the alloy disappears quickly under the surface and the distribution of the REM's throughout the ingot body is easily insured by resumption of teeming to fill the hot top volume (18, 19). No other metal can be added to steel using that simple practice without risking non-homogeneous distribution.

On the other hand, the fifth property is a serious limitation of the role of the lanthanides in steelmaking as it prohibits any solid solution alloying and thus forces the metallurgist to carefully avoid excess mischmetal addition for fear of making the steel "hot-short." In Figure 1, it can be seen that a low melting point eutectic develops with any excess metallic REM content present in the steel towards the end of solidification, and concentrates at the "as-cast" grain boundaries. This grain boundary film is liquid at all hot rolling temperatures and thus makes the steel highly "hot-short" as exemplified by an industrial accident pictured in Figure 3. This same grain boundary eutectic is often interpreted as "dirt" or oxide inclusions because during polishing of the samples, the eutectic which is highly concentrated in REM's (some 90 to 95%) oxidizes rapidly, and requires special precautions to be observed unaltered (18).

Rare Earth Silicide (RES). Developed by Vanadium Corporation of America, now part of Foote Mineral Company, and Molycorp during the early and mid-sixties, this alloy was then and still is now cheaper than mischmetal to produce, per unit REM. It is produced in the submerged arc furnace by direct reduction of purified bastnasite ore, quartz, iron ore or scrap and carbonaceous reducants. Composed roughly of 1/3 mischmetal, 1/3 silicon and 1/3 iron, the alloy was marketed at 40¢/lb in 1968, about 42% of the price of electrolytic mischmetal per unit REM. This attractive pricing played a key part in the development of the high strength low alloy steel (HSLA) market when it started at Jones & Laughlin Steel Corp. in 1968-9 (20), and Stelco in 1970 (21). The disadvantages of the alloy center around its physical properties as compared to mischmetal. Its lower density, higher melting point (about 2200°F) and "chill effect" or the need to supply sensible heat from the steel melt to three times more material than for mischmetal, have contributed alloying difficulties particularly with the popular mold additions. It is virtually impractical, for example, to plunge rare earth silicide in a steel ladle because of the excessive buoyancy and chilling effects. In mold additions, rare earth silicide is more conducive to surface and subsurface defects than mischmetal and cannot be added late at the hot top junction. Although the ferroalloy reached high consumptions in North America, capturing up to 90% of the total REM market in steel, with a peak of about 1800 tons of REM equivalent in 1972, its current share of the market is now down to less than 15% of that market, because of its unfavorable alloyability. Attempts at reaching higher REM

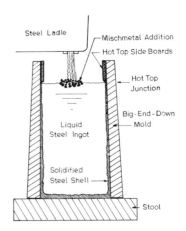

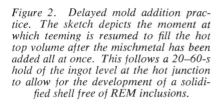

Figure 2. Delayed mold addition practice. The sketch depicts the moment at which teeming is resumed to fill the hot top volume after the mischmetal has been added all at once. This follows a 20–60-s hold of the ingot level at the hot junction to allow for the development of a solidified shell free of REM inclusions.

Figure 3. Hot shortness—large and deep tears and holes in a slab of carbon steel treated with 6 lbs of mischmetal per ton instead of 2 lbs, by accidental malpractice

concentrations (40 to 50%) pushed the submerged arc furnace closer to its thermodynamic limits and also resulted in an unstable alloy showing spontaneous decrepitation in storage. Production costs increased faster for the submerged arc process than for the electrolytic cell, at least for REM production, over the last decade so that the price ratio RES/MM has moved progressively from 0.42 to 0.65, reducing further the main attractiveness of the rare earth silicide alloy for steelmaking.

Even today, however, the alloy is favored over mischmetal for multiple ladle practices and for a combined deoxidation-desulfurization-sulfide shape control effect using large ladle additions in the production of critical line pipe qualities. This latter application is threatened by substitution with calcium injection as we will see later. Because it was based on bastnasite, an exclusively American ore at the time, and because of its metallurgical limitations, RES never took hold extensively in Europe and in Japan. The recent emergence of a very large Chinese bastnasite deposit may prompt renewed interest in some sort of direct reduced REM alloy during the eighties.

Other REM Alloys. None of the many other REM containing alloys are used in steelmaking today with the possible exception of Russian alloys of which we know little. Their "ferrocerium" is in fact very similar to our mischmetal in most references (8). The only other REM compound still in use in a few U.S. shops is called by its trade name "T-compound." This mixture of REM oxides and fluorides was used during World War II as a fluxing agent for non-metallic inclusions in the early production of aircraft quality alloy steels in electric arc furnaces (22).

Physico-Chemistry and Ferrous Metallurgy of the REM's.

Replacement of FeS by MnS. To focus on the essential, temporarily irreplaceable, properties of the REM's in steelmaking, we have to highlight their affinity for sulfur. From the beginnings of the iron age, sulfur has had deleterious effects in steelmaking (23). After it almost bankrupted Henry Bessemer's new steelmaking process in 1860 (24), sulfur was prevented from making the steel "hot-short" during rolling by manganese additions.

Since then, 99.9% of the steel made has used manganese as an absolute must for that reason. Much later, it became clear that hot shortness is the result of iron sulfide, which precipitates at the as cast grain boundaries of the steel ingot, being liquid at hot rolling temperatures. As the affinity of manganese for sulfur is substantially higher than that of iron for sulfur, all of the sulfur will precipitate as MnS rather than FeS provided a high enough Mn/S ratio is achieved to counterbalance the large Fe/Mn ratio. Fortunately, MnS is a rather plastic solid at hot rolling temperatures and thus eliminates hot-shortness.

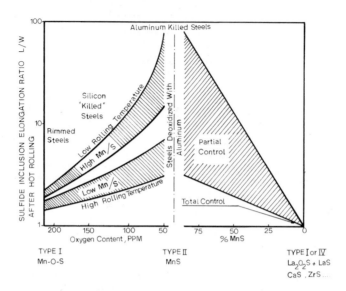

Figure 4.   Hot plasticity of sulfide inclusions during hot rolling of steel as a function of oxygen content, Mn/S ratio, rolling temperatures, and substitution by stronger sulfide formers. The hot plasticity is measured in length-to-width ratio of elongation after hot rolling, in longitudinal sections.

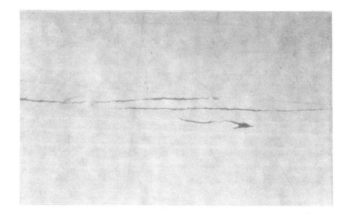

Figure 5.   Elongated manganese sulfide inclusion in aluminum killed steel after hot rolling; unetched, 300×

Limitations of the MnS Approach. For eight decades, the manganese solution was acceptable, particularly because most early
steels were not thoroughly deoxidized and the plasticity is drastically reduced by the presence of oxygen in the sulfide (20) as
depicted on the left side of Figure 4. However, with the growing
use of aluminum as a deoxidizer instead of silicon, particularly
in hot rolled steels in which inclusions are not broken up by cold
rolling, it was found that the MnS inclusions were extremely elongated and the mechanical properties were substantially degraded
particularly in the directions perpendicular to rolling.

Some relief was obtained with cross rolling of the plates but
this is not applicable to continuous hot rolling. Also some relief was obtained with lower sulfur contents but there is a limit
there too because the plasticity of the manganese sulfide increases with the Mn to S ratio (20). Over the last 30 years, manganese
has also been assigned other metallurgical functions of strength-
ening and phase control so that most high strength low alloy
steels (HSLA), contain over 1% Mn and sometimes up to 2% Mn, ag-
gravating considerably the plasticity of the manganese sulfides
during hot rolling.

In conventional aluminum-deoxidized steels, the extra-low
dissolved oxygen content maintains the sulfur in solution in the
liquid steel until the end of the solidification process. Since
sulfur exhibits virtually no solubility in the solid steel -- less
than 0.001% in the bcc structure -- a MnS-Fe eutectic suddenly
precipitates at the as cast grain boundaries, the so called "Type
II" structure described by Sims (25). This weakens the as cast
structure and also results in elongated MnS inclusions in the hot
rolled steel plates, coils, sheets, bars, wires etc, as shown in
Figure 5.

Substitution of MnS. Aside from eliminating the sulfur content to less than 0.001%, which is impractical in tonnage steelmaking, the only solution is substitution of manganese in the sulfide by elements which combine a higher affinity for sulfur than
manganese with a non-plastic sulfide during hot rolling, see right
side of Figure 4. In Figure 6, a comparison of potential elements
organized by increasing negativity of their free energies of formation (26), shows an apparent large choice of alternatives including titanium, zirconium, calcium and the lanthanides.

Not only do the lanthanides outperform most other substitutes
for sulfide stability, they also show a unique feature, the formation of an extremely stable oxysulfide of the La_2O_2S type. Its
free energy of formation is so highly negative, close to that of
the most stable oxides, Figure 7, that, when REM's are added to
liquid steel predeoxidized with aluminum, generally no rare earth
oxides are formed, at least as such (27-29). Samsonov (30) had
already studied the REM oxysulfides, which helped Luyckx identify
the phase in non-metalic inclusions based on microprobe analysis
in 1969 (18), Figure 8.

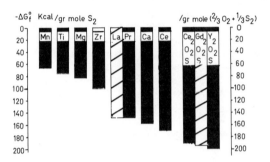

Figure 6. *Free energy of formation of some sulfides and REM oxysulfides at 3000°F (19).*

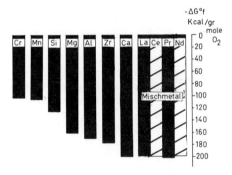

Figure 7. *Free energy of formation of some oxides at 3000°F (19)*

In the search for substitutes, other considerations than just sulfide stability have to be considered. These include the possible interference of the newly introduced element with other steel porperties, the plasticity of the new sulfides, the physical alloyability of the additive and, of course, the cost effectiveness of the additive. Zirconium and titanium interfere with other properties of the steel because of the excessive stability of their nitrides, Figure 9, and carbides, Figure 10. Although considerable usage of these two elements has played a part in sulfide substitution -- over 500 metric tons of nuclear zircalloy scrap were used in 1974 -- it appears that their role will progressively fade away primarily because of poor low temperature impact properties of steels treated with Zr and Ti.

Calcium and particularly magnesium show excessive vapor pressure at steelmaking temperatures, Table I, but this alloyability problem has been somewhat alleviated by submerging the introduction of the calcium alloy under 3 meters of liquid steel (31). However, independently of vapor pressure, it is the low solubility of calcium in liquid iron which limits the effective substitution of MnS by CaS to extremely low sulfur levels, particularly when the manganese content is high, 2% for example (32).

Replacing MnS by RES. Using incremental quantities of mischmetal (and also of rare earth silicide) it was demonstrated in laboratory heats at the Graham Research Laboratory of Jones & Laughlin Steel in 1968, that the predictability and control of the morphology of the sulfide inclusions can be achieved (20). This control could not even be approached using calcium alloys in large multiple additions. With the rare earth metals, all that has to be ascertained is a REM/S ratio of at least 3/1 in weight%. No other properties were affected and thus no interference was detected. With a retained REM/S ratio of between 3 and 6/1, the manganese sulfide inclusions were totally eliminated and replaced with small undeformable round or blocky REM oxysulfides and sulfides, Figure 11.

The most dramatic results were, however, the complete elimination of cracking of the test plates when they were bent over a sharp radius in the transverse direction, Figure 12, and the more than doubling of the transverse shelf energy as measured by 2/3 Charpy tests, Figure 13 (20). The latter also shows the progressive improvements with incremental additions of REM's.

Commercial Applications. Immediate commercial application of these results to an 80,000 psi HSLA steel grade fully confirmed the superiority of the approach in terms of reproducibility, cleanliness of the steel, excellent properties and limited cost, $2.00/ ingot ton using rare earth silicide at the time. The practice was an extra-simple mold addition by gravity of 5 lbs of RES per ingot ton during the first half of the teeming of each ingot. The technique coined as "SULFIDE SHAPE CONTROL with REM's" spread

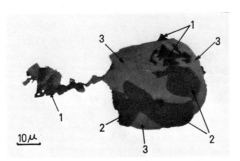

*Figure 8.   Complex rare earth inclusion in hot rolled 80,000 psi HSLA steel. This
is one of the largest inclusions found after scanning many longitudinal cross sections
in commercial 0.325 inch sheet to show the three main phases: 1, the darkest gray
phase is a REM modified alumina; 2, the medium-gray phase is the REM oxysulfide; 3, the light-gray phase is the REM sulfide, RE_xS_y, with x and y close to 1.
Unetched, 350×. The entire inclusion is bright-red in polarized light. Microprobe
analysis shows a 1.4 to 1.6 La/Ce ratio in phases 2 and 3, contrasting with the 0.5
to 0.7 La/Ce ratio in the RE silicide mold additive.*

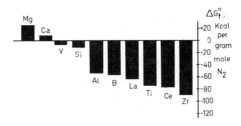

Figure 9.   Free energy of formation of some nitrides at 3000°F

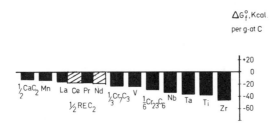

Figure 10.   Free energy of formation of some carbides at 3000°F

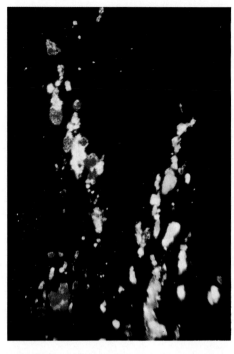

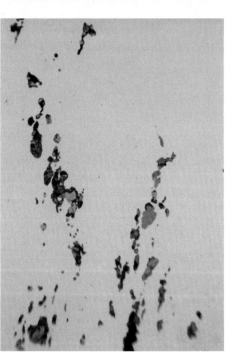

Figure 11. Subsurface concentration of REM oxysulfides and sulfides (left micrograph) in normal light and right micrograph; in polarized light. Magnification, 285×.

In the general area, about two thirds of the inclusions appeared bright red under polarized light and were identified by microprobe scanning as are earth sulfides. Most of the remainder show bright orange colors under polarized light and were identified as oxysulfides of the REM. Darker areas under direct light show white-grayish polarized effects, and are the result of dishing out of inclusion material during polishing and replacement by polishing compounds and residues.

AIME—NOHC
Steelmaking Proceedings

Figure 12. Badly cracked outer radius of a transverse bend around a ½ thickness radius in untreated 80,000 psi HSLA steel (top); Similar steel plate and sheet after REM treatment (bottom) (33)

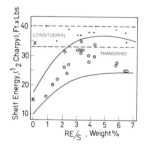

Figure 13. Impact energy at 100% ductile fracture temperature, which is "shelf energy," as a function of REM-to-sulfur ratio retained in the 80,000 psi steel. Note the progressive effect of increasing REM additions on the transverse impacts while the longitudinal values remain virtually unchanged. The X points represent untreated steel.

at lightning speed to other steelmaking plants in the U.S., Canada and Europe. However mischmetal quickly displaced RES in market share as discussed earlier.

After an early start in HSLA steels for automotive applications as exemplified in Figure 14 (33), the bulk of the usage of mischmetal shifted to line pipe steel, a market that was very active from 1970 to 1974 and caught most steelmakers off guard without other alternatives to control MnS inclusions. A recent application involving the node of an offshore platform with complex welding of tubular shapes is shown in Figure 15 (33). Other applications which developed during the past decade were all directly related to sulfide shape control. Resistance to spalling during cold punching of high carbon plow wheels for agricultural machines is one example. Resistance to lamellar tearing of welded structures (34), in which the elimination of elongated MnS inclusions is essential, is an other example.

Finally, since late 1976, a large tonnage application has developed in the U.S. involving high strength welded tubes for deep oil well casing and drilling, competing head-on with the more conventional seamless tubes produced through the Mannesman process. About 1500 tons of mischmetal per year are consumed for this latter application. This total consumption is expected to increase at least until 1983, when complete predesulfurization of the steel will reduce the REM consumption per ton of steel by more than 50%. Today's average consumption per ton of steel treated is about 1 3/4 lbs of mischmetal or equivalent in rare earth silicide. It should drop to 3/4 lbs / ton by 1990.

Steelmaking Practices. There are four techniques for adding mischmetal to liquid steel, two involving the ladle and two involving the ingot mold. Without entering the details that can be found in the literature (18, 19, 32), the ladle techniques are: one, the plunging of a canister containing from 100 to 1,000 lbs of cast mischmetal alloyed with a little magnesium to promote agitation and mixing (35); and two, an introduction through the alloy feeding system of a ladle degasser, after degassing has been completed and an aluminum "trimming" addition has completed the deoxidation prior to REM feeding (36).

The two mold practices involve hand feeding of preweighed bags during the early part of mold filling to promote maximum mixing (37), and the "DELAYED MOLD ADDITION PRACTICE" described while discussing the physical properties of mischmetal (18). Other practices used less extensively and mostly in Europe and Japan include the feeding of a wire containing the alloy into the tundish or the mold of slab casters, the hanging of a mischmetal bar in the ingot mold during bottom pouring and the injection of REM alloy powders with or after calcium silicon injection to improve sulfide shape control after desulfurization with calcium. Recoveries of the REM units vary from as low as 25% with the second ladle practice to as much as 80% with the delayed mold addition and 95% with wire feeding in the slab casting mold.

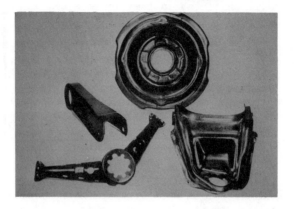

AIME–NOHC Steelmaking Proceedings

Figure 14.   Examples of some automotive parts produced commercially using the cold formability introduced by the REM addition (33)

Figure 15.   Off-shore platform node construction showing the complex welding assembly job requiring outstanding resistance to lamellar tearing in the electric-resistance-welded (ERW) steel pipe stock. Excellent through-thickness ductility is obtained by low sulfur plus REM treatment in the ladle, plunging a mischmetal canister.

Problems With REM Treatment.

Subsurface Defects in Ingots. The precipitation of RE_2O_2S and RE_xS_y as solid particles in the liquid steel immediately after the addition is conducive to inclusion clustering, the forming of large -- up to inches in diameter -- spatial networks of small -- 1 to 10 micron -- non-metallic particles adhering to each other by surface tension (38). In addition, slow melting and dissolution particularly of rare earth silicide leads to oxidation of the alloy during mold addition resulting in solid scums and subsurface entrapments, which ultimately result in surface defects on the finished rolled product, Figure 16. The delayed mold addition technique all but eliminates these problems and the use of rare earth silicide in the mold has all but disappeared largely because of these problems.

Ladle and Tundish Nozzle Blockage. The same clustering mechanism is responsible for this serious operating problem which is not specific to the use of REM's, but to any additive conducive to solid inclusions in the liquid steel. Deoxidation with aluminum, zirconium, titanium, even high additions of calcium, all can lead to Al_2O_3, ZrO_2, TiO_2, CaS inclusions which tend to accumulate in the nozzle throat and ultimately stop the flow of liquid steel completely. An obvious solution would appear to be the feeding of REM's after the nozzle, for example in the form of wire. However, there is then maximum tendency for the problem described above to develop in the slab casting mold. The best solution to this problem is to minimize the volume of inclusions passing through the nozzle by upgrading the ladle refractory and performing a suitable stirring after the REM treatment to give the inclusion clusters maximum chance to separate out of the melt by adherence to the ladle slag or to a refractory wall (39). Above all, this problem can only be solved when initial sulfur levels are low, ideally less than 0.007%, but no more than 0.012%.

Bottom Cone Segregations. Layered accumulations of RE sulfides and oxysulfides near the bottom of the ingot (the maximum concentration is at about 25% of the ingot height) is observed practically in all large ingots with sulfur content over 0.010% and treated with REM's in the mold. This condition degrades the through thickness properties of steel plates because of the large concentration of small inclusions acting as notches. Among others, a strong research team at Kawasaki Steel, Chiba Works, headed by Drs. Sanbongi, Emi, Habu and others has made an exhaustive and constructive study of the phenomenon (32, 40, 41). They proposed the following complete solution: with the required RE/S ratio of 2.7/1 for total MnS substitution, the controlling factor in the severity of segregation is the RE x S product or, ultimately, the

Figure 16.   Shallow surface crack at the outer radius of a sharp ½T bend on 80,000 psi steel sheet (top).   Corresponding subsurface concentration of REM oxysulfides and sulfides in a slab cross section near the surface.   The parent ingot was treated with 5 lbs of rare earth silicide per ton of ingot steel (bottom).   The bottom picture is from a Baumann print or sulfur print, not sensitive to the oxides and thus eliminating the argument of reoxidation as main cause of surface defects in REM treated steels.   Magnification, 2.5×.

sulfur content. For a RE x S product which they call K_{RE} below or equal to 13 x 10^{-5} the "bottom sedimental zone" disappears, leaving faintly "enriched A and V segregations" and less top segregation. This, in turn, corresponds to a sulfur content of 0.007% maximum. However, a S_{max} of 0.005% is preferred with the corresponding K_{RE} product of 10 x 10^{-5}, because then all segregations disappear and the resulting steel reaches its maximum attainable properties with total shape control without side effects, Figure 17.

  REM Alloy Costs. For a typical North American sulfur specification of 0.015% max., a minimum retained REM content of 0.045 is required to insure full MnS substitution, i.e. a REM/S ratio of minimum 3/1. Using the delayed mold addition practice with at least 75% recovery and mischmetal @ $5.30/lb the current cost of a typical treatment is:

$$\$5.3 \times \frac{0.00045 \times 2,000}{0.75} = \$6.35/\text{net ton of ingot steel.}$$

With ladle plunging or additions through a degassing unit, the costs per ton can go as high as $12.00 per ton for guaranteed sulfide shape control and maximum transverse properties which generally require a RE/S equal to 4 instead of 3.

  The direct and simple solution to this cost is obviously to lower the sulfur content prior to mischmetal addition. For every 0.001% reduction in sulfur, there is a minimum 42¢/ton saving using the delayed mold addition technique and the saving potential increases with other, less efficient practices. However, desulfurization costs increase rather sharply when reaching down to the low contents below 0.005%. In Figure 18, the preceeding discussion is summarized showing a minimum in the area of about 0.007% S which is also desirable from a product quality standpoint. This minimum is the total cost of sulfide shape control + desulfurization. This was first presented in 1973 (19) but has been readjusted to the new cost structures.

  Solutions to the Problems with REM. To summarize the solutions to all of the problems associated with REM additions to liquid steel, first it is essential to try and operate at much lower sulfur contents than normally practiced in North America, ideally about 0.005 to 0.007% prior to REM addition. For ingot casting, the delayed mold addition, particularly coupled with low sulfur concentrations is sufficient and economical for most applications. For severe property requirements and for continuous casting, the REM's should be introduced in the ladle, using improved refractories and slags, and a good stirring practice after the treatment. These requirements are essentially the same ones imposed by the vendors of the competing calcium practice. Wire feeding in the slab casting mold is not recommended.

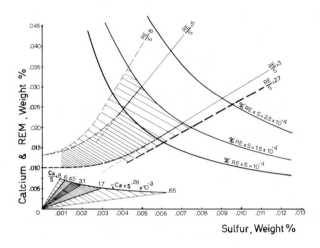

*Figure 17. Representation of the analytical limits to be kept for defect-free REM-
or Ca-treated steel. The shaded areas (deep shade only for calcium) are considered
safe by the Kawasaki team.*

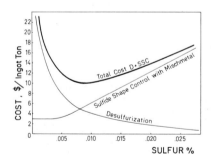

*Figure 18. Economic optimization of
desulfurization plus sulfide shape control,
using mischmetal at 50% recovery, by
ladle addition for critical applications*

Competing Techniques for Manganese Sulfide Control.

    In large part because of the problems described above, par-
ticularly the nozzle blockage problem, intensive development efforts have centered on desulfurizing the steel to the point at
which shape control would no longer be required. Among the several techniques existing today, those combining injection of calcium
alloys, basic slag mixtures and improved ladle linings have, in
effect, substituted the need for REM additions in 80 to 90% of the
potential use in Europe and Japan. The original claims that when
0.005% S is reached, no more shape control is needed (31), have
been replaced by the new claims that calcium also provides total
shape control as well or better than the REM's (42, 43).
    As the Kawasaki research team mentioned earlier have conclud-
ed, there is also, with calcium, a Ca/S requirement as with the
REM's for total MnS substitution (32). They have proposed the
most reliable estimate so far of retained calcium requirement for
"homogeneous sulfide shape control" which is summarized in Table
IV and Figure 17.

Table IV: Minimum Ca/S Ratio Requirement
             in Weight% for Shape Control.

Criticality Level of Properties		Manganese Content		
		1%	1½%	2%[*]
Improvement in Toughness:	partial	0.65	1[*]	1.5[*]
	total	1.3	2.5	3.2[*]
Prevention of Hydrogen Cracking:	partial	1.3	2.5	3.2[*]
	total	1.7	3.1	4.5[*]

[*]Extrapolations from the discussions in the text (32).

The three manganese levels are typical of, respectively, Electric
Resistance Welded pipe (ERW) at 1%; U.O pipe at 1½% (a newly developed forming technique for the manufacture of very large pipe
out of heavy plate steel); and the new Mn-Mo-Cb steels developed
mainly in the U.S. by Amax (44). Because of the limited solubility of calcium in steel, the only way these ratios can be achieved,
particularly in high Mn steels and for the most critical property
levels, is by extreme desulfurization down to 0.004% max. in the
easiest case and 0.001% max. in the most unfavorable situation.
    This discussion indicates that most steels produced today us-
ing the low sulfur practices, typically at 0.005% S, are not showing complete substitution of MnS inclusions. Fortunately, the
property improvement is generally sufficient to satisfy almost all
specifications. However, the possibility exists of a partial re-
turn to a final REM addition at the low sulfur levels obtained by
calcium injection to achieve much easier shape control at low cost
and without side effects, when critical performances are essential.

Hydrogen-induced Cracking, the New REM Application Since 1977.

Mechanism of Failure. Catastrophic failures of large diameter gas and oil line pipe in seawater and in hydrogen sulfide contaminated waters over recent years have been traced to disintegration of the steel structure by hydrogen. At the surface of the pipe, hydrogen atoms are liberated by an electro-chemical reaction and penetrate quickly by diffusion inside the steel structure to recombine in molecular hydrogen as soon as they meet with a discontinuity in the steel such as non-metallic inclusions. This molecular hydrogen can reach local pressures of 10,000 atm and more, developing tremendous localized stresses. Elongated inclusions, particularly in groups as frequently exhibited by MnS, will tend to open up under the applied stress and initiate cracking at their tips, ultimately joining other cracks in a step fashion until macrocracks develop initiating the catastrophic failure. When the steel is itself under constant stress, for example from natural gas pressure, the hydrogen induced cracking is greatly accelerated. The same phenomenon occurs in deep sour gas wells only at even greater speed on account of H_2S concentrations.

The Sulfide Shape Control Effect. Italian (45) and Japanese (46) steel researchers have shown that sulfide shape control is clearly more important in this case than sulfur reduction. Figure 19 shows the progressive improvement in crack appearance after standard exposure time, using progressively improved steelmaking practices in which the REM treatment introduces the most significant progress (45). Figure 20 shows similar results, this time on commercial seamless steel as opposed to line pipe steel, and clearly demonstrates that, even at 0.003% S, a REM addition can bring very substantial improvements in resistance to hydrogen-induced stress corrosion cracking (46). The interpretation of these results is simple: the replacement of elongated manganese sulfide inclusions by numerous, small REM oxysulfide and sulfide inclusions multiplies precipitation points for the transformation of hydrogen from atomic to molecular form and eliminates the severe weakening effect at the tips of elongated inclusions. As long as the REM/S ratio is of the order of 3 to 6, this is a satisfactory theory and in the above mentioned examples, it is probably correct.

The REM Hydride Effect. In a research report entitled "Inhibition of Hydrogen Embrittlement in High Strength Steel" C.S. Kortovich broke new ground when he added very large excess lanthanum and cerium to a 4340 steel melt at 0.004% S (47). His retained REM/S ratios in the five (5) laboratory heats which were treated with up to 0.2% La and Ce, varied from 8/1 to 46/1. This large excess, predictably, resulted in precipitation of the low melting La-Fe or Ce-Fe eutectic at the primary grain boundaries as described earlier in this paper and in hot shortness and loss of impact properties. All this was confirmed by the report, except

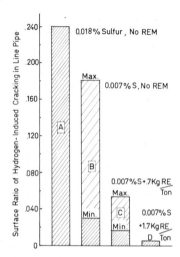

Figure 19. Dramatic prevention effect introduced by REM additions against disintegration of line pipe steel by hydrogeninduced cracking (HIC)

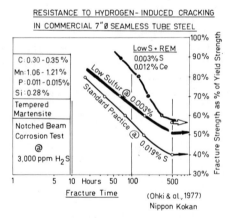

Figure 20. Improvement in lower critical stress as well as delayed cracking initiation introduced by REM additions even when the steel is down to 0.003% sulfur

that Kortovich misidentified the eutectic as a grain boundary oxide, the same error made by many steel mill metallurgists. Dramatic improvement in resistance to hydrogen embrittlement was
achieved by moving from the low cerium and lanthanum levels practiced by the other researchers aiming only at sulfide shape control, to 3 to 5 times that level, aiming at REM hydride formation.
That is the breakthrough. In addition, there are inconsistent in-
dications that the properties of the highly "doped" steel improved
after hydrogen charging, certainly a startling observation. In
Figure 21, the grain boundary precipitates are sketched and in
Figure 22, a summary of the hydrogen cracking results is given
with similar coordinates and units as in Figure 20, for comparison.
It is nearly certain that hydrides have formed in this application, as suspected by Kortovich. It is also highly probable that
these hydrides have simply formed at the site of the grain boundary eutectics which contain about 92.5% Ce in the Ce-Fe system and
95% La in the La-Fe system. This area of development is perceived
by this writer as having the most promising potential for new volume usage of the REM's in steelmaking during the eighties.

Summary of the Metallurgical Effects of REM's in Steel.

In Figure 23, a qualitative plotting of the effects of growing additions of REM's to steel on the most affected properties is
proposed. In this plot, it is clear that cold formability, impact
resistance and hot workability -- also improved weld integrity --
quickly reach a maximum with fairly small, economical additions
because all of these improvements are directly related to sulfide
shape control, and tramp element control in the case of stainless
steels. For details on the latter mechanism, not discussed in
this paper because it has now become a minor application, please
refer to the literature of the fifties (48). Two other properties, high temperature oxidation resistance (49, 50) and hydrogen
cracking resistance, follow a distinctly separate course because
the mechanism of action has little or nothing to do with manganese
sulfide inclusions. It can be seen also that the latter two effects severely conflict with basic requirements of hot workability
and plain strength of most steel grades. Ingenious manipulation
of the "as-cast structures" may be one way to minimize the deleterious effects of the grain boundary eutectic while capitalizing on
higher additions to stretch the resistance of our future steels to
high temperature oxidation or hydrogen embrittlement.

History of the Industrial Use of Mischmetal in Steels.

Origins. Since the 1890's, monazite, the first commercial
rare earth ore, was mined from black beach sands in Brazil and
shipped to Austria for its 5 to 10% thorium oxide content. Carl
Freiherr Auer von Welsbach spent 20 years of research work developing a bright incandescent gas mantle he discovered in 1866 with

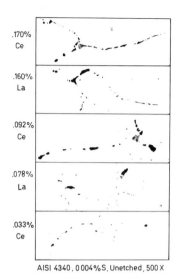

Figure 21. Sketches of the grain boundary eutectic, RE–Fe at various La and Ce concentrations

AISI 4340, 0.004% S, Unetched, 500 X

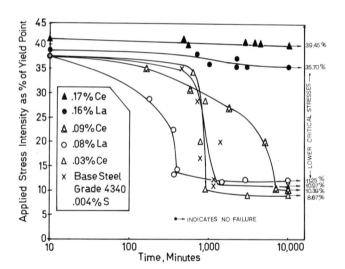

Figure 22. Summary of HIC results with increased REM additions showing significant improvement only over 0.1% Ce or La in lower critical stress, suggesting hydride formation in the RE–Fe eutectic.

ZrO_2 doped by La_2O_3. He capitalized on the longevity of ThO_2 and the white brightness given by a few percent of CeO_2 in order to meet the growing competition with Edison's new electric lamp.

Dissatisfied with having to discard over 90% of the ore value, a phosphate of cerium, lanthanum and "didymium" after extracting the thorium as a nitrate, Auer von Welsbach researched and found the first metallurgical use for the light lanthanides as a flint for cigarette lighters. To produce the pyrophoric alloy, which he coined "mischmetall," he used the then recently developed fused salt electrolysis processes of Hillebrand & Norton, 1875 and of Muthmann, Hofer & Weiss, 1902. In 1908 the first company involved in the commercial production of rare earth metals was founded by von Welsbach at Treibach in Karinthia. Today the company is known as Treibacher Chemische Werke.

In the U.S., Ronson Metals quickly followed suite starting production of lighter flints around 1915. It did not take long for curious ferrous metallurgists to try out the newly available metal. As early as 1913 in iron (4), and 1922 in steel (3), the first reports showed promise or dismal failure. With today's knowledge of the mechanisms involved (20), it is not surprising that Gillet and Mack at the Bureau of Mines, although reporting a drop in sulfur, showed dirty steel and poor mechanical properties as a result of the first mischmetal trial. This and other experiments with similarly dismal results put a considerable damper on the use of REM's in steelmaking. It took almost half a century to understand steel thermodynamics and inclusion separation mechanisms to overcome this "dirt problem" and to harness the lanthanides for economical and critical use in massive steel production. During World War II, however, renewed interest centered around the use of rare earth fluoride fluxes as cleansing agents for aircraft landing gear steels and the likes (22).

Early Success. After fast progress in magnesium alloys spurred by aircraft materials needs during the thirties and after a brilliant but brief flash of success in the first nodular irons in 1948 (but unfortunately quickly substituted by Mg) mischmetal finally struck it rich in steel around 1950. With almost "miraculous effect" on the hot workability of highly alloyed stainless steel ingots, mischmetal entered the hall of fame of steelmaking history with the then popular appellation of "penicillin of steel." U.S. patent #2,553,330 to Carpenter Steel Co., the paper by Post, Schoffstall and Beaver (48), and other subsequent papers described the practice. They discussed the dramatic improvements achieved and tried to theorize on the mechanisms by which "Lanceramp," the popular alloy of the times (1), affected the properties. One clear-cut effect depicted in Figure 24 from the fifties, shows a refinement of the as-cast grain size in certain grades such as AISI 310. Amidst confusion, there was evidence already of the beneficial neutralization of the tramp elements, Pb, Sn, As, Bi etc., and of the extreme reactivity with sulfur and oxygen.

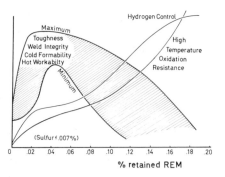

Figure 23. Qualitative summary of the evolution of steel properties discussed in this chapter as a function of the retained REM content showing an early maximum for all properties associated with sulfide shape control and tramp element control but quite a different story for hydrogen and oxidation resistance

Electric Furnace Proceedings

Figure 24. The mechanism that created the first REM boom in steelmaking in 1950 (58). Cross section of S.A.E. grade 310 stainless steel billets pickled to show the solidification structure. On the left, normally coarse structure causing hot shortness; on the right, effect of 2 lbs of mischmetal added to the ladle to improve hot workability.

Partly because of high mischmetal prices, substitution by boron alloys took most of the glitter out of the market for a decade.
The Carpenter application is now a negligible fraction of the total consumption of mischmetal in steels.

Almost ignored at the time but a harbinger of today's main REM
role in steels, were papers such as the one by Berry and Dorvel in
1951 (51), reporting the elimination of low ductility and low impact strength in aluminum deoxidized cast steels by adding mischmetal after all other additions, "changing the shape and distribution of non-metallic inclusions." Such papers reflected Clarence
Sims' views already published in 1935 (25) but not in vogue at the
time.

By the late fifties, it became increasingly clear that the affinity of the REM's for sulfur to the point of occasionally causing some startling desulfurization, was one of the main features
distinguishing them from other "deoxidizers," Ti, Al, Zr, V, etc.
being tested at the time to improve steel cleanliness. The deter-
mination of cerium-sulfur solubility products in steels by Langenberg and Chipman in 1958 (52), is a manifestation of this early
understanding. However, because of the pervasive fashion from
1950 to 1965 of concentrating all metallurgical efforts on deoxidation processes for steel cleanliness and property control, the
main marketing efforts for the development of mischmetal usage in
steelmaking centered on the low oxygen equilibrium obtained in
steel by REM additions. Limited industrial tests along these
lines in critical bar steel grades, for example, failed to bring
the desired improvements largely from totally neglecting the sulfur component. Instead of analyzing subsurface "dirt" concentrations which would have revealed high sulfur contents, the problem
was attributed to reoxidation of the teeming stream. As a result,
"ductile iron and magnesium alloys shared with lighter flints and
small stainless steel usage the main uses for mischmetal and rare
earth silicide in all metallurgical fields as late as 1968" (53).
Total world consumption was probably less than 100 tons per year
in steel in 1968.

The Second and Major Success. As with the first breakthrough,
at Carpenter Steel, a pressing problem had to be solved fast to
salvage four years of arduous and successful development on a new
steel grade at Jones & Laughlin Steel. All systems were "go" on
the first 80,000 psi vanadium-aluminum-nitrogen HSLA steel con-
trol-cooled on the new hot strip mill of the Cleveland Works, except for an unforeseen, nagging problem when the first 200 tons
hit the market. When the steel was bent on a tight radius in a
press-brake, with the axis of the bend parallel to the hot rolling direction, deep cracks developed on the outer diameter of the
bend, prompting scrapping of the part or extensive welding repair.
It was the manganese sulfide exacerbated by lower than normal rolling temperatures necessitated by the new structure technology

(54), by extra-low oxygen contents of the aluminum deoxidation and by the vastly increased Mn/S ratio.

Early substitution tests using zirconium resulted in a loss of 15,000 psi because of predictable precipitation of all the nitrogen as ZrN in the liquid, removing an essential building block from the VAN-80 construction. In laboratory tests in 1968 the REM's met with total and instant success at low and reproducible levels (20). Unlike the Carpenter application, the HSLA class of steel responded to a massive tonnage need both in oil and gas transportation and in automotive truck frame, car weight reduction programs of the early seventies (55).

Except for a few German and Japanese mills, the steel industry was not prepared to take the other route, the extra-low sulfur alternative at 0.005% maximum which is now common practice in many large steel plants around the world. The REM's became locked in with most HSLA steels for critical formability or impact applications and the consumption of REM's in steels peaked in 1974 with nearly 6,000 metric tons of mischmetal equivalent, at least a 60 times rise in six years. In Figure 25, this evolution of consumption is estimated from approximate figures compiled by Molycorp, the major world producer of the bastnasite ore. It also differentiates between mischmetal, rare earth silicide and foundry alloy consumption of REM units. This world consumption diagram clearly demonstrates the astronomical impact -- at the rare earth scale -- of the simple mold addition technique requiring zero investment to achieve vastly improved engineering properties in line pipe and automotive steels from 1970 to 1974.

After the Boom, The Bust in Europe in 1975. In the midst of euphoria and hasty production capacity enlargements in 1974-75, the four European mischmetal producers were stunned by a sharp downturn in orders. This was first attributed to the combination of a deep world-wide steel recession with the invasion of the market by a flooding of cheap Brazilian imports. In a record time since 1972, the Brazilians had built not less than three mischmetal production plants to take maximum value out of their ore but they came on stream just after the peak. However, mischmetal consumption kept dropping through 1976 and 1977 while the steel market was recovering, which clearly demonstrated substitution.

What happened? The German and Japanese steel metallurgists had understood much earlier in the game, during the sixties, the paramount importance of eliminating the manganese sulfide inclusions. Their equipment and highly quality-oriented minds allowed them to tackle the difficult orders ahead of everybody else. They firmly selected the low sulfur route and embarked in heavy investments for hot metal desulfurization equipment and later in steel desulfurization (56). Until 1973, however, the sulfur levels achieved by hot metal desulfurization did not help the final sulfur content because of the contaminating effect of cooling scrap in the Basic Oxygen Furnace (BOF), except in Japan where

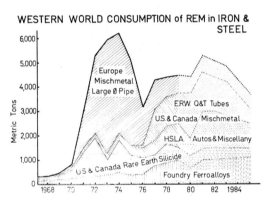

Figure 25.   Evolution of commercial consumption of contained REMs in iron and steel starting in 1967 and projecting tentatively through 1985. Other metallurgical uses of mischmetal and RES are not included but amount to no more than 15% of the totals of the graphs.

only ore was used as coolant. This is the basic reason why the
mischmetal market in steel was never large in Japan.

From the Niederrhein division of Thyssen Stahl in Oberhausen,
West Germany, came the first comprehensively engineered steel desulfurization process based on calcium compounds and alloys in-
jected deep in the steel ladle (31). The sharp contrast of smooth
slab casting operation by using this technique with the nozzle
blockage and subsurface contamination characteristic of the REM
practice in the ladle was the major drive for the switch. A much
advertized lower alloy cost per ingot ton, using calcium alloys
helped swallow the royalty and equipment costs estimated at over
$1 million per unit in 1974. What prompted steelmakers to move so
fast was the large looming orders, mostly from the U.S.S.R., for
low price gas line pipes with increasingly critical low temperature properties. The only way they could compete was by using the
much lower cost slab casting route in which, precisely, the REM
practice was causing so much trouble. In a matter of months 15
units were sold around the world and installation of the equipment
was given top priority and urgency. The claims of metallurgical
superiority of calcium treated steels as compared to high sulfur
REM treated steels were overwhelming: better cleanliness, higher
impacts, sulfur content easily maintained below 0.005% and total
sulfide shape control of the remaining sulfur by CaS left little
or no hope for the alternate route, once the investment had been
committed.

The problems associated with the so called CAB or TN (for
Thyssen-Niederrhein) practice surfaced only much later. They include much higher refractory costs in the ladle, expensive fume
collection systems over the ladle, the injection of unwanted silicon with the calcium silicon alloy, the need for a new slag cover
on the ladle of steel, the pick-up of 1 to 3 ppm of hydrogen with
the injection and of 10 to 40 ppm of nitrogen. The worst observation, which is hotly disputed by the proponents of the TN technique, is the general absence of total sulfide shape control in
slab-cast steels, particularly with high manganese contents and
lengthy ladle holds typical of continuous casting operations.
None of these problems, however are likely to deter steel operators from pursuing the injection practices which give them little
or no trouble at the slab caster.

There are now of course many competing steel desulfurization
techniques and the recent trend has been away from injection and
towards more sophisticated new slag compositions to reach the
0.005% max. S without the pick-up of nitrogen and hydrogen and
without the expensive basic ladle refractories. Japanese metallurgists who are currently in the lead have recognized the shape
control difficulties associated with calcium and are reconsider-
ing the use of the REM's in small, critically adjusted quantities
(32, 46), as an alternative to the need for a second calcium feeding in the tundish or the mold for total shape control of the sulfide inclusions.

The Contrasting U.S. Boom of the Late Seventies. While convulsions racked the European mischmetal market, consumption in the U.S. increased steadily from 1973 to 1976, even through the 1975 steel recession. From a modest 1 million lbs per year market in 1973, mischmetal first started substituting for rare earth silicide from 1974 to 1976 and then struck it rich again in late 1976 with a new application in ERW high strength tubes for oil well casing and drilling, to stabilize around 6 million lbs per year today in the U.S. and Canada. A small fraction of that figure still goes to ductile iron, lighter flints and magnesium alloys, samarium oxide reduction for magnets and other more sophisticated applications.

In Figure 25, discussed earlier, the market transfer from Europe to the U.S. around the mid-seventies is quite evident. There is now a net import situation to satisfy the demand while the American producers have increased their capacity for the third time in a decade.

The Outlook for This Decade and Beyond. Strong signs of substitution by low sulfur practices have appeared on this side of the Atlantic. U.S. Steel at Baytown, Texas in 1976, Lukens Steel in Coatesville, PA in 1975, Stelco in Hamilton, Ontario in 1979 and IPSCO, in Regina, Saskatchewan in 1980 have purchased and installed a TN unit essentially for large diameter pipe production. Other steelmakers have preferred competing devices. Oregon Steel has installed a Scandinavian Lancers Unit in 1978, Bethlehem Steel has installed its internally developed unit at Burns Harbor in 1979 and Republic, Armco and Jones & Laughlin are developing their own injection systems as well.

While the above mentioned installations have already substituted the entirety of the REM usage for arctic line pipe application, they are only starting to make a dent in the HSLA automotive market, with Bethlehem Steel announcing the first extra-low sulfur HSLA sheet steel called XF, to replace their previous titanium bearing grades (57). The substitution of REM's in the high strength oil country goods will not likely happen before 1983 in the major producing plant at Lone Star Steel, Texas while it will happen much sooner at National Steel, Granite City Division, who embarked on a slab casting investment due to start before the end of the year 1980.

Unless a major breakthrough in REM application occurs before 1983, such as the demonstration of drastically reduced susceptibility of pipes and tubes to hydrogen embrittlement (47), the domestic mischmetal market in steelmaking will fall fairly sharply by 1984-85, despite the metallurgical inferiority of the substitutes. If mischmetal was showing signs of pick-up in steel in Japan, there would be a high probability of similar trends in Europe and the U.S. after a delay period of 6 to 12 months, an eventuality that has not showed up yet in the Japanese steel industry.

As the steel market for mischmetal has been marked by quick booms followed by substitutional busts, it is not wise to make predictions of market size much beyond 1985, pending an other potentially massive application. The base level, however tends strongly upwards, indicating an encouraging underlying current of increased confidence of the steelmakers towards the lanthanides. The trauma caused by severe operational and quality problems using the REM's without precautions gave the metal the black eye and an underdog status which will require time and enlightened marketing efforts to overcome on the long term. With ever increasing demands on the engineering properties of our steels, I am confident that its superiority over all substitutional systems will eventually give mischmetal not only the market volume but also the status that it deserves in the steelmaking community.

Literature Cited

1. Trombe, Felix. Rev. de Met., 1956, 53, 31-33.

2. Savitskii, E. M. "Rare Metals & Alloys", Technology House (Dom Tekhniki), Moscow, 1959.

3. Spedding F. H.; Daane A. H. "The Rare Earths", American Society for Metals; R. E. Krieger Publishing Co. Inc. Huntington N.Y., 1961; p. 501.

4. Kleber, E. V.; Love, B. "Technology of Sc., Y, and the Rare Earth Metals". Pergamon Press, 1963.

5. LeRoy Eyring. "Progress in the Science and Technology of the Rare Earths" Vol. II, Pergamon Press, London, 1964, p. 193-197.

6. Anderson E.; Spreadborough J. Rev. Met., 1967, 64, 177-183.

7. Hirschhorn I. S. "Use of Mischmetal (Mixed Rare Earth Metals) in Steels". Private Publ. by Ronson Metals Corp. 8/1968.

8. Kippehan N.; Gschneidner, K. A., Jr. "Rare Earth Metals in Steels", IS-RIC-4; Rare Earth Information Center, Iowa State Univ., Ames, IA, 1970.

9. Reinhardt K., Goldschmidt Informiert, 4/1974, (31), p. 2,7,33.

10. Raman A. Z. Metallk.; 1976, 67, 780-789.

11. Waudby, P. E. Intern. Met. Reviews, 1978, 23, (2), 74-98.

12. American Metal Market, Summer 1980, Rare Earth Metals Price List.

13. Bohunovsky, O. Proceedings of Metal Bulletin's First International Ferro-alloys Conference, Oct. 9-11, 1977, Zurich; Metal Bulletin Ltd, London, 1978, p. 86-89.

14. Industrial Minerals, 3/1979, (138), 36-37.

15. Private Communication with Santoku Metal Corporation.

16. Hultgren, R.; Desai, P. D.; Hawkins, D. T.; Gleiser M.; Kelley, K. K.; Wagman, D. D. "Selected Values of the Thermodynamic Properties of the Elements", American Society for Metals, Metals Park, OH, 1973.

17. Hilty, D. C.; Farley, R. W.; Sims, C. E. "Electric Furnace Steelmaking Vol. II, Theory and Fundamentals" Iron & Steel Div. of AIME, 1967, p. 45.

18. Luyckx, L. "Mechanisms of Rare Earth Action on Steel Struc-
    tures". American Society for Metals, Materials Science Sympo-
    sium, Cincinnati, Nov. 1975, Private Publ. by Reactive Metals
    & Alloys Corp., 9/1976, p. 1.

19. Luyckx, L.; Jackman, J. R. Electric Furnace Conference Pro-
    ceedings, 1973, 31, 175-181.

20. Luyckx, L.; Bell, J. R.; McLean, A.; Korchynsky, M. Met.
    Trans., 1970, 1, 3341.

21. Private Communications with Steel Company of Canada and Moly-
    corp, 1970.

22. Phelps, H. E. U.S. Patent #2,360,717, 1944.

23. Overview, Molycorp, No 23, 12/1970, p. 1.

24. McGannon, H. E. "The Making, Shaping and Treating of Steel",
    United States Steel Corp., Herbick & Held, Pittsburgh, 1970,
    9th Ed., p. 24.

25. Sims, C.E. Trans. Met. Soc. AIME, 1959, 215, 382-88.

26. Gschneidner, K. A., Jr.; Kippenhan, N. "Thermochemistry of the
    Rare Earth Carbides, Nitrides and Sulfides for Steelmaking",
    IS-RIC-5; Rare Earth Information Center, Iowa State Univ.,
    Ames, IA, 1971.

27. Gschneidner, K. A., Jr.; Kippenhan, N.; McMasters, O. D.
    "Thermochemistry of the Rare Earths, I Oxides, II Oxysulfides
    III Compounds with B, Sn, Pb, P, As, Sb, Bi, Cu, and Ag", IS-
    RIC-6; Rare Earth Information Center, Iowa State Univ., Ames,
    IA, 1973.

28. Wilson, W. G.; Kay, D. A. R.; Vahed, A. J. Metals, 26, 1974,
    (5), 14.

29. Lu, W. K.; McLean, A. Ironmaking Steelmaking, 1, 1974, 228.

30. Samsonov, G. V. "High-Temperature Compounds of Rare Earth Me-
    tals with Non-metals"; 1965, New York, Consultants Bureau, p.
    211.

31. Spetzler, E.; Wendorff, J. AIME-NOHC Steelmaking Proceedings,
    58, 1975, 358-377.

32. Sanbongi, K. Transactions ISI Japan, 19, 1979, 1-10. (Special
    lecture).

33. Selleck, L. J.; Thompson, G. W.; Croll, J. E.; MacDonald, J. K. AIME-NOHC Steelmaking Proceedings, 61, 1978, 143-153.

34. Farrar, J. C. M.; Dolby, R. E. "Sulfide Inclusions in Steel", American Society for Metals, Metals Park, OH, 1975, p. 252-268.

35. Jackman, J. R. U.S. Patents #4,022,444 and #4,060,407, 1977.

36. Bennett, H. W.; Sandell, L. P., Jr. Electric Furnace Proc., 31, 1973, 167.

37. Bingel C. J.; Scott, L. V. Electric Furnace Proc., 31, 1973, 171-174.

38. Torsell, K.; Olette, M. Rev. Met., 66, 1969.

39. Luyckx, L. "Ladle Treatment of Carbon Steel", McMaster Symposium, McMaster Univ., Hamilton, Ontario, 5/1979, p. 12-1 to 13.

40. Emi, T.; Haida, O.; Sakuraya, T.; Sanbongi, K. AIME-NOH-BOSC Proceedings, 61, 1978, 574-584.

41. Nakai, Y.; Kurahashi, H.; Emi, T.; Haida, O. Transactions ISI Japan, 19, 1979, 401-410.

42. Scott, W. W., Jr.; Swift, R. A. AIME-NOH-BOSC Proc., 61, 1978, 128-132.

43. Tivelius, B.; Sohlgren, T. "Ladle Treatment of Carbon Steel", McMaster Symposium, McMaster Univ., Hamilton, Ont., 5/1979, p. 3-16.

44. Mihelich, J. L.; Cryderman, R. L. "Low-Carbon Mn-Mo-Cb Steel for Gas Transmission Pipe"; ASME publication, Petroleum Mech. Eng. & Pressure Vessels & Piping Conf., New Orleans, 9/1972, p. 1-11.

45. Parrini, C.; DeVito, A. "High Strength Microalloyed Pipe Steels Resistant to Hydrogen-Induced Failures", Presented at Micon '78 Conf., Houston, Texas, April 3-5, 1978, Private Publ. by Italsider, Taranto, Italy, also, ASTM book STP 672, Baltimore, 7/1979, p. 62.

46. Ohki, T.; Tanimura, M.; Kinoshita, K.; Tenmyo, G. "Effect of Inclusions on Sulfide Stress Cracking", 1/1977, Private Publ. by Nippon Kokan Kabushiki Kaisha Technical Research Center, Japan.

47. Kortovich, C. S. "Inhibition of Hydrogen Embrittlement in High Strength Steel"; Technical Report #ER-7814-2, Prepared by TRW, Equipment Mat. Tech. for the Office of Naval Research, Contract #N00014-74-0365, 2/1977.

48. Post, C. B.; Schoffstall, D. G.; Beaver, H. O. J. Metals, 3, 1951, 973.

49. Hessenbruch, W. "Metalle und Legierungen fur Hohe Temperaturen"; Julius Springer, Berlin, 1940. The influence of minor elements on the heat resistance of standard alloys.

50. Bailey, R. E.; Shiring, R. R.; Anderson, R. J. "Superalloys: Metallurgy and Manufacture", 3rd Internat. Sympos., Seven Springs, PA, 9/1977, p. 109.

51. Berry, C. D.; Dorvel, A. A. American Foundryman, 20, (12), 1951, 45.

52. Langenberg, F. C.; Chipman, J. Trans. Met. Soc. AIME, 212, 1958, 290-93.

53. Hirschhorn, I. S. "The Industrial Status of Mischmetal" Proceedings, 11th Rare Earth Conf., Traverse City, MI, 10/1974, p. 754-763.

54. Leclerc, J.; Beernaert, C.; Bouchon, J. Can. Met. Quart., 12, (2), 1973, 201.

55. Dumont, T. C. Iron Age, (3), 1974.

56. Luyckx, L. "Sulfide Inclusions in Steel", American Society for Metals, Metals Park, OH, 1975, p. 44-69.

57. "Bethlehem Develops New Sheet to Provide Better Formability", American Metal Market, Sept. 12, 1980.

58. Electric Furnace Proceedings, 1955, A75.

RECEIVED February 18, 1981.

MIXED RARE EARTH USES—
NONMETALS

The Use of Rare Earths in Glass Compositions

L. W. RIKER

Schott Optical Glass Incorporated, Duryea, PA 18642

The use of rare earth oxides by glassmakers is relatively new when we consider that glass has been produced for over 4,000 years. Modern glass technology started about 1880 when Otto Schott in Jena, Germany made systematic studies of the affects of various oxides on the mechanical and optical properties of glass. He studied cerium oxide as a constituent in glass but did not put it to any practical use. (1) Winkleman and Straubel studied rare earth fluorescence at this time. In 1896, Drossbach patented and manufactured a mixture of rare earth oxides for decolorizing glass. This was the first commercial use of cerium. It was in a crude form with other rare earth oxides including neodymium. In 1912, Crookes of England made systematic studies on eye protective glasses and found cerium excellent for ultra violet absorption without giving color. The first use of lanthanum in optical glasses was in 1935 by Morey. (2)

The most rapid growth of the use of rare earth oxides has taken place since World War II. New technology glasses have been developed requiring the use of purer materials. These have been successfully obtained through more advanced separation techniques by the rare earth manufactureres with purities up to 99.999%. Cerium has increased in use as a stabilizer against browning of glass by cathode ray and gamma rays. Most cathode ray tube faceplates use cerium stabilized glass. The nuclear industry has required large quantities of radiation shielding windows which provide very high light transmission without darkening due to formation of color centers. Much of the development work to understand the mechanism of browning by gamma radiations was done during the 1950's and early 1960's in conjunction with the work on use of nuclear energy.

New developments have been made in the photographic and optical field with the design of more sophisticated lenses. The lanthanum optical glasses with a high index of refraction and low dispersion have been an outgrowth of the post war period.

Another growth area is the glass container industry. Cerium is used here to decolorize glass and to stabilize against solarization caused by U. V. rays.

0097-6156/81/0164-0081$05.00/0

Neodymium oxide, which is used as a coloring oxide in hand crafted glass, is also used in doping laser glasses which is another growing field.

There are approximately 350 tons of rare earth oxides used yearly for glass making. Cerium concentrate makes up the biggest share of the market. This is in the form of a mixed rare earth material containing about 88% CeO_2/Total REO and the balance is made up of La_2O_3, Pr_6O_{11}, and Nd_2O_3. The ratios will vary with the supplier and raw material source. Lanthanum oxide has the next largest market followed by 95% to 99.9% purity cerium oxide, neodymium oxide and small amounts of praeseodymium and erbium oxides.

Glass is a unique material, appearing as a solid although often referred to as a super cooled liquid. There have been many definitions of glass by dictionaries, encyclopedias, scientists, and government agencies. From a technical standpoint, one can define it as "an inorganic product of fusion which has been cooled to a rigid condition without crystallization."(3)

The most common commercial glasses are called soda-lime glasses. They are made from silica which is the glass or network former. The melting temperature of the silica is reduced by the addition of soda and potash which are fluxing agents. To promote chemical durability and stabilize the viscosity, lime, magnesia, and alumina are added. The glass must be refined to remove gaseous inclusions. This is done chemically by the addition of sodium nitrate and sulfate, arsenic oxide and antimony oxide. The soda-lime glasses are used for plate and window glass, containers, light bulbs and ophthalmic lenses.

There are many other families of glasses including lead-alkali-silicates, borosilicate, barium-borosilicates and aluminosilicate glasses. In addition, there is the broad range of various optical and other technical glasses using a variety of glassmaking raw materials.

Of the important properties of glass, color is one of the most interesting. Color is usually achieved by the addition of various metal oxides. The strongest of these are titanium, vanadium, chromium, manganese, selenium, iron, cobalt, nickel and copper. Silver and uranium will give weak colors. Some of the rare earths are also used as colorants with sharp absorption bands in contrast to the broad bands given by most colorants. (4)

Color can be a desired property when purposely making a colored glass or it can be detrimental such as iron and chrome impurities when making a high transmission optical glass. Since iron is a common impurity in many glass making raw materials it must be removed during the material processing. Otherwise, it will contribute a yellow-green color to the glass. To offset this problem, several materials act as decolorizers which lighten the color of the iron or neutralize it. This will be discussed later along with the function of rare earth oxides in achieving decolorization.

Having briefly reviewed glass as a material and some of its properties, we should look at specific properties where rare earth oxides are used.

The Coloring Effects of Rare Earth Oxides

When transparent glasses absorb portions of the visible spectrum from 400 to 700nm, they will appear colored. The color is determined by the transmitted portion of the visible spectrum after subtracting certain wavelengths by absorption from the illuminating source.

The rare earth oxides have absorption spectra consisting of a large number of relatively narrow bands through both the visible and invisible parts of the spectrum. It is interesting that there is little change in the characteristic absorption spectra of rare earth oxides in various compounds, solutions and glasses.

The colors in rare earth glasses are caused by the ion being dissolved and they behave uniquely because the 4 f electrons are deeply buried. Their colors depend on transitions taking place in an inner electronic shell while in other elements such as the transition metals, the chemical forces are restricted to deformation and exchanges of electrons within the outer shell. Since the rare earth's sharp absorption spectra are insensitive to glass composition and oxidation-reduction conditions, it is easy to produce and maintain definite colors in the glass making process. (5)

Rare earth oxides used for coloring glass are neodymium, praeseodymium, and erbium. Cerium is only used in conjunction with other coloring oxides. Neodymium is the most commonly used oxide for coloring glass and gives a delicate pink tint with violet reflections. The hue of the color varies with glass thickness and concentration of neodymium and also the source of illumination. It goes from a light pink in thin sections to a beautiful blue-violet in thicker pieces. This characteristic is called dichroism. It is primarily used in art glasses in concentrations of 1% to 5% and for special filters. Neodymium welding glasses are used by lamp workers and welders to protect their eyes from the yellow flare emitted by sodium vaporized from hot glass or fluxes. This is due to the narrow absorption peak of neodymium between 589 and 590 nm where sodium atoms emit their characteristic yellow light. A typical transmittance curve of a neodymium containing glass is shown in Figure 1.

Praeseodymium is the next strongest rare earth oxide, giving a green color very similar to the eye as chromium containing glasses. Since the cost of praeseodymium is high compared to chrome oxide it is not used to any extent except in special filter glasses, and in combination with neodymium in didymium welding glasses. See Figures 2 and 3.

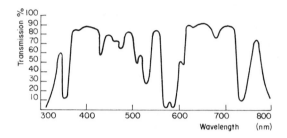

Figure 1.   Transmittance curve of a glass containing Nd_2O_3

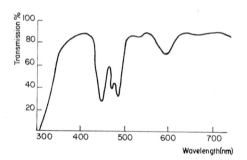

Figure 2.   Transmittance curve of a glass containing Pr_6O_{11}

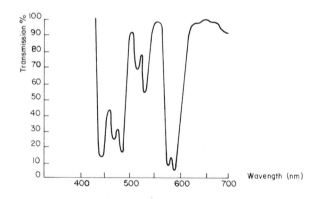

Figure 3.   Transmittance curve of a glass containing a mixture of Pr_6O_{11} and Nd_2O_3

Originally due to the difficulty in separating the various oxides, so called didymium oxides were used for glasses such as these special welding glasses and Crookes absorptive sun glasses. They contained the natural ratios of neodymium and praeseodymium along with the high amounts of cerium which gave a good U. V. cut-off. Most of the other rare earth oxides were present along with some thorium oxide. This made an inexpensive rare earth coloring material but was not always reproducable. Today for example, a lanthanum rare earth oxide can be used and by knowing the ratios of the neodymium and praeseodymium to the cerium and lanthanum, corrections can be made with 95% purity oxides to get the desired absorption characteristics.

Erbium oxide gives a pale pink to the glass which cannot be obtained by any other means. As seen in Figure 4, it has only one absorption peak in the visible range. It is expensive and is used on a limited basis in photochromic glasses and some crystal glasses. Erbium is stable compared to CdS, copper, selenium and gold which require controlled redox and/or striking conditions to produce a red or pink color. (5)

Figure 5 shows the absorption band of cerium as being very weak in soda-lime glasses in the blue and violet regions. When used in large concentrations it gives a weak yellow color, and in combination with titania it produces an attractive yellow color. This is often used in table ware but requires up to 3% of each oxide to produce a satisfactory color. In order to intensify the color, the cerium concentration is kept constant and the titania increased. (6)

In ophthalmic glass production, the cerium-titania complex is combined with manganese to produce the pink U. V. absorptive tinted glasses. The manganese which normally gives a purple color is toned down with the yellow color giving a yellowish pink. In addition, the cerium absorption in the U. V. is an important property of the glass.

Discoloration of Glass by Radiation

Cerium plays an important part in stabilizing glass against solarization and browning due to irradiation. In the case of solarization, the glass discolors due to absorption of ultra violet rays from sun light. In the case of browning, the source is from higher energy radiations.

Solarization is a photochemical reaction which leads to a change in color in glass. It is the result of long term exposure to the ultra violet radiation from sunlight. When certain multivalent ions or combinations of ions are present, their valence can be changed by the ionizing radiation.

For example, if manganese in a two valent form absorbs a photon from the U. V. portion of the spectrum, it changes to a three valent form plus an electron which becomes trapped in the glass structure, usually by ferric iron in a commercial glass.

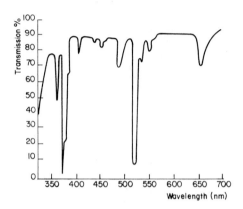

Figure 4.   Transmittance curve of a glass containing Er₂O₃

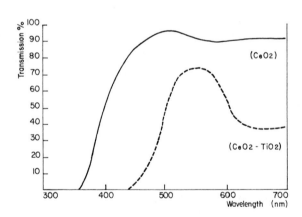

Figure 5.   Transmittance curve of a glass containing CeO₂ and CeO₂ and TiO₂

The ferric iron is then changed to ferrous iron and with the oxidized manganese forms a purple color. This is characteristic of bottles which have been subjected to the sun's rays for a period of time. The manganese is added initially to the glass as a decolorizer to offset the yellow color of the iron. (7)

Other ions, especially arsenic in combination with iron, enhance the color from solarization. This is especially critical in window glass where the glass is clear and solarizes to a yellow-brown. It has been found that more than 0.005% cerium oxide in combination with arsenic will cause this yellowing effect with the strongest color being at 2.5% cerium. Higher cerium contents tend to reduce solarization by filtering off the actinic radiation. (1) By removing the arsenic completely, small amounts of cerium can be added as an oxidizing agent for decolorizing glass and will aid in stabilizing against solarization. (8)

Browning is another type of discoloration caused by x-rays, gamma rays and cathode rays. Cerium oxide is an important ingredient in specialty glasses to reduce this browning characteristic. Ceric ions act as electron traps in the glass and absorb electrons liberated by these high energy radiations which keep the color centers from forming. Cerous ions are formed which have little visible color and protect the glass from discoloration by high energy and nuclear radiations. Some of the uses of these nonbrowning glasses are in radiation shielding windows, television and other cathode ray faceplates. (3, 7, 9)

The radiation shielding windows are made from high density lead glasses. They are used as viewing windows placed in thick lead and concrete walls for nuclear and radiochemical laboratories. In addition, cerium stabilized borosilicate cover plates are used on the hot side.

Since the unstabilized glasses will darken from a radiation source such as cobalt - 60, the transmission of the windows decreases making them difficult for viewing. The intensity of the darkening effect is a function of the energy of ionizing radiation, the intensity of radiation and the radiation dose. The darkening effect is not stable and will fade slightly after exposure. Since these windows can be in excess of a meter thick, maximum transmission is a necessity. Figure 6 illustrates the results on transmission of a 3.23 density lead glass stabilized with 1.5% CeO_2 subjected to various radiation doses compared to a similar glass that is not stabilized. To produce the required nonbrowning stability, cerium oxide is used in various amounts up to 2.5%. In the high lead glasses containing over 60% PbO, cerium additions make the glass amber prior to irradiation and reduce the overall transmission. These glasses are naturally resistant to coloration by irradiation and any color that develops, fades quickly. Therefore, cerium stabilization is usually used only on the lower density glasses. The stabilized glasses are normally used toward the hot side with the denser glasses used on the cold

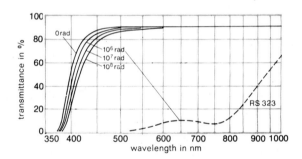

*Figure 6.   The effect of various irradiation levels on (solid curves) Ce-stabilized
and (curve labeled RS-323) nonstabilized lead glass*

side of the window. A typical window cross section is shown in
Figure 7 utilizing cerium stabilized 2.53 density borosilicate
glass on the hot side with 3.23 density stabilized, and 5.2 and
2.53 density unstabilized toward the cold side.

Decolorizing of Glass

Iron oxide is always present as an impurity in glass. It is
introduced through the natural raw materials such as sand and
limestone. Another source is from trap iron mixed in the cullet
and abraded metal from the handling of batch. All of this adds
up to several hundred parts per million which causes light
absorption at the ends of the spectrum rather than the middle and
causes a yellow-green color in the glass. This can be overcome
by a process known as decolorization. There are two types:
chemical and physical decolorizing. (6)
To chemically decolorize a glass, oxidizing materials are
added to change the iron from the ferrous to the ferric state.
This shifts the maximum light transmission towards the yellow by
absorbing more in the blue. Several of the more popular materials
have been arsenic and manganese. In recent years, cerium has
been substituted for these materials. An advantage of cerium is
solarization does not occur as long as arsenic is not present.
Also, when the cerium is used in conjunction with selenium and
cobalt, the addition of 2-3 ounces per ton of batch can give a
reduction in the usage of these two materials. (8)
Physical decolorizing is accomplished by making the color
of ferric iron in the glass with complimentary colors. This
makes the transmittance across the spectrum fairly constant
giving a neutral color. Physical decolorizing reduces part of
the transmittance of the glass in getting rid of the green color.
A true colorless glass such as an optical glass must be made with
very low iron materials since decolorizing agents would reduce the
transmission. The main physical decolorizers are manganese,
selenium, cobalt and neodymium oxides. Manganese with a little
cobalt is effective in complimenting the iron in the ferric state.
Selenium is one of the better decolorizers in tank melting.
The iron is neutralized by the pink tint of the selenium. Since
a yellow shade is still present, the decolorizing is completed
with the addition of a small amount of cobalt. Arsenic helps
to stabilize the decolorizing with selenium but as the arsenic
content increases more selenium is required.
The third oxide used for physical decolorizing is neodymium
oxide. Its absorption curve closely compliments an average
mixture of ferrous and ferric oxides especially with the strong
absorption band at 589 nm. Neodymium oxide is also stable against
any state of oxidation change in the furnace. Neodymium is
exceptionally good as a decolorizer for potassium silicate and
lead glasses. If the redox balance is not quite correct for the

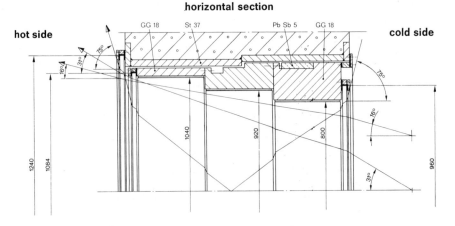

vertical section

horizontal section

hot side   cold side

Figure 7. Radiation shielding window showing Ce-stabilized borosilicate glass cover plates (RS 253 G 18) on the hot side, stabilized lead glass (RS 323 G 15), nonstabilized high density lead glass (RS 520) and borosilicate glass cover plate

iron, corrections can be made using small amounts of manganese oxide, nickel oxide, selenium or erbium oxide.

It must be remembered that the quantities of rare earth materials being used for decolorizing are quite small per batch. The use of 25 grams of neodymium per 100 kg of sand is all that is required. To reduce the cost of cerium, it can be introduced as a cerium concentrate containing 60% CeO_2 which is a relatively inexpensive form.

Optical Glass

Up to this time, we have been discussing the influence of rare earth elements on the color and transmission characteristics of glass. The use of rare earths in optical glass is different since they must not give any absorption in the visible range and are often used as major ingredients up to 40% of the batch. This compares with fractions of a per cent added for use as a decolorizer and coloring oxides up to 5%.

The properties of optical glasses differ substantially from other glasses. These glasses are used for optical lenses and elements to function in a wide variety of systems. Optical glasses are classified by their index of refraction and Abbe-number or reciprocal of its dispersive power. They must also meet special quality requirements such as a high degree of transparency or light transmission and be reasonably free of bubbles and solid inclusions. The glass must be homogenous and free of striations and be annealed to reduce internal stresses to a minimum.

Optical glasses are classified by various families determined by their chemical compositions. Originally, there were two types; crown glass which is a soda-lime-silicate and flint glass which is a lead-alkali-silicate. The addition of other oxides such as boron, barium, zinc and lanthanum have created new families designated as borosilicate crowns, zinc crowns, barium crowns, barium flints, and lanthanum crowns and flints. Each one of these glasses has its own characteristic optical properties as can be seen by the map of optical glasses in Figure 8.

The raw materials going into an optical glass differ greatly in purity levels compared to other commercial glasses. Due to the high degree of light transmission required, it is necessary that the chemical purity of the materials used be extremely high. For example, a normal silica sand used in glass may have iron oxide in purity levels around 300 ppm or more while in optical glass it is in the range of 10 to 50 ppm or lower. Impurities from any of the transition metal oxides such as chrome, cobalt and nickel which could add color to the glass, must be limited to under 1 ppm.

The rare earth materials must go a step further and be introduced as a 99.9% to 99.995% rare earth oxide purity. It is absolutely essential that no color occurs from the absorption

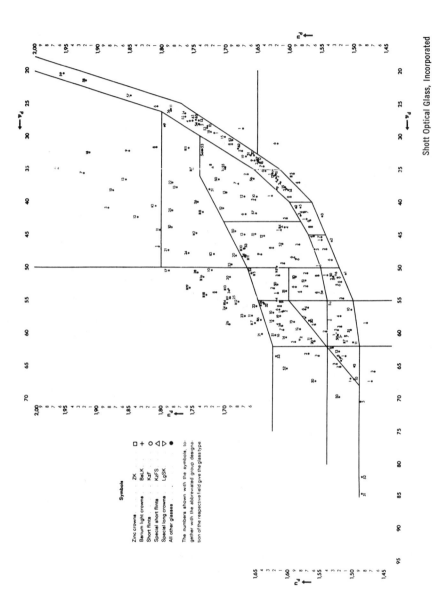

Shott Optical Glass, Incorporated

*Figure 8. Optical map designating glass groups (letters) and glass types (numbers)
as defined by index of refraction (n_d) and Abbe-number (v_d)*

Symbols

□	+	○	◁ ▷ ●

Zinc crowns	ZK	BaLK
Barium light crowns		KzF
Short flints		KzFS
Special short flints		LgSK
Special long crowns		
All other glasses		

The numbers shown with the symbols, together with the abbreviated group designation of the respective field give the glass-type

bands of neodymium and praeseodymium. Traces of cerium must be eliminated to minimize U. V. absorption.

It is due to these stringent requirements on raw material purity along with the type of glass making oxides used that optical glasses in general are rather expensive compared to other commercial glasses.

The primary rare earth material used is lanthanum oxide. Another material, thorium oxide, although not a rare earth oxide but an element extracted from monazite sand, has been used along with lanthanum as a major ingredient. Since thorium is a radio-active material, it is no longer being used and new glasses have been developed to replace the thorium based glasses. Other rare earth oxides used in very small amounts are gadolinium, ytterbium, and another related element, yttrium.

Lanthanum oxide is added primarily to obtain a high index of refraction and high Abbe-number. The result is a low dispersion glass. Looking at the optical map, it can be seen that the highest index of refraction glasses are usually extra dense flints due to the high lead oxide content. These glasses have a low Abbe-number. The borosilicates have a low index of refraction and high Abbe-number. Barium crowns result in a high Abbe-number but an intermediate index.

The lanthanum glasses were not developed until after 1935 and much of the experimentation on improvement of chemical durability and crystallization characteristics was performed during the 1950's. These glasses have played a big part in over-all improvements in many optical systems such as the modern camera.

Lanthanum glasses are usually low silica and consist sub-stantially of boric acid, zirconia, barium oxide and lanthanum with various other additives to help stabilize the viscosity and liquidus or crystallization temperature. (2, 10)

Fluorescence

Fluorescence in glass is the result of atoms being excited by the absorption of light resulting in light emission. This is a phenomenum normally associated with certain minerals and other crystalline materials when subjected to ultra violet light. Most rare earth ions when added to glass exhibit fluorescence. (1, 5)

Practical application of the fluorescence of glass is limited. With the development of the optical laser in 1960, neodymium doped glasses became important in the operation of high powered lasers. Neodymium glass lasers emitting at 1060 nm have received the greatest attention because they can operate at room temperature with relatively high efficiencies. Of importance as glass hosts are alkali-alkaline-earth-silicates and recently the fluoro-phosphates which help contribute to high efficiency. The neodymium oxide used in these glasses is at least 99.9% purity and gives a purple colored glass. E. Snitzer's paper on "Lasers and Glass Technology" gives a comprehensive review of this subject. (11)

Summary

A historical review of the uses of rare earths in glass
indicates that as new technology develops, the use of rare earths
increase in glassmaking. The use of cerium oxide in stabilizing
high energy radiation effects on glass, lanthanum oxide for new
optical glasses and neodymium doped laser glass are all products
of technology developed in the past 30 years. The classical
uses of rare earths for coloring and decolorizing glass continue
to grow.

Literature Cited

1. Weyl, W. A. "Coloured Glasses"; Dawson's Pall Mall: London,
   England, 1959; pp. 218-234, 439-514.
2. Tooley, F. V. Ed. "Handbook of Glass Manufacturing"; Books for
   Industry: New York, 1974; Chapt. 18.
3. Shand, E. B. "Glass Engineering Handbook"; McGraw-Hill Book
   Company Inc.: New York, 1958; pp. 3-9, 81-88.
4. Morey, G. W. "The Properties of Glass"; Reinhold Publishing
   Corporation: New York, 1938; pp. 435-436.
5. Herring, A. P.; Dean, R. W.; Drobnick, J. L. "The Use of Rare
   Earth Oxides to Give Color or Visible Fluorescence to Soda-
   Lime Glasses"; presented at Am. Ceramic Society 70th Annual
   Meeting, Chicago, Ill., April 28, 1968. Reprints available
   from Molybdenum Corporation of America.
6. Scholes, S. R. "Modern Lass Practice"; Seventh Revised
   Edition, Rev. by C. H. Greene; Cahners Publishing Company:
   Boston, 1975; pp. 307-315.
7. Harding, F. L. "Introduction to Glass Science"; L. D. Pye,
   H. J. Stevens and W. C. LaCourse, Eds.; Plenum Press: New
   York, 1972; pp. 417-423.
8. Schutt, T. C.; Barlow, G. "Practical Aspects of Cerium
   Decolorization of Glass"; Amer. Ceram. Soc. Bull., 1972, 51,
   (2), 155-157.
9. Kreidl, N. J.; Hensler, J. R. "Formation of Color Centers in
   Glasses Exposed to Gamma Radiation"; J. Amer. Ceram. Soc.,
   1955, 38, (12), 423-432.
10. Kutzchmann, R. "Influence of La_2O_3 and ThO_2 on the Crystalline
    Behavior of Optical Glasses"; Glass Tech., 1965, 6, (5),
    156-160.
11. Snitzer, E. "Lasers and Glass Technology"; J. Amer. Ceram.
    Soc., 1973, 52, (6), 516-525.

RECEIVED March 3, 1981.

Rare Earth Polishing Compounds

ROBERT V. HORRIGAN

8416 West Country Club Drive, North, Sarasota, FL 33580

There is little information in the literature regarding the first applications of cerium oxide or cerium-rich rare earth oxide mixtures in glass polishing. Duncan (1) mentions that the application began in the European glass industry about 1933, spreading to the Canadian optical industry about 1940. During World War II, an employee of German-American descent working for the W. F. & J. Barnes Co. of Rockford, Illinois, introduced on August 31, 1943 a rare-earth oxide (45% CeO_2) polish called Barnesite which enjoyed immediate success in the polishing of precision optics such as bombsights, range finders, periscopes, and other fire control instruments. The Lindsay Chemical Co. of West Chicago, Ill., early in World War II, introduced a high cerium oxide (90+% CeO_2) polish called Cerox for ophthalmic use. Other more specialized cerium-based products were added, a few competitors entered the field, and by 1960 more than 340 metric tons per year were being used for polishing mirrors, plate glass, television tubes, ophthalmic lenses and precision optics. The advent of the Pilkington process, 1972-1973, for large scale plate glass manufacture severely reduced the market for cerium oxide, but still today over 1000 metric tons per year are sold in the U.S.

From 1940 to 1965, the principal source of these rare earth products was the mineral monazite (Th, RE orthophosphate) which fortunately or unfortunately, depending on one's point of view, contains 4-6% thorium. Today, there is essentially no market for thorium in the U.S. The expense of separating out thorium-free rare-earth products from monazite is not only excessive, but bound tightly in governmental red tape because of the mild radioactivity of the thorium. This situation does not apply in France, Brazil, or India, whose governments are wisely stockpiling all extracted thorium for future atomic energy needs.

Luckily, the U.S. has the largest bastnasite (R.E. fluocarbonate) mine in the world located at Mountain Pass, California, owned and operated by Molycorp, Inc., a subsidiary of Union Oil

Co. of California. Proven orebody reserves at the end of December
1978 were 365,000 metric tons, with indicated reserves of over 3
million metric tons of rare earth oxide (REO). Current mine production capacity is 27,000 metric tons per year of bastnaesite
concentrate produced in 3 grades: a 60% REO unleached concentrate,
a 70% REO leached concentrate (SrO and CaO removed), and a 90% REO
calcined concentrate (CO_2 removed). In 1977, shipments totaled
13,521 metric tons of contained REO. Polishing compounds consumed
approximately 10% of this production.

With suitable chemical, mechanical and heat treatment, glass
polishing compounds of high quality have been produced from bastnaesite concentrates since 1965.

The Scientific Basis for the Uses

A brief description of glass surfacing techniques will be
useful prior to our discussion of the three principal theories of
the polishing mechanism. In the ophthalmic factory or prescription laboratory, an optical glass blank is firmly fastened to a
lens chuck, which is then pressed down on a curved grinding tool
and rotated at high speed. To achieve the desired lens curvature,
one or two stages of diamond grinding (generation) suffice. Al-
ternately one diamond generating step followed by grinding (or
fining) with loose powdered abrasives (such as corundum, emery,
garnet, or silicon carbide) suspended in a water slurry may be
employed. This is rough treatment, and we may well expect to find
some subsurface damage which hopefully can be repaired during the
polishing step.

The "fined" lens, still attached to the lens chuck, is rinsed
free of any adhering abrasive, and placed in a polisher. Here the
tool contacted by the lens is called the "lap" and may consist of
a wide variety of materials depending on the goal to be achieved.
In the ophthalmic factory, for example, thick, hard thermoplastic
pads have good surface quality, curve control, long life, and the
ability to operate well under high speeds and pressures. On the
other hand, the prescription laboratory will favor a paper-thin
plastic or cloth pad which is used only once. The polishing compound, usually ceric oxide, zirconium oxide, ferric oxide (jewel-
er's rouge), or silica (white rouge) is slurried in water in a
concentration of 5-25% by weight, and is recirculated constantly
over the lap and lens. In the factory, large central systems col-
lect the polishing slurry and pumps furnish the slurry to the
polishing bowls constantly. The lens weight loss, while not
great, is readily measured, and glass removal rate is of prime
importance in measuring the efficiency of a polishing compound.
In our view, the polishing slurry would have an indefinite life
were it not for the fact that the glass products gradually dilute
and contaminate the slurry. The build-up of alkali ions is so
great, that daily pH adjustments are necessary in large central
system slurry tanks.

Over three hundred years ago Isaac Newton concluded that polishing was nothing more than fine-scale abrasion. Early in the twentieth century, Lord Rayleigh found that a polished surface was entirely different from a ground, or abraded surface, and suggested that the polished surface was smooth on a molecular scale, like the surface of water. Later the British chemist, Sir George Beilby, applying chemical etchants to a polished surface, found original grinding scratches to reappear. He concluded that a molecular flow of material (the "Beilby Layer") from high to low spots took place, thus covering the scratches. (2, 5) Bowden and Hughes (2) at the University of Cambridge in the 1930's reasoned that if abrasion were the fundamental mechanism, then the hardness of the polishing material should correlate with ability to polish; they found this not to be the case, but did find a remarkable correlation between the melting point of the polishing material and the rate of polish. They concluded that polishing was a melting phenomenon, not abrasion.

Let us test their hypotheses against the melting points of known good polishing oxides: ZrO_2, 3000°C; CeO_2, 1950°C; SiO_2, 1700°C; Fe_2O_3, 1565°C; SnO_2, 1127°C. Except for stannic oxide, these high melting point values support the melting hypothesis of Bowden and Hughes.

Here the matter rested for twenty years or so, abrasion or melting, take your pick, and each side had its adherents. But now a third hypothesis was proposed and gradually took precedence over the first two. In 1931 Grebenschikov (3) noted that the presence or absence of water influenced the polishing of glass, and suggested that a layer of silicic acid would build up on the surface of the glass being polished. This layer would protect the glass from further erosion were it not for the fact that the polishing agent was at work to sweep away this layer and expose a fresh surface.

Further work by Cornish and Watt (4) and Silvernail and Goetzinger (5) established the active role played by the presence of water, and these authors concluded that a chemical-mechanical hypothesis would fit the observed data. In the case of ceric oxide polishing of glass, Cornish and Watt suggest the formation of a "CeO-Si" activated complex which permits the rupture of the O-Si-O bonds by hydrolysis. The complex "CeO-Si" then breaks apart, the hydrated silica is swept away along with alkalis released from the glass surface, and the process repeats.

The above is a good example of CeO_2 acting like a catalyst. The author would like to suggest another possibility which may add to the chemical theory. The efficient polishing compounds previously mentioned have not only high melting points, but also have large unsatisfied coordinate valencies. Typically, for example, the zirconium atom will attract a cloud of hydroxyl radicals to satisfy its coordinate valences. Thus, a high concentration of hydroxyl radicals are readily available at the glass surface to speed the hydrolysis reaction.

The free world market for cerium-oxide based polishing compounds is not large--approximately 4400 metric tons per year--,
and we do not see a substantial growth potential despite the 11%
annual growth in sales of spectacle lenses. The reason is two-
fold: first, faster more efficient polishing compounds are available which can be used in slurry concentrations one-half that of a
few years ago; second, fully half the market for ophthalmic glass
lenses has been captured by plastic lenses of CR-39 polymer.
Cerium oxide is ineffective in polishing this material; specially
treated alumina or stannic oxide are used.

Table I shows our estimate of 1979 cerium-oxide based polishing product consumption.

TABLE I.   CONSUMPTION OF CERIUM-OXIDE BASED
POLISHING COMPOUNDS (1979) a

COUNTRY	CONSUMPTION (METRIC TONS/YR.)
United States	1,600
Canada	200
South America	350
Far East	850
Western Europe	1,400
	4,400

a. CeO_2 content varies from 45-90%.

The estimated end-use pattern for cerium oxide based polishing compounds in the U.S. (1979) is illustrated in Table II.

TABLE II.   ESTIMATED END USE PATTERN
IN THE UNITED STATES FOR
CERIUM-OXIDE BASED POLISHING COMPOUNDS (1979) a

END USE, U.S.	CONSUMPTION METRIC TONS	PERCENT
Glass lenses, ophthalmic	720	45
Glass lenses, precision	192	12
Mirrors	320	20
TV tube faceplates	240	15
Misc. - photomasks, gem stones	128	8
	1,600	100

a. CeO_2 content varies from 45-90%.

Competitive Advantage of the Rare Earths - Competition from Other Materials

As our sales force never tires of repeating, "It isn't the
cost per pound of cerium oxide that matters; what matters is your

TABLE III. REPRESENTATIVE SPHERE AND TORIC
POLISHING MACHINE CHARACTERISTICS, 1930 - 1980

MANU- FACTURER	MODEL	APPROX. ERA OF ORIGIN	NORMAL SPINDLE SPEED	TYPICAL SPINDLE FORCE	TYPICAL SPINDLE TIME
SPHERES					
Bausch & Lomb	Hand Pan	1930's	300 RPM	Variable	15 Min.
Robinson- Houchin	Greyhound #113	1950's	450 RPM	30 Lbs.	8 Min.
CMV	1CM-10	1970's	Upper=1,200 RPM Lower=1,800 RPM	90 Lbs.	1 Min.
Coburn	608	1970's	2,400 RPM	100 Lbs.	3/4 Min.
TORICS					
Bausch & Lomb (used to "rock" a torric)	Hand Pan	1930's	300 RPM	Variable	30 Min.
American Optical	427	1940's	Upper= 400 RPM Lower= 30 RPM	20 Lbs.	15 Min.
Optek	400	1960's	400 CPM*	30 Lbs.	5 Min.
American Optical	Super Twin	1970's	550 CPM*	40 Lbs.	4½ Min.

*Cycles Per Minute.

cost per thousand polished surfaces!" A high quality cerium oxide polish may be priced at $3.50 per pound; a good quality zirconia-based polish may be $1.50 per pound; red rouge (ferric oxide) may be priced at $0.40 per pound; and white rouge (precipitated silica) at perhaps $0.20 per pound. Without getting into details, a recent example may clarify the competitive advantage of cerium oxide. One of the largest lens manufacturers in America was persuaded to switch from zirconia to a high quality cerium oxide. In the first nine months a savings of $400,000 was realized by more than halving the amount of powder used, shortening the time required for polishing each lens, and increasing the yield of finished lenses in the bargain.

Other factors are important, too. Zirconia has a nasty tendency to settle out rock-hard in tanks and pipes, and besides the material loss, clean-up costs are severe. Ceria will settle eventually, but always is soft and easy to re-suspend. Ferric oxide (red rouge) is an excellent, but slow polish, and a bad pollutant due to its irreversible staining quality. White rouge is a very slow polish, and is rarely seen in use today.

High polishing speeds are essential in todays economy, and the latest equipment employs much higher spindle speeds and pressures than those used just a few years ago. Cerium oxide is ideal under these more modern conditions. A spherical lens that required 8 minutes to polish 15 years ago is now polished in less than one minute. A toric (cylinder) lens that previously took 15 minutes to polish, now requires 4-1/2 minutes.

Table III illustrates the progress which has been made in polishing machines over the last fifty years.

BIBLIOGRAPHY

1. Duncan, L. K. "Cerium Oxide for Glass Polishing" Glass Industry, (1970), 41 (7), 387-393.

2. Cornish, D. C. "The Mechanism of Glass Polishing" B.S.I.R.A. Research Report R267, British Scientific Instrument Research Association, South Hill, Chislehurst, Kent (1961).

3. Grebenschikov, I. V. Keram. i Steklo, (1931), 7, 36.

4. Cornish, D. C.; Watt, J. M. "The Mechanism of Glass Polishing" a report presented at the Symposium on the Surface Chemistry of Glass, Am. Ceramic Soc. Meeting, Wash. D.C. (May 11, 1966).

5. Silvernail, W. L.; Goetzinger, N. J. "The Mechanism of Glass Polishing" Glass Industry, (1971), 52 (4), 130-152, 52 (5), 172-175.

RECEIVED February 18, 1981.

The Use of Rare Earth Elements in Zeolite Cracking Catalysts

DAVID N. WALLACE

W. R. Grace & Company, Davison Chemical Division, Columbia, MD 21044

There are many areas of application of the rare earth metals and their oxides including those in metallurgy, their well known use as polishing compounds, and their ability to provide unique glass compositions. One of the largest single uses for rare earth mixtures is in fluid cracking catalysts made for the petroleum refining industry. It is with fluid cracking catalysts that refiners produce the bulk of gasoline and fuel oil required by the general public. (1)

Fluid cracking catalysts manufactured prior to 1960 were amorphous mixtures of silica and alumina, combined in such a manner that the mixture could be spray dried into a roughly spherical shape about 70 microns in diameter. Today's cracking catalyst in addition contains an inert filler and zeolite: the principle active ingredient of today's cracking catalysts.

To give a perspective of cracking catalyst usage world wide, we note that world wide oil refining capacity is about 50,000,000 barrels per day 15% of which can be catalytically cracked. Cracking catalyst usage to handle this amount of oil runs to about 550 tons per day, of which 90 to 95% contain zeolites. The total yearly value of cracking catalysts is in excess of $100,000,000. The geographic distribution of cracking catalyst usage, Figure 1, shows that in the United States today zeolite cracking catalysts are primarily used due to their preferential selectivity for gasoline production. Other areas of the world which do not have such a dependency on gasoline use both zeolite catalysts and amorphous catalysts to produce a mix of gasoline and fuel oils.

Following their introduction to the refining industry in 1962, zeolite cracking catalysts, have virtually replaced the amorphous silica alumina cracking catalysts that had previously dominated the marketplace. To the rare earth industry the development of zeolite catalysts represented a new end use without precedent. Nearly all zeolite cracking

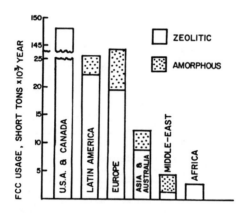

Figure 1. *Geographic distribution of fluid cracking catalyst (FCC) usage*

catalysts currently manufactured contain rare earth oxides
present as a mixture of the rare earth elements.

Today about 250 thousand tons per year of fluid cracking
catalysts are sold throughput the world. Of this amount
about 220 thousand tons are zeolite cracking catalysts. In
the early days of zeolite catalysts, the catalysts contained
on the average between 5 and 10% zeolite. Today, however,
average zeolite contents run in the range of 10 to 14 percent
with selected grades containing as much as 35 percent zeolite.

Assuming for the moment that the average level of rare
earth oxides on these catalysts is 2% by weight, the
estimated 1980 rare earth oxide usage would be about 4,400 tons.
This estimate is on the low side and is based on the 10%
zeolite level. A more accurate zeolite content estimate
would be 15% in which case 6,600 tons would be consumed.

Data obtained from a 1979 U.S. Bureau of Mines report
by C. M. Moore, (2), Figure 2, indicates that a sharp rise
in United States rare earth demand accompanied the development
of rare earth exchanged zeolite cracking catalysts and their
rapid acceptance by the United States petroleum refining
industry. Although usage in cracking catalysts seems to have
levelled off, total U.S. demand continues to swing upward
suggesting that other segments of U.S. industry have increased
their usage of rare earth.

The growth of zeolite containing fluid cracking catalysts
skyrocketed during the mid-1960's, Figure 3, and today it is
safe to say that without exception all fluid cracking unts
in the United States employ some form of zeolite catalysts.

Zeolite Catalytic Cracking

Why was there such a phenomenal growth of zeolite
catalysts in the refining industry? The answer lies in two
parts. Zeolite catatalysts containing rare earth are
structurally more stable and maintain their hydrogen transfer
(cracking) properties better during use than the older
amorphous silica alumina cracking catalysts. These catalysts
are capacity expanders by which refiners are able to increase
the amount of oil processed and still obtain the desired
product distribution.

In general, refinery catalytic cracking units are
limited in their throughput by the amount of coke produced
that has to be burned off in the regenerator. Coke is a
by-product of the cracking reaction. Zeolite cracking
catalysts lowered the coke production significantly, thus
allowing refiners to increase their throughput substantially
while staying within coke burning limitations.

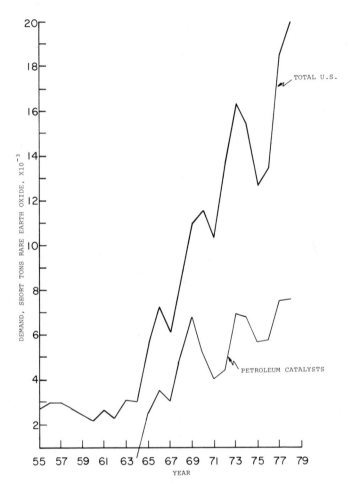

Figure 2.   Rare earth usage in petroleum cracking catalysts as a function of total U.S. rare earth demand

The ability of catalysts to convert or crack large molecular weight, high boiling point organic molecules into smaller molecular weight, lower boiling molecules depends to a large extent on their acidic properties. In zeolites the acid site population and strength are several orders of magnitude higher than in the older amorphous silica-alumina gel catalysts and are believed to be primarily Brønsted acid sites. Further, the addition of rare earth to the zeolite enables it to retain its inherent acidic properties better in the harsh high temperature reaction system of the refinery cat cracker than it can without rare earth.

This ability is measured throughout the petroleum industry by a tool referred to as the microactivity test. In this test an oil feedstock, boiling in the range of roughly 400-950°F, is passed under controlled flow rate conditions over a fixed bed of the catalyst at a temperature of about 900°F. Chromatographic analysis of the product stream from this reaction for material boiling below about 420°F is made. The amount of this product found determines the conversion level. Conversion is usually expressed in volume percent and includes gasoline range compounds and lighter materials.

While the number of fluid cracking units in the United States switching to zeolite catalysts was increasing, the microactivity value of an average equilibrium mixture of cracking catalysts also increased as seen in Figure 4. This meant that more of the oil feed to the fluid catalytic cracking unit was being converted to the more useful lower boiling compounds on the first pass through the unit. With the older amorphous catalysts a significant fraction of the oil fed to the unit was found to be relatively unconverted on the first pass and had to be recycled back to the unit increasing the coke burning load of the regenerator and restricting fresh feed throughput.

A higher catalyst microactivity implies a reduced amount of unconverted material recycled to the catalytic cracker, thus increasing not only first pass feed conversion to desirable products but also permitting higher throughput of fresh feedstocks due to the reduction in recycle material. Consequently, the development of zeolite catalysts proved a major boon to the refining industry.

The Zeolite of Cracking Catalysts

As mentioned earlier, fluid cracking catalyst are presently comprised of three principal ingredients, an amorphous silica-alumina refractory binder, a generally inert filler and the zeolite.

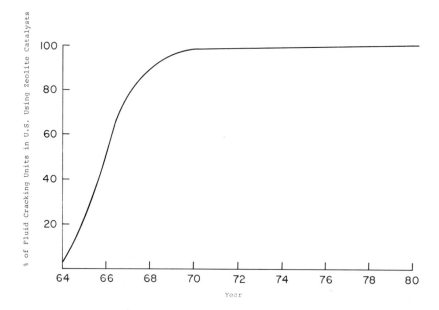

Figure 3.   Growth of zeolite catalyst use in U.S. fluid cracking units

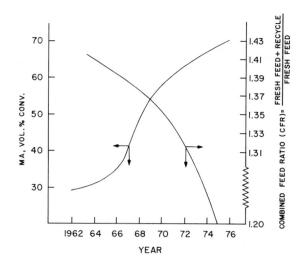

*Figure 4.   Yearly increase in microactivity (MA) and decrease in recycle caused
by zeolite catalyst usage*

The zeolite component belongs to a broad class of minerals composed of crystalline hydrous alumino silicates containing one or more alkali or alkaline earth metals. Some of the naturally occuring zeolites are analcite, chabasite, mordenite, natrolite and faujasite, all of which are generally found in small deposits.

The zeolites used in cracking catalyst compositions are synthetically made members of the faujasite family including X and Y types. These designations are based on specific X-ray diffraction patterns but are commonly discussed on the basis of silica to alumina ratios. Y zeolite (at $SiO_2/Al_2O_3 > 3.0$) is the preferred type for cracking catalyst use since it tends to be more hydrothermally stable than the lower ratio X variety, which has a SiO_2/Al_2O_3 ratio of <3.0.

The fundamental building block of the X and Y faugasites is a truncated octahedron referred to as a sodalite cage, Figure 5, having hexagonal faces and square faces.

The crystal structure of the faujasite is built up by linking the sodalite cages tetrahedrally through their hexagonal faces forming connecting hexagonal prisms.

As the sodalite cages are stacked up in this fashion we note, Figure 6, that a channel develops through the structure. This channel has a well defined spatial geometry and is referred to as a super-cage, being bounded by six membered and four membered ring surfaces of the sodalite cages and the connecting hexagonal prisms. (A change in the stacking arrangement can lead to an equally well defined but different channel structure with different catalytic properties). Charge balance or neutrality is maintained in these structures in the "as prepared" form by alkali or alkaline earth cations.

Zeolite Cation Exchange

The presence of the alkali or alkaline earth metals in the zeolite provide the extremely important property of cation exchange capacity. However, not all of the cations are easily exchanged from the more popular Y faujasite form. As we see in Figure 7, where the SI, SII, SIII and SI', SII' designations represent the site positions available to the cations, there are geometry impediments caused by the small free diamter (~2.2Å) of the hexagonal ring and accessibility of the hexagonal prism cage.

Because of these restrictions it is sometimes desirable to heat the zeolite to an elevated temperature in order to expand the kinetic diameter of the entrance ring, as well as to dehydrate the cationic species present, facilitating the relocation and subsequent removal of the cation by exchange.

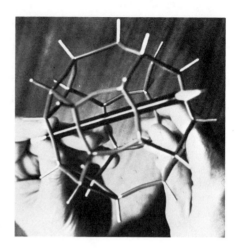

Figure 5.   Sodalite cage

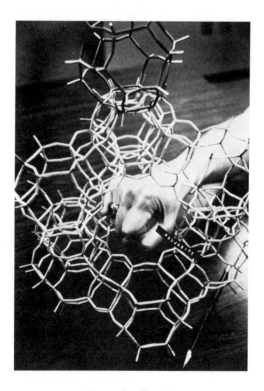

Figure 6.   Faujasite

Over the past 2 decades zeolites have been exchanged with just about every imaginable cationic species in an attempt to find something that works as well as rare earth does in maintaining zeolite structural stability and catalytic activity. As yet no commercially viable substitute for rare earth has been found which provides the same zeolite stability, activity and product selectivity at a commercial price.

An indication of the difficulties encountered is expressed in Figure 8 (3). The catalytic response of calcium and manganese exchanged faujasites is compared with the response of a rare earth exchanged faujasite as a function of the relative acid character of the zeolite. Note the large activity advantage and the higher acidity level of the rare earth exchanged zeolite.

The Cracking Catalyst Environment

In a typical fluid catalytic cracker, catalyst particles are continuously circulated from one portion of the operation to another. Figure 9 shows a schematic flow diagram of a typical unit (4). Hot gas oil feed (500°-700°F) is mixed with 1250°F catalyst at the base of the riser in which the oil and catalyst residence times (from a few seconds to ~1 min.) and the ratio of catalyst to the amount of oil is controlled to obtain the desired level of conversion for the product slate demand. The products are then removed from the separator while the catalyst drops back into the stripper. In the stripper adsorbed liquid hydrocarbons are steam stripped from the catalyst particles before the catalyst particles are transferred to the regenerator.

The regenerator section represents the most severe environment for today's cracking catalyst. The coked catalyst particle,with some hydrocarbons still adsorbed,passes directly into an oxidizing temperature zone of 1250°F or higher. In this environment coke is burned off the catalyst particle, regenerating it for further use.

It is important to note that in burning off the coke, catalyst particle temperatures generally exceed the average bed temperature by several hundred degrees. In laboratory work catalyst particles have been observed to scintillate during burning, suggesting temperatures well in the excess of 1500°F.

Recent legislation has required industry to reduce stack emissions of such things CO, SO_x, NO_x and particulate matter. Although some of these problems are still being addressed, a catalytic method has been found for significantly reducing CO emissions from the regenerators of catalytic cracking units. This is achieved by burning CO within the regenerator stage. Doing this generally eliminates the need for expensive

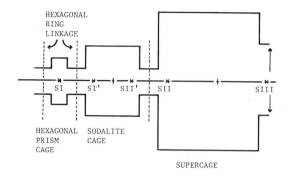

Figure 7. Diagram of synthetic faujasite cages showing cation positions (SI, SI', SII', SII, SIII) and pore openings

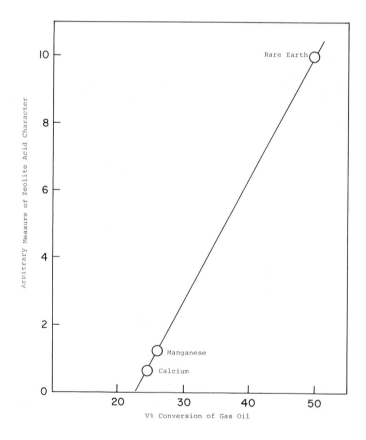

Figure 8. Correlation between catalyst activity for gas-oil cracking and Brønsted acidity of Ca, Mn, and REX zeolites

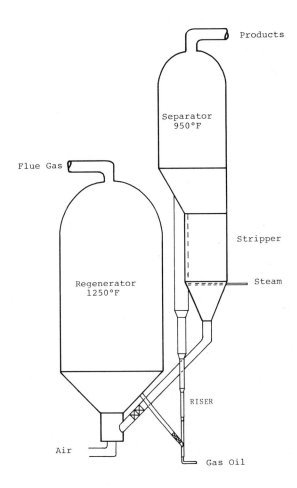

Figure 9.   Diagram of a fluid catalytic cracking unit

capital investment in CO boilers, yet provides the heat
necessary for maintaining efficient refinery operations. This
technique causes regenerator temperatures to rise requiring
improved regenerator metallurgy and stable cracking catalysts.

Zeolite Rare Earth Level Effects

Zeolite stability can be partially controlled by the
exchange level of rare earth, as shown in Figure 10. Zeolite
thermal stability is measured as a function of the retained
surface area following a 2 hour air calcination at 1650°F. In
this particular case maximum thermal stability was obtained
at about 20 Wt.% rare earth oxide (RE_2O_3) on zeolite. At this
level of rare earth, which is fairly typical, nearly complete
exchange of the supercage and sodalite cage sodium ions by
rare earth ions is obtained. If a high level of sodium were
to remain in the zeolite after rare earth exchange, for
example, due to poor pH control, the zeolite structure would
collapse. Consequently, it is desirable to exchange out as
much sodium as possible, replacing it with rare earth.

Hydrothermal (steam) stability is also important, in as
much as the catalyst must pass through a high temperature
stripping zone in which the usual fluid stripping medium is
steam. In our laboratory, zeolite hydrothermal stability
is measured by comparing the x-ray crystallinity of the
unknown faujasite sample with that of a fully rare earth
exchanged reference standard following a 3 hour, 100% steam,
1500°F treatment.

Figure 11 shows that maximum hydrothermal stability for
this faujasite was obtained a rare earth oxide level of only
7 Wt.%. However, since maximum thermal stability was achieved
at abou the 20% rare earth oxide level, the exchange should
be carried out to the 20% level in order to maximize overall
stability characteristics.

Thermal and hydrothermal stability are necessary but not
sufficient criteria for an acceptable cracking catalyst,
since both the life expectancy and the activity of the zeolite
catalyst is of importance to the refiner. Activity
is controlled by the catalyst manufacturer in one of two ways,
by either adding more zeolite or increasing the stability
and activity of the zeolite.

Like both thermal and hydrothermal stability, activity
is a function of the level of rare earth exchange as shown
in Figure 12. This graph indicates that maximum activity
following a simulated commercial deactivation is obtained
by exchanging into the zeolite 20% by weight rare earth
(as the oxide) replacing sodium and/or the preexchanged
ammonium cation used in this study to provide a constant base
zeolite Na_2O level. (Ammonia was driven off during deactivation)

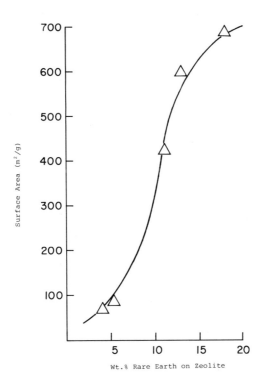

Figure 10. Zeolite thermal stability response to rare earth content

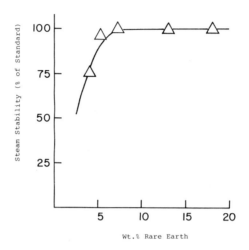

Figure 11.   Zeolite steam stability response to rare earth content

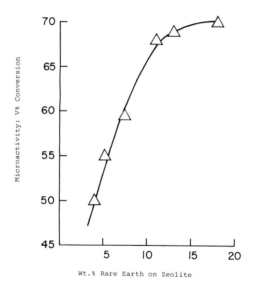

Figure 12.   Microactivity response of zeloite cracking catalyst to rare earth content

While further exchange with rare earth beyond the 20 Wt.
percent level is possible, it is economically impractical
principally due to the energy required to dislodge the
remaining Na_2O and the limited activity benefits which accure.

The Future Role of Rare Earth Exchanged Zeolites in Catalytic Cracking

What about the future? Like many other industries,
catalyst manufacturers are dependent on refinery requirements
and crude oil availability. Although crude oil supplies
may become limited and catalyst usage reduced, rare earth
usage in cracking catalyst may be unaffected. This is
because crudes that are likely to be processed are expected
to be more difficult to crack requiring higher stability
and activity and thus more rare earth exchanged zeolite per
unit of catalyst.

If gasoline demand continues to slacken, more feedstock
may be targeted for either fuel oil, or diesel production.
In this case less of the rare earth exchanged zeolites would
be required.

Finally, the product slate (e.g. olefin production,
petrochemical feedstock production), or the product quality
(e.g. gasoline octane improvement) may dictate a reduction
in rare earth usage.

Which of these will come to pass is uncertain.
However, we do know that in the long term the feedstocks will
be generally more difficult to crack requiring process as
well as cataltyic improvement, and rare earths will continue
to play a major role in fluid cracking catalysts.

The author gratefully acknowledges the contributions of
Drs. J. S. Magee and E. W. Albers in preparing this work,
and the support of the Davison Chemical Division of W. R.
Grace and Co.

"Literature Cited"

1. Venuto, P. B.; Habib, E. T., Jr. "Fluid Catalytic
    Cracking with Zeolite Catalysts".
    Marcel Dekker, Inc.: New York 1979.

2. Moore, C. M.; Rare Earth Minerals and Metals.
    Preprint from 1977 Bureau of Mines, "Minerals Yearbook",
    U.S. Department of Interior, Bureau of Mines:
    Washington, D.C.

3. Gates, B. C.; Katzer, J. R,; Schuit, G.C.A.;
    "Chemistry of Catalytic Processsess:.
    McGraw-Hill Book Co.: New York 1979.

4. Wollaston, E. G.; Haflin, W. J.; Ford, W. D.; D'Souza
    G. J.; Hydrocarbon Processing, Vol. 54, September 1975.
    p. 93.

RECEIVED March 30, 1981.

Rare Earths in Noncracking Catalysts

ALAN W. PETERS and GWAN KIM

W. R. Grace & Company, Davison Chemical Division, Columbia, MD 21044

Since 1962 rare earths have been used to stabilize zeolite cracking catalysts for the petroleum industry ($\underline{1}$, $\underline{2}$). Until recently this application to catalysis has been the only commercially significant one. Currently, however, a number of new applications of potential commercial significance are appearing. One of the most important of these is the use of cerium in catalysts for automobile exhaust emission control. We will emphasize this application in our review without neglecting other applications.

The rare earth oxides have a number of distinguishing properties important in catalytic applications. The oxides are basic ($\underline{3}$) compared to alumina, lanthanum oxide (La_2O_3) being the most basic. The oxides also have good thermal stability, a valuable characteristic in most industrial applications. Some rare earths including cerium, praseodymium, and terbium form non-stoichiometric oxides ($\underline{4}$), an important property shared by many good oxidation catalysts. These mixed valence state compounds are typically polymorphic.

Cost and abundance are important properties to be considered for any commercial application. Table I lists recent cost and abundance data of individual rare earths derived from major ores. The expensive oxides are the least abundant. Of the catalytically interesting rare earths forming non-stoichiometric oxides, cerium is by far the most abundant and least expensive.

Important potential catalytic applications include:
- Ammonia Synthesis
- Hydrogenation/Dehydrogenation
- Polymerization
- Isomerization
- Oxidation
- Auto Exhaust Emission Control
- Applications of Perovskites

Some of these areas have been recently reviewed by Rosynek ($\underline{5}$), polymerization of olefins has been reviewed by Mazzei ($\underline{6}$), and Minachev ($\underline{7}$) in a recent paper summarized some experimental results in the areas of isomerization, hydrogenation, and oxidation. We will try not to overlap these recent reviews.

0097-6156/81/0164-0117$05.00/0

TABLE I   Rare Earth Oxides Abundance[a] and Cost[b]

	$/lb.	Abundance in Ores			
	Pure Oxide	Monazite	Bastnaesite	Xenotime	U Residues
CeO_2	7.50	45	49	5	4
La_2O_3	7.25	20	32	0.5	0.8
Nd_2O_3	18.00	18	13	2.2	4.1
Pr_6O_{11}	32.00	5	4	0.7	1.0
Sm_2O_3	32.00	5	0.5	2	4.5
Gd_2O_3	55.00	2	0.3	4	9
Eu_2O_3	700.00	0.1	0.1	0.2	0.2
Tb_4O_7	350.00			1.0	1.2
Dy_2O_3	45.00			8.7	11.2
Ho_2O_3	120.00			2.1	2.6
Er_2O_3	45.00			5.4	5.5
Tm_2O_3	1000.00			0.9	0.9
Yb_2O_3	85.00			6.2	4.0
Lu_2O_3	2000.00			0.4	0.4
Y_2O_3	30.00	2.1	0.1	61	51

Concentrates

Cerium	0.85	(a)	Mineral Facts and Problems, 5th.
Lanthanum	1.05		Ed., U.S. Bureau of Mines, 1975.
REO	0.80		
		(b)	Minerals Yearbook, Volume 1, 1977,
			U.S. Bureau of Mines, 1980.

TABLE II   Performance of the Cerium Promoted Lummus Catalyst

Average Reactor	% NH_3 in Product		
Temperature, °F	Equilibrium	Conventional	Ce Promoted
710	39	10.4	13.5
840	22.4	12.8	17.8
910	16.8	12.7	15.6
ΔT (T Max. − T inlet)		∿250°F	∿330°F

Conditions:

150 atm pressure

Gas hourly space velocity = 16,000

Mole Ratio H_2/N_2 =   ∿2.8

Ammonia Synthesis

Catalytic ammonia synthesis has been recently reviewed by Ertl (8) and by Emmett (9). The catalytic reactions can be written:

$$N_2(g) \rightleftarrows N_2(ad)$$

$$N_2(ad) \rightleftarrows 2N(ad)$$

$$H_2(g) \rightleftarrows 2H(ad)$$

$$N(ad) + 3H(ad) \rightleftarrows NH_3(ad)$$

$$NH_3(ad) \rightleftarrows NH_3(g)$$

The step:

$$N_2(ad) \rightleftarrows 2N(ad)$$

is rate determining, although at high conversions the removal of NH_3 from the catalyst surface may be important.

A typical NH_3 synthesis catalyst (10) contains iron oxide plus 1% K_2O, 1-2% Al_2O_3, and may contain ∿1% CaO on the surface. After fusion and reduction the surface is largely metallic iron plus reduced promoters concentrated on the surface (8). Sze and Wang (11) have shown that a catalyst washed with $Ce(NO_3)_3$ and subsequently reduced is much more active than the conventional catalyst, Table II. Mischmetal salts may be substituted for the cerium salt.

Since industrial catalysts can be very sensitive to pretreatment, the source of the activity improvement is unclear. For example, washing even in the absence of cerium may have some catalytic effect.

Hydrogenation

In an interesting series of experiments Van Mal and co-workers (12, 13, 14) have found that if rare earths are combined with transition metals at high temperatures, the alloy will absorb large amounts of hydrogen as hydrides under mild conditions; 1 atm. H_2 and room temperature. Some examples of these compounds and their hydrides are:

Compound	Hydrides
Ce_3Ni	$Ce_3NiH_{8.4}$
$LaNi$	$LaNiH_{3.1}$
$LaNi_5$	$LaNi_5H_6$
YFe_3	$YFe_3H_{4.8}$
YFe	$YFe_2H_{4.2}$

Catalytic applications of these materials to hydrogenation
(15), methanation (16) and ammonia synthesis (17) have been described and some information concerning the structures of these
materials is available (18).

By themselves, rare earths are less active than the conventional nickel/molybdenum/cobalt, tungsten combinations, the Raney
Ni alloys, or the noble metal catalysts.

Polymerization

A recently developed class of compounds called "Super Slurpers"
based on starch-polyacrylonitrile copolymers are able to
absorb as much as 500 to 1000 times their weight of water, depending on the purity of the water (19, 20, 21). The formation of
these copolymers is catalyzed by Ce^{4+} ion. These polymers were
developed by the U.S. Department of Agriculture and have potential
agricultural uses as water storage additives as well as obvious
consumer and industrial applications.

Oxidation

A redox mechanism involving lattice oxygen originally proposed in 1954 by Mars and Van Krevelen (22) for hydrocarbon oxidation over V_2O_5 can be applied to a variety of catalytic oxidation reactions (23). The following illustrates a lattice redox
mechanism for CO oxidation:

1. CO Adsorption

$$CO(g) \;\rightleftharpoons\; CO(ad)$$

2. CO Oxidation by Lattice Oxide, Catalyst Reduction

$$\boxed{O}^{2-} + CO(ad) \;\rightleftharpoons\; CO_2(ad) + \square^{2-}$$

3. Desorption of CO_2

$$CO_2(ad) \;\overset{\longrightarrow}{\underset{\longleftarrow}{}}\; CO_2(g)$$

.4. Regeneration of Lattice Oxygen, Catalyst Oxidation

$$\boxed{}^{2-} + 1/2\ O_2 \;\overset{\longrightarrow}{\underset{\longleftarrow}{}}\; \boxed{O}^{2-}$$

The rare earth oxides possess a degree of oxygen mobility compatible with a lattice redox mechanism (4, 24). Minachev (7) has shown that the oxides of the rare earths Pr, Nd and Tb exchange oxygen readily with gas phase oxygen molecules and that these same compounds are active oxidation catalysts for hydrogen, Figure 1. Similar results were obtained for the oxidation of NO (25), except that cerium in this case was also found to be active, Figure 2.

Applications to Automobile Exhaust Emissions

Recent automobile exhaust emissions standards are summarized in Table III, and a review of the catalytic systems designed to meet these standards has recently appeared (26). Catalytic converters have been used as a part of emission control systems since 1975. One approach has been to use a dual bed catalytic converter where the reduction of NO to N_2 occurs over the first bed, and excess O_2 is provided to the second bed to oxidize the CO and hydrocarbons more completely. Typically, the exhaust contains compounds listed in Table IV plus some poisons containing Pb, P, S etc. (27). The catalytic system must reduce concentrations of CO, hydrocarbon and NO_x to legally acceptable levels. The engine is designed in such a way that an oscillation from rich (oxygen deficiency) to lean (oxygen excess) occurs about once/ second. The following illustrates some of the reactions that are thought to occur on the rich and lean side over an active three-way exhaust catalyst.

Some Net Exhaust Gas Reactions

Hydrocarbon $+\ \boxed{O} \;\longrightarrow\; CO_2 + H_2O$ (Lean)

$ CO + H_2O$ (Rich)

$CO + \boxed{O} \;\longrightarrow\; CO_2$ (Lean)

$CO + H_2O \;\overset{\longrightarrow}{\underset{\longleftarrow}{}}\; CO_2 + H_2$ (Water-Gas Shift)

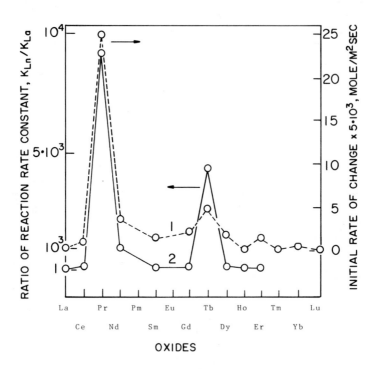

Figure 1. Initial rate of isotopic exchange of the oxygen of oxides with molecular oxygen at 370°C, Curve 1; and their relative activity in hydrogen oxidation at 340°C, Curve 2. The activity of lanthanum oxide is taken to be unity (7).

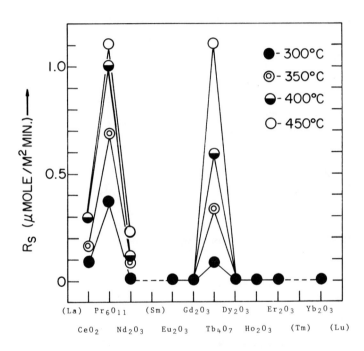

Figure 2.   Specific activities of the rare-earth oxides in the oxidation of nitric oxide
(25)

TABLE III	Federal Exhaust Emission Standards for Passenger Cars (grams/mile)		

Model Year	HC[a]	CO	NO$_x$
1968 (Est.)	10	80	5
1975	1.5	15	3.1
1977	1.5	15	2.0
1980	0.41	7.0	2.0
1981	0.41	3.4(7.0)[b]	1.0(1.5)[b]
1983	0.41	3.4	1.0(1.5)[b]
1985	0.41	3.4	1.0

a HC = Hydrocarbon

b (   ) Waiver to the indicated level is possible.

TABLE IV   Exhaust Gas Composition

Rich		Lean
CO	•	CO
Hydrocarbon	•	Hydrocarbon
NO	•	NO
CO$_2$		CO$_2$
H$_2$O		H$_2$O
O$_2$ (deficiency)		O$_2$ (excess)
Poor CO Conversion		Poor NO Conversion

⟵———————— 1 Hz ————————⟶

$$\text{Hydrocarbon} + H_2O \rightleftharpoons CO + H_2 \quad \text{(Steam Reforming)}$$

$$CO + NO \rightleftharpoons CO_2 + 1/2\ N_2$$

$$NO + [H] \rightleftharpoons NH_3 + H_2O$$

$$NO + 2/3\ NH_3 \rightleftharpoons 5/6N_2 + H_2O$$

It is clear that on the rich side, oxidation will be inhibited, while on the lean side, NO_x reduction to N_2 will be limited. Conversion efficiencies for a typical three-way catalyst over a rich to lean cycle are shown in Figure 3.

The Catalyst. Three catalyst shapes are typically used, Figure 4. The most active and durable catalysts contain the noble metals, especially Pt, Pd and Rh on an alumina support. The catalytic material is thinly coated on the walls of the monolithic support or the catalytic metals are placed at or near the surface of either beads or extrusions for maximum activity (28).

A role for CeO_2 or another oxide catalyst occurs as a result of oscillation of the exhaust gas mixture from lean to rich. On the rich side, there is a lack of oxygen. If the CeO_2 can provide lattice oxygen for the reaction, improved levels of CO conversion to CO_2 can be realized. Figure 5 illustrates the oxygen storage effect. At the time indicated and at a certain CO conversion level, the oxygen source is shut off. After a delay, the CO conversion drops. A catalyst with a CeO_2 or other oxygen storage component may exhibit a longer delay time. The delay time will be a measure of oxygen storage. Figure 6 shows the effects of CeO_2 content on the CO conversion delay time. It has been suggested the CeO_2 may also promote the water-gas shift reaction. Figure 7 shows CO conversion by water-gas shift reaction as a function of CeO_2. The water-gas shift reaction may operate via a lattice redox mechanism similar to the oxidation mechanism or via a formic acid intermediate (29, 30).

Hegedus et al. (28) discussed the effect of ceria on the noble metal catalyst system. The overall effect of CeO_2 during operation of the catalyst is illustrated in Figures 8 and 9. Recently Summers and Ausen (31) showed, however, that CeO_2 can significantly degrade the activity of a supported Pt catalyst after a thermal aging cycle, Figure 10, but does not degrade supported Pd catalysts.

Perovskites. Materials of the formula ABO_3 having the perovskite structure (32) can be prepared in a form containing lanthanum. Some perovskites containing cobalt and strontium, $LaCoO_3$

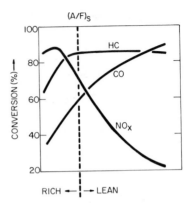

*Figure 3. Three-way catalyst perform-
ance in a cycling test at 1 Hz. The air to
fuel weight ratio, A/F, is ~14.6 at the
stoichiometric point, shown by the dotted
line.*

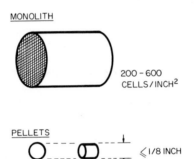

Figure 4.   Typical auto exhaust catalysts

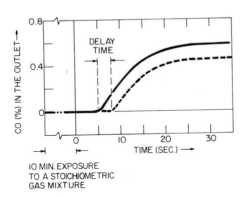

Figure 5.   Measurement of CO activity delay time

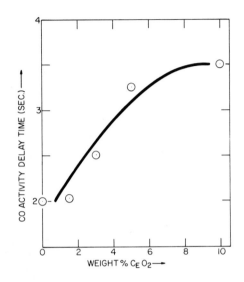

Figure 6.   Effect of CeO₂ on CO activity delay time

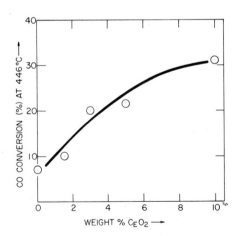

Figure 7.   CO conversion via water-gas shift reaction

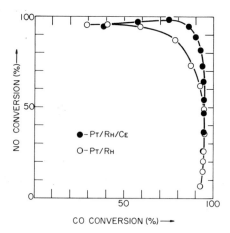

Figure 8.   Effect of Ce on the cycled dynamometer performance of Pt/Rh catalysts (28)

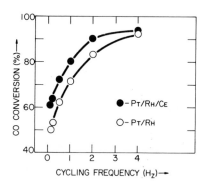

Figure 9.   Effect of Ce on the performance of Pt/Rh in a laboratory cycling test (28)

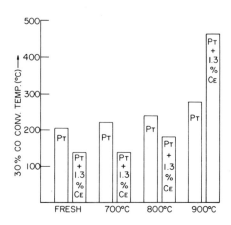

Figure 10.   Thermally aged Pt and Pt/ Ce catalysts for CO conversion (31)

and $Sr_{0.3}La_{0.8}CoO_3$, have been suggested as oxidative auto exhaust catalysts (33, 34). Other compounds containing lead, $La_xPb_{1-x}MnO_3$, have NO_x reduction activity (35) and can provide an especially active and stable support for platinum, appearing to impart resistance to SO_2 poisoning (36, 37). Recently, rare earth-copper double oxides have been studied for catalytic activity (38).

During the last three years, thirty patents have been published describing the use of rare earths in exhaust gas purification. In the event that all automotive catalysts in the USA were to contain 1% rare earth oxide, the market volume would be approximately 100 tons/year. It is probable that where CeO_2 is used, the level will be between 1% and 10% in the catalyst.

Literature Cited

1. Wallace, D. N., The Use of Rare Earth Elements in Zeolite Cracking Catalysts; Chapter 6 this volume.
2. Venuto, P. B., and Habib, E. T., "Fluid Catalytic Cracking with Zeolite Catalysts"; Marcel Dekker, Inc.: New York, 1979.
3. Moeller, T., "The Chemistry of the Lanthanides"; Reinhold Pub. Corp.: New York, 1963; p. 60.
4. Eyring, L., "High Temperature Oxides, Part II." Alber, A. M., Ed., Academic Press: New York, 1970.
5. Rosynek, M., Catal. Rev. - Sci. Eng. $\underline{16}$, 111 (1977).
6. Mazzei, A., Nato Adv. Study Inst., Ser. C, 1978.
7. Minachev, Kh. M., in "Proceedings, 5th International Congress on Catalysis." Hightower, J. W., Ed. $\underline{9}$, p. 219. American Elsevier, New York, 1973.
8. Ertl, G., Catal. Rev. - Sci. Eng., $\underline{21}$, 201 (1980).
9. Emmett, P. H., "Fifty Years of Progress in the Study of the Catalytic Synthesis of Ammonia," in the "Physical Basis for Heterogeneous Catalysis," Drauglis, E. and Jaffee, R. I., Ed., Plenum Press, 1975.
10. Bridger, P. and Beinlich, T., Chem. Eng. Progr., $\underline{43}$, 291, (1947).
11. Sze, M. C., and Wang, R. H., U.S. Patent 3,992, 328; Sze, M. C., Hydrocarbon Processing, December, 1977, p. 127.
12. Kuijpers, F. A., and Van Mal, H. J., J. Less-Common Metals, $\underline{23}$, 395 (1971).
13. Van Mal, H. H., Buschow, K. H. J., Miedema, A. R., J. Less-Common Metals, $\underline{49}$, 473 (1976).
14. Also see the International Symposium on the Properties and Applications of Metal Hydrides, Colorado Springs, Colorado, U.S.A., April 7-11, 1980, in the J. Less-Common Metals, $\underline{73}$, (1980) and the Proceedings of the "Hydrogen in Metal" Meeting at the University of Birmingham, U.K., January 5-6, 1976, Chemical Society (Faraday Division) published in J. Less-Common Metals, $\underline{49}$, (1976).
15. Soga, K., Imamura, J., Ikeda, S., J. Phys. Chem., $\underline{81}$, 1762 (1977).
16. Luengo, C. A., Cabrera, A. C., Mackay, H. B., and Maple, M. B., J. Catal. $\underline{47}$, 1, (1977).
17. Schlapbach, L., Seiler, A. and Stucki, F., Mat. Res. Bull., $\underline{14}$, 785 (1979).
18. Takeshita, T., Wallace, W. E. and Craig, R. S., J. Catal. $\underline{44}$, 236 (1976).
19. This information was brought to the authors' attention by K. A. Gschneidner.

20. Weaver, M. V., Montgomery, R. R., Miller, C. D., Sohns, V. E., Fanta, G. F. and Doane, W. M., Die Starke 29, (1977) No. 12, p. 413-422.

21. Weaver, M. O., Cruglimelli, L. A., Doane, W. M. and Russell, C. R., J. Appl. Polym. Sci., 15, 3015 (1971) and Chem. and Eng. News, Nov. 5, 1979, p. 23.

22. Mars, J. and Van Krevelen, D. W., Chem. Eng. Sci. 3, Spec. Suppl., 41 (1954).

23. Keulks, G. W., Krenzke, L. D. and Notermann, T. M., Advan. Catal., 27, 183 (1978).

24. Sayonov, L. A., Artawonov, E. V. and Mitrofanova, G. N., Kinet. Katal., 12, 329 (1971).

25. Takasu, Y., Nishibe, S., Matsuda, Y., J. Catal., 49, 236 (1977).

26. Hegedus, L. L. and Gumbleton, J. J., Chemtech, 10, 630 (1980).

27. Shelef, M., Otto, K., and Otto, N. C., Adv. Catal., 27, 311 (1978).

28. Hegedus, L. L., Summers, J. C. Schlatter, J. C. and Baron, K., J. Catal., 56, 321 (1979).

29. Shchibrya, G. C., Morozov, N. M., and Temkin, M. I., Kinet. Katal., 6, 955 (1965).

30. Newsome, D. S., Catal. Rev. - Sci. Eng., 21, 275 (1980). (A review of water-gas shift reactions).

31. Summers, J. C. and Ausen, S. A., J. Catal., 58, 131 (1979).

32. Roth, R. S., J. Res. Nat. Bur. Std., 56, 75 (1957).

33. Mendovercraft, D. B., Nature, 226, 847 (1970).

34. Pedersen, L. A. and Libby, W. F., Science, 176, 1355 (1972).

35. Voorhoeve, R. J., Remeika, J. P. and Johnson, Jr., D. W., Science, 180, 62 (1973).

36. Katz, S., Croat, J. J. and Laukonis, J. V., Ind. Eng. Chem., Prod. Res. Dev., 14, 774 (1975).

37. Johnson, Jr., D. W., Gallagher, P. K. Wertheim, G. K. and Vogel, E. M., J. Catal., 48, 87 (1977).

38. Arakawa, T., Takeda, S., Adachi, G. and Shiokawa, J., Mat. Res. Bull., 14, 507 (1979).

RECEIVED April 24, 1981.

USES INVOLVING THE INDIVIDUAL
RARE EARTH ELEMENTS

Discovery and Commercial Separations

J. KACZMAREK

Rhone Poulenc Chemical Company, Chemicals Division, P.O. Box 125,
Monmouth Junction, NJ 08852

Initial Discovery

The rare earths have their origin in the accidental
discovery by the Swedish Army Lieutenant, C. A. Arrhenius in
1787 of an unusual black mineral specimen at a quarry at
Ytterby, a small community not far from Stockholm. In 1794
Johan Gadolin, a Finnish chemist at the University of Abo,
separated from a sample of this mineral about 38% of a new and
previously undescribed "earth" (oxide in our modern terminology),
and set the basis for a series of investigations extending
through the present. A. G. Ekeberg, at Uppsala, suggested in
1797 the name of gadolinite for the mineral and the name yttria
for the "new earth".

Shortly thereafter (1803) M. H. Klaproth, a German investigator, and, independently, the renowned Swedish chemist,
J. J. Berzelius and his collaborator Wilheim Hisinger, isolated
from a heavy mineral found in 1781 in a mine at Bastnas, Sweden,
another similar and yet somewhat different "earth". This one
was named ceria and the mineral cerite after the then recently
discovered planetoid Ceres. It was believed at the time, that
both yttria and ceria were single elements, but subsequent
study showed each to be a mixture of oxides, the complete separation and identification of which required more than a century
of effort.

History of the Study of the Composition of Ceria and Yttria

The ultimate composition of ceria was established many years
after its isolation by C. G. Mosander, a Swedish surgeon, chemist
and mineralogist, who was for a time assistant to Berzelius.
During the period 1839-1841, Mosander thermally decomposed a
nitrate obtained from ceria and treated the product with dilute
nitric acid. From the resulting solution, he then isolated first
a new earth, "lanthana", and then another new earth, "didymia"
(the twin brother of lanthana), of similar chemical but slightly
different physical properties. (Figure 1)

0097-6156/81/0164-0135$08.00/0
© 1981 American Chemical Society

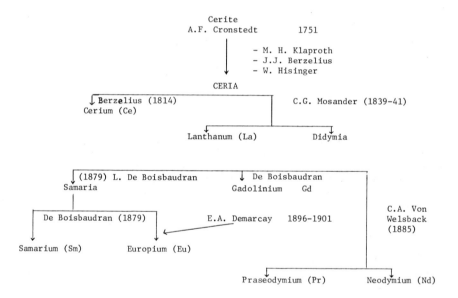

Figure 1.   The study of cerite

Similarly, in 1843, Mosander separated from the original yttria three oxide fractions, one white, one yellow (old erbia) and one rose colored (old terbia). (Shown in Figure 2)

There followed a long period of tedious research effort that culminated in the ultimate identification of the composition of two complex mixtures of oxides.

In Figures 1 and 2, the history seems clear cut and orderly, but one should keep in mind that for a long time there was an understandable confusion of names due to the poor communication among workers in the 19th and early 20th century. What was thought to be a new element was in most of the cases, a mixture of the closely related rare earths. It took years to clarify the confusion.

A case in point includes gadolinium, first isolated from yttria by the Swiss chemist, DeMarignac, in 1880 and later in 1885, was also obtained from ceria by the French investigator, DeBoisbaudran; and lutetium, announced in 1905 by the Frenchman, Urbain, but obtained nearly simultaneously by both the Austrian, Von Walsbach, and the American, James.

The following Figure, 3, gives the origin of the names of these elements.

The separation and identification of the components of yttria and ceria came along with the development of new laboratory and industrial techniques, analytical instruments and procedures. Prominent among the latter are those of emission and absorption spectroscopy, without which confirmation of purity would have been impossible.

Because the elements of this series were obtained originally as earths (oxides) from relatively rare minerals, they were named "rare earths". Although this name is still used, it should be noted that rare earths are not so rare.

Minerals and Ores

Crustal content data, as summarized in Table I, indicate clearly that the lanthanides are at least as abundant as many of the elements considered common and supplies are potentially unlimited.

The similar atomic structure of the rare earth elements is not only reflected in their chemical and physical properties, but also in their close geochemical association. As a group, the rare earths behave almost as a coherent individual entity. Because of their large ionic size they are incompatible with the earlier formed silicates, and have thus migrated in the pegmatitic and hydro-thermal fractions of granitic and syenitic rocks. A certain degree of selective deposition is evident in the yttrium subgroup of the rare earths, which is more closely associated with granitic magmas, in the form of monazite, and the cerium subgroup that tends to prevail in the undersaturated syenitic rocks in the form of bastnasite.

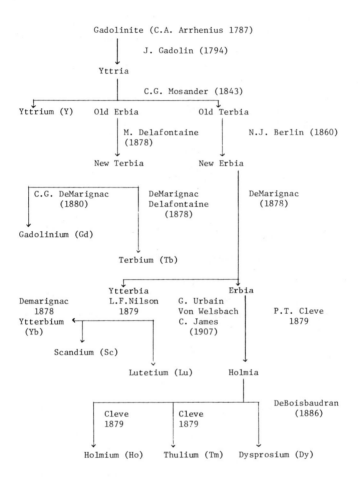

Figure 2.   The study of gadolinite

LANTHANUM	–	To lie hidden
CERIUM	–	Planetoid Ceres
PRASEODYMIUM	–	Green Twin
NEODYMIUM	–	New Twin
SAMARIUM	–	Mineral Samarskite
EUROPIUM	–	Europe
GADOLINIUM	–	Gadolin
YTTRIUM		
YTTERBIUM	–	Ytterby
ERBIUM		
TERBIUM		
DYSPROSIUM	–	Difficult of access
HOLMIUM	–	Stockholm
THULIUM	–	Thule – ancient name of Scandinavia
LUTETIUM	–	Lutetia – ancient name of Paris
SCANDIUM	–	Scandinavia

Figure 3.   Origin of the rare earth names

TABLE I

ABUNDANCE OF ELEMENTS IN IGNEOUS ROCKS OF CRUST OF THE EARTHS

Rare Earth Elements			Common Elements		
Symbol	Atomic Number	Abundance g/MT	Symbol	Atomic Number	Abundance g/MT
Sc	21	5	Be	4	6
Y	39	28.1	B	5	3
La	57	18.3	N	7	46.3
Ce	58	46.1	Co	27	23
Pr	59	5.5	Cu	29	70
Nd	60	23.9	Ga	31	15
Pm	61	0	Ge	32	7
Sm	62	6.5	As	33	5
Eu	63	1.06	Br	35	1.6
Gd	64	6.4	Mo	42	2.5 - 15
Tb	65	0.9	Ag	47	0.1
Dy	66	4.5	Cd	48	0.2
Ho	67	1.2	Sn	50	40
Er	68	2.5	Sb	51	1
Tm	69	0.2	1	53	0.1
Yb	70	2.7	Pb	82	16
Lu	71	0.8	Bi	83	0.2

The rare earths (see table II) have a marked geochemical affinity for fluorine, calcium, titanium, niobium, zirconium, and the phosphate and carbonate ions. The most important, from an economic viewpoint, are the carbonatites and the phosphates.

Carbonatites. Carbonatites are igneous mixtures of essentially carbonate minerals found in the form of intrusions and lavas, associated with highly undersaturated alkali igneous complexes along major rift zones, cutting old stable continental shield areas.

Current theories on their genesis revolve around a mechanism of mass gas transfer of material rich in carbonate derived from the upper mantle deep within the earth. The three most significant commercial carbonatite deposits are at Mountain Pass, California in the U.S.A., Palabora in South Africa and Paotou, Inner Mongolia in the Peoples Republic of China, see Figure 4. The Mountain Pass, California deposit now supplies nearly 100% of the world's bastnasite. Palabora deposits are mainly used for copper production but have given some rare earths concentrates in the past. The rare earths distribution in bastnasite, a fluorocarbonate, is given in Table III.

Phosphates. The two major phosphate bearing ores are monazite and xenotime, the former being a source of light lanthanides and the latter a source of the heavy rare earths, see Table IV. Deposits in the form of heavy mineral sands are the major source of monazite. They are usually exploited as a byproduct of rutile, ilmenite, and zircon mining operations.

These deposits are formed in the natural process of weathering, transportation, and concentration at the site of heavy minerals originating from some primary source rock. Commercially, beach placers are the most important along with alluvial streams; aeolian deposits are insignificant.

The reworking of the heavy minerals by the action of the sea enables accumulations to build up especially in areas where the coastline is indented and the beaches are gently sloping. Large deposits of this type occur in Australia, India, Brazil, South Africa and the U.S.A., see Figure 5.

A similar type of deposit of monazite and xenotime is in the placer tin deposits especially in Southeast Asia.

Major Rare Earths Ore Producers. Australia, Brazil, India and Malaysia are the major monazite producing countries. Together they supplied almost 98% of the total world production of monazite in 1976. Australia and Malaysia have little or no domestic processing facilities beyond concentrating the monazite at the mine.

Both Australia and Malaysia have, so far, remained free of government controls on monazite production and export, unlike India and Brazil. Hence, all the monazite produced is exported, mainly to the U.S.A., France, and the UK.

TABLE II

MINERALS CONTAINING RARE EARTHS

GADOLINITE	$Be_2FeY_2Si_2O_{10}$
CERITE	$CaCeSi_3O_{13}$
XENOTIME	YPO_4
BASTNASITE	$CeFCO_3$
MONAZITE	$(Ce,Y)PO_4$
APATITE	$(CaCe)_5 (P,Si)O_4 {}_3(O,F)$
PYROCHLORE	$(NaCaCe)_2Nb_2O_6F$
FERGUSONITE	$(Y,Ce,U,Th,Ca)(Nb,Ta,Ti)O_4$
SAMARSKITE	$(Y,Ce,U,Ca)(Nb,Tu_2,Ti)_2O_6$
EUXENITE	$(Y,Ca,Ce,U,Th)(Nb,Ta,Ti)_2O6$
ALLANITE	$(Ca,Ce,Th)_2(Al,Fe,Mn,Mg)_3(SiO_4)_3OH$
FLUOCERITE	CeF_3

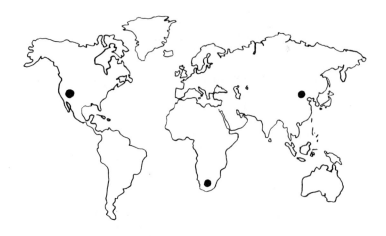

Figure 4.   Location of the world bastnasite deposits

TABLE III

BASTNASITE COMPOSITION

La_2O_3	32	
CeO_2	49.5	98.7%
Pr_6O_{11}	4.2	
Nd_2O_3	13	
Sm_2O_3	0.8	
Eu_2O_3	0.11	
Gd_2O_3	0.15	
Tb_4O_7		
Dy_2O_3	0.12	
Ho_2O_3		1.3%
Er_2O_3		
Tm_2O_3		
Yb_2O_3	0.01	
Lu_2O_3		
Y_2O_3	0.1	
ThO_2	0.5%	

TABLE IV

COMPOSITION OF

MONAZITE AND XENOTIME

	MONAZITE	XENOTIME
La_2O_3	23	
CeO_2	46.5	
Pr_6O_{11}	5.1 } 93%	} 10.6%
Nd_2O_3	18.4	
Sm_2O_3	2.3	1.2
Eu_2O_3	0.07	0.01
Gd_2O_3	1.7	3.6
Tb_4O_7	0.16	1
Dy_2O_3	0.52	7.5 } 89.4%
Ho_2O_3	0.09 } 7%	2
Er_2O_3	0.13	6.2
Tm_2O_3	0.013	1.27
Yb_2O_3	0.061	6
Lu_2O_3	0.006	0.63
Y_2O_3	2	60
ThO_2	10%	

The major rare earths mineral producers are listed in Table V along with their claimed yearly capacities. It is seen that the capacity of the Molycorp bastnasite facility exceeds the total world monazite capacity (22,000 MT/year).

Bastnasite. As shown in Figure 6 bastnasite can be decomposed by concentrated sulfuric acid giving an aqueous solution of the water-soluble rare earth sulfate with the evolution of carbon dioxide and hydrogen fluoride gas. This process is used by a few companies to purify the rare earths from the other common elements, such as iron, lead, silicon and barium, which are found in the ore body.

The next figure, 7, shows the process used by Molycorp. The bastnasite ore is calcined after concentration by flotation, then a hydrochloric acid attack under certain operating conditions solubilize most of the trivalent rare earths. The residue, which is recovered by filtration contains the tetravalent component of bastnasite along with 65 to 80% cerium oxide.

This fraction after calcination can be used directly as a glass polishing compound.

Monazite or Xenotime. The rare earth phosphate containing ores are attacked with either concentrated sulfuric acid or sodium hydroxide solution. The processing involves cracking the ore, removing the thorium, and separating the lanthanides. The chemical treatment used depends upon the composition of the mineral. The sodium hydroxide treatment of monazite, Figure 8, is preferably used since it has the advantage of removing phosphates more readily than the sulfuric acid procedure.

The finely ground monazite is mixed with a concentrated sodium hydroxide solution and maintained at 140-150°C for a few hours. After addition of water and settling, the hydroxides of rare earths and thorium are recovered by filtration.

Several processes have been used to eliminate the thorium from the rare earths. The precipitated hydroxides, could, for example, be dissolved in an acid medium, then the thorium hydroxide selectively precipitated by careful and progressive addition of an alkaline solution, such as sodium hydroxide, or ammonium hydroxide, etc., see the left hand column of Figure 9.

It is also possible, if the proper conditions are set, to dissolve selectively the rare earth hydroxides which are more basic than thorium hydroxide, see the right hand column of Figure 9. In such a case, the mixed hydroxide water slurry is brought to a pH of 3.4 by a slow and careful addition of hydrochloric acid. The undissolved thorium hydroxide is then separated from the solution by filtration.

In addition to the above two mentioned procedures, selective extraction into non-aqueous solvents can be used. Tri-n-butyl phosphate or certain higher amines will extract thorium more

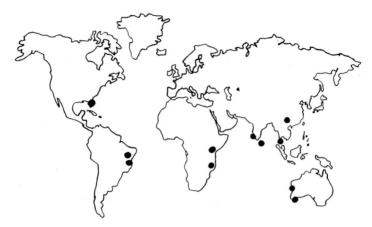

Figure 5.   Location of the world monazite deposits

TABLE V

MAJOR RARE EARTH MINERAL PRODUCERS

		MT/year
AUSTRALIA		
Allied Eneabba	MONAZITE	5000
Associated Minerals	MONAZITE	2500
Cable Sands Pty Ltd.	MONAZITE	Small
Westralian Sands	MONAZITE	2-3000
BRAZIL		
Nuclei de Monazita	MONAZITE	3000
INDIA		
Indian Rare Earths	MONAZITE	4500
MALAYSIA		
Beh Minerals Sdn	MONAZITE	2000
	XENOTIME	200
U.S.A.		
Molycorp	BASTNASITE	27,000 REO
Titanium Enterprises	MONAZITE	1000
Humphreys Mining Co.	MONAZITE	Small

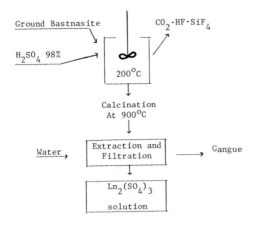

Figure 6.   *Bastnasite ore attacked with sulfuric acid*

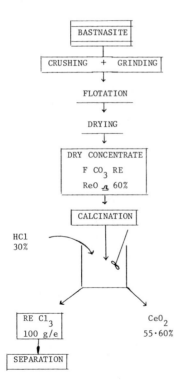

Figure 7.   *Probable Molycorp bastnasite treatment*

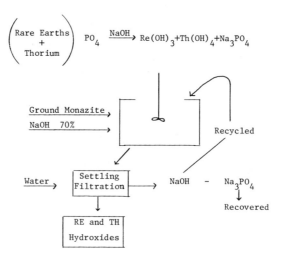

Figure 8. Possible sodium hydroxide process

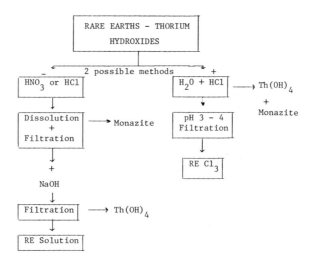

Figure 9. Possible thorium removal processes

readily than the lanthanides from the aqueous phase. The amines function best with a sulfate solution from which thorium is removed completely and in a high state of purity as the amine salt of a sulfate complex, that is to say,

$$(RNH)_2 \left[Th(SO_4)_2 \right]_3$$

where R represents an organic group.

The elimination of thorium is of prime importance to Rhone-Poulenc and we have done a considerable amount of research to find a solution to this problem. Actually, the thorium level of our rare earth product is comparable to, if not better than, that of other products available on the market. Most of the time thorium is not even detectable.

Separation of the Lanthanides and Yttrium

The identical structure of the external electron shells (3 external electrons - $5d^1 6s^2$ - as shown on table VI) gives these 14 elements very similar chemical properties, and makes the separation of the different rare earths elements particularly difficult. Be that as it may, the physical and chemical properties are not as close as it might be expected in view of the difficulties experienced by pioneers in the field.

The rare earths have ion radii that vary 1.5% from one element to the next - the size decreases while the atomic number increases from lanthanum to lutetium. This is what is commonly called the "lanthanides contraction", see Figure 10.

Atomic and ionic radii affect the attraction, for electrons and anions, and govern such properties as basicity. Basicity differences affect in the hydrolysis of ions, the solubilities of salts, the thermal decomposition of oxysalts and the formation of complex species.

Thus separation may be effected by one or another, or by some combination of the following procedures involving:
1) fractional crystallization of isomorphous salts,
2) selective oxidation or reduction, and
3) basicity differences:
    a)   ion exchange, and
    b)   solvent extraction.

All procedures, with the exception of those involving oxidation or reduction, are fractional in nature; that is to say, in each step there is some concentration differences of one species to the other, but a good separation results only if that step is repeated many times.

It is important that the path taken by each component is followed analytically as fractionation proceeds, preferably by a rapid procedure that is specific for each cation. Spectrophotometric procedures are those that are generally used.

The efficiency of the fractionation is determined by the magnitude of the separation factor. For two lanthanides A and B

TABLE VI

ELECTRONIC STRUCTURE OF THE LANTHANIDES

	Atomic Number	K	L		M			N				O				P
		1s	2s	2p	3s	3p	3d	4s	4p	4d	4f	5s	5p	5d	5f	6s
Y	39	2	2	6	2	6	10	2	6	1		2				
La	57	2	2	6	2	6	10	2	6	10		2	6	1		2
Ce	58	2	1	6	1	6	10	2	6	10	1	2	6	1		2
Pr	59	2	2	6	2	6	10	2	6	10	2	2	6	1		2
Nd	60	2	2	6	2	6	10	2	6	10	3	2	6	1		2
Sm	62	2	2	6	2	6	10	2	6	10	5	2	6	1		2
Eu	63	2	2	6	2	6	10	2	6	10	6	2	6	1		2
Gd	64	2	2	6	2	6	10	2	6	10	7	2	6	1		2
Tb	65	2	2	6	2	6	10	2	6	10	8	2	6	1		2
Dy	66	2	2	6	2	6	10	2	6	10	9	2	6	1		2
Ho	67	2	2	6	2	6	10	2	6	10	10	2	6	1		2
Er	68	2	2	6	2	6	10	2	6	10	11	2	6	1		2
Tm	69	2	2	6	2	6	10	2	6	10	12	2	6	1		2
Yb	70	2	2	6	2	6	10	2	6	10	13	2	6	1		2
Lu	71	2	2	6	2	6	10	2	6	10	14	2	6	1		2

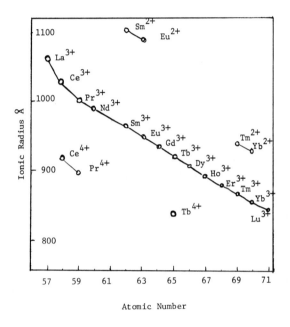

Figure 10.   The lanthanide contraction

being changed from initial condition (1) to a final condition
(2), the separation factor may be defined as

$$\alpha = \frac{CA_2/CB_2}{CA_1/CB_1} = \frac{CA_2 \cdot CB_1}{CA_1 \cdot CB_2}$$

No separation results if α =1 but the more it exceeds the ratio
of 1, the more efficient the process becomes. Below are some
typical separation factors:

> precipitation or crystallization = 1.1 - 5,
> ion exchange   = 1.1 - 10, and
> liquid-liquid extraction   = 1.1 - 5 .

    Fractional Crystallization. Today fractional crystalliza-
tion is not used anymore, but has to be mentioned because of its
historical value.

    At the end of the 19th century, Urbain, using the fractional
crystallization method, prepared 60g of dysprosium oxide after
10,000 crystallizations; then, in 1907, after 15,000 successive
nitrate crystallizations from nitric solution, he separated
lutetium and ytterbium.

    The most suitable compounds which have been used for separa-
tion via fractional crystallization are:

1) the double ammonium nitrates, $RE(NO_3)_3 \cdot 2NH_4NO_3 \cdot 4H_2O$, for the
   removal of lanthanum and the separation of praseodymium from
   neodymium.

2) the double manganese nitrates, $2RE(NO_3)_3 \cdot 3Mn(NO_3)_2 \cdot 24H_2O$,
   for the separation of the ceric group, but not the yttric
   group.

3) the bromates, $RE(BrO_3)_3 \cdot 9H_2O$, and the ethyl sulfates,
   $RE(C_2H_5 SO_4)_3 \cdot 9H_2O$ for the separation of the yttric group.

    Separation by Selective Oxidation or Reduction. Since a
change of oxidation is accompanied by a substantial change in
properties, selective oxidation or reduction provides a remark-
ably clean and efficient way of separating specific lanthanides.

    The reduction to the divalent state involves samarium,
europium, and ytterbium. In 1906 C. Matignon and E. Cazes
obtained samarium(II) chloride by reducing the trichloride with
hydrogen. In 1911, G. Urbain and F. Bourion prepared
europium(II) chloride by a comparable reduction involving
gydrogen, and in 1929 ytterbium(II) chloride was similarly
obtained by W. Klemm and W. Schuth.

    On an industrial scale, only the reduction of europium(II)
with zinc, followed by its recovery as a divalent sulfate from
chloride solution is useful. In practive, it is possible to
recover europium from mixtures containing only trace quantities
by adding zinc, barium chloride and sulfuric acid; the mixed

barium europium(II sulfate precipitate is then washed with an oxidizing acid solution which oxidizes europium(II) to europium(III) which is soluble, while the barium sulfate remains undissolved. This method was described by McCoy in 1935.

Commercial separations involving the oxidation to the tetravalent state are limited to the removal of cerium after oxidation. These separations, which are based upon reduced basicity in the tetravalent state, include:

1) <u>selective oxidation</u>, anodically or chemically with bromate, hydrogen peroxide or chloride followed by nearly complete precipitation of cerium(IV) from the buffered solution.

2) <u>selective extraction into non-aqueous solvents</u>, especially tri-n-butyl phosphate in which Ce^{+4} and Th^{+4} are readily soluble. Reduction and extraction of this fraction with aqueous sodium nitrate returns cerium (as Ce^{+3}) to the aqueous phase, but leaves thorium in the non-aqueous phase.

<u>Ion Exchange Separation.</u>   In 1893, Hoffmann and Kruss demonstrated for the first time that yttrium and gadolinium could be purified by adsorption on activated carbon, but the first systematic cation separation study was not done until 1943. Russell and Pearce from Purdue University showed that tripositive lanthanides were adsorbed on an exchanger but their removal at that time by elution with sodium chloride effected no greater degree of separation than fractional crystallization or precipitation. The modern ion exchange process using a suitable eluting complexing agent (buffered citric acid solution) came from the work directed by Spedding and by Boyd and Tompkins under the Manhattan Project.

The ion exchange technique uses either natural zeolites or synthetic resins. It is a familiar process used in water softening where a calcium ion is exchanged for a sodium ion.

The exchange of metal ions in solution with protons on a solid ion exchanger is an equilibirum process, as shown in Figure 11.

Rare earths are easily adsorbed on a solid ion exchanger, but their affinities to the exchanger are quite similar. The actual separation is brought about by the complexing eluting agent. Adaptation of these techniques to macro-scale was due to the work of F. H. Spedding and J. E. Powell at Iowa State University. They found that a 5% ammonium citrate eluting solution at pH 2.5 - 3.2 which was effective on a laboratory scale as shown in Figure 12, could not be used on a macro-column, because of the extensive overlapping of the elution curves. This could be reduced somewhat by increasing the column length.

However, in order to remain reasonable, a more effective eluting agent, such as the solution of 0.1% ammonium citrate at pH 5.0 - 8.0 which gives the $\left[Ln\ (Cit)_2\right]^{-3}$ species had to be used. This system was utilized to separate kilogram quantities of rare earths with a purity better than 99.99% but because of its low total capacity it was commercially unattractive.

$$Ln^{3+} + 3HR \rightleftharpoons Ln\ R_3 + 3H^+$$

aq sol   solid   solid   aq sol

Figure 11.   The ion exchange equilibrium

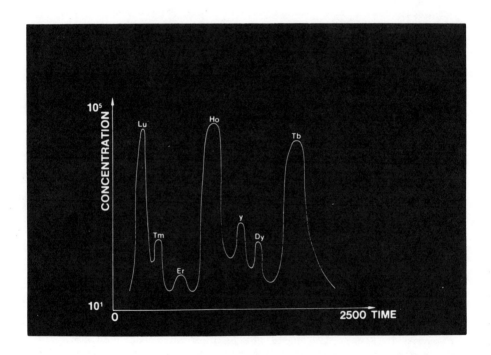

Figure 12.   Laboratory scale elution of an ion exchange column; 5% citrate at pH 3.20

In the early 1950's, Spedding and Powell showed that by
using a much stronger complexing agent, such as ethylene-
diaminetetracetic acid (see Figure 13), much more effective
separations could be realized. This improvement was sufficient
and this process became the main commercial process for separating rare earths from the mid-1950's to the mid-1970's. It is
still used by a number of companies today.

Other chealting agents, as shown in Figure 13, may be used
advantageously. Both the acids H_3HEDTA and H_5DTPA allow the
rapid recovery of yttrium by first concentrating this element
with the ceric group.

By increasing the temperature of an ion exchange system,
more rapid separation can be performed. In fact, temperature
modifies the separation factor of two neighbor elements. For
example, by increasing the temperature from 25^oC to 95^oC, the
1.5 samarium-europium separation factor becomes 1.8 and the
europium-gadolinium 1.1 separation factor goes to 1.5. Thus the
difficult Eu-Gd separation at 25^oC becomes "easy" at 95^oC.

Figure 14 shows the Rhone-Poulenc ion exchange columns which
had been used up to 1965.

Liquid-Liquid Extraction

The pioneering work of W. Fisher and his associates at
Hannover (reported in 1937) wherein small differences in the
distribution of the rare earth tribhlorides between water and
partially miscible alcohols, ketones, or others were recorded,
established a foundation for the future successful development.

Highly significant was J. C. Warf's observations (1949) that
cerium(IV) can be separated readily and completely from the
trivalent cations by extraction from an aqueous nitric acid
solution using tri-n-butyl phosphate.

The importance of this system for the separation of the
trivalent species from each other was recognized in 1953 by
D. F. Peppard and his collaborators at the Argonne National
Laboratory. This was followed in the same year by the isolation
of the "first kilogram" of pure gadolinium by B. Weaver and his
co-workers at the Oak Ridge National Laboratory using the same
method. Subsequently, the method has been used on both a laboratory and a commercial scale.

Liquid-liquid solvent extraction is the most important
process used to separate the rare earths today.

Liquid-Liquid Extraction Principle. If a liquid solvent
which is either immiscible or only partially miscible is mixed
with a solution containing solute A, the solute will distribute
between the two liquids until equilibrium is established. The
solute's concentration in the two phases at equilibrium will
depend on its relative affinity for the two solvents. Although

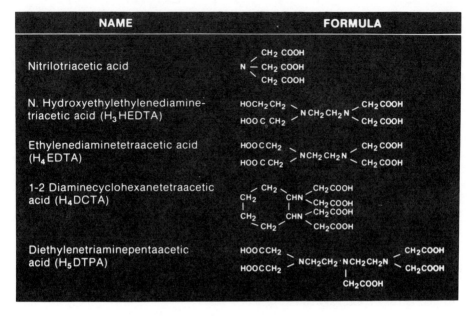

Figure 13.   Aminecarboxylic acids

Figure 14.   Rhone Poulenc ion exchange columns

it is inevitable that two solvents should be involved, it is conventional to refer to the added liquid as the solvent; the product of the desired solute in the solvent as the extract, and the residue left in the initial phase as the raffinate.

At equilibrium, the ratio of the concentration of the solute in the extract, y, and raffinate, x, is called the <u>distribution coefficient</u>, D:

$$D_A = \frac{Y_A}{X_A}$$

The coefficient is a measure of the affinity of the solute for the two phases.

Since consideration of thermodynamics demand that the activity (or chemical potential) of a solute should be equal in the two phases at equilibrium, a distribution coefficient of other than unity implies that the solute must have different activity coefficients in the two phases. The origin of such a difference usually resides in the degree of interaction between the solute and the two solvents.

While no sharp dividing line can be drawn, it is possible to distinguish two broad categories of solvent extraction processes, depending on whether the solute-solvent interaction is nonspecific or specific. The former implies some from of "physical" interaction as the one that might arise from polarity differences or hydrogen bonding. In the case of the latter, a more defined "chemical" interaction can be distinguished.

<u>The Flow Sheet - Extraction and Scrubbing</u>. The amount of solute that can be recovered from a particular feed solution by equilibration with a solvent depends on both the distribution coefficient and the volumetric ratio of extract to raffinate phase.

An increase in the amount of solvent gives a greater recovery of solute but produces a more dilute extract. In order to meet the criteria of a reasonable concentrated extract and a high recovery of solute from the raffinate phase, it is best to employ multi-stage countercurrent contacting (as shown in Figure 15). This is the best way of obtaining separations on a continuous flow basis.

As no solvent is perfectly selective for a given solute, the extract often contains higher concentrations of impurities that should be removed. This is done by "scrubbing" the extract in a second stage, usually involving the original solvent under such conditions that the desired solute is largely retained in the extract while the impurities are washed out.

The heart of an extraction process plant is the solvent, it is the essential element of a given extraction process. It determines the efficiency and the economics of a process. In general, the solvent is a mixture of several organic compounds, which include the diluent, the extracting agent, and the modifiers.

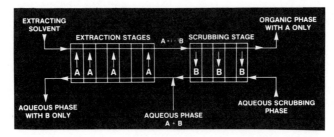

Figure 15.   Association of two extraction units to separate two constituents, A and B

TABLE VII

SOME COMMERCIAL DILUENTS			
HIGH AROMATICS	Specific Gravity 20°C	Boiling Point °C	Flash Point °C
Solvesso 100	0.876	157	44
Solvesso 150	0.985	188	66
HAN	0.933	180	41
Chevron 3	0.888	182	63
Chevron 25	0.875	157	46
MEDIUM TO LOW AROMATICS			
Escaid 100	0.790	191	76
Napoleum 470	0.811	210	80
LOW AROMATICS			
Isopar L	0.767	191	62
Isopar E	0.723	115	7
Isopar M	0.782	210	78
Norpar 12	0.751	195	69
Shell 140	0.785	184	61

The Diluent. The diluent or carrier solvent is mainly required as a diluting medium, to lower the viscosity of the organic phase and facilitate the contact between the two phases. It may also have some additional properties and should: 1) retain in solution both the complexed and uncomplexed extractant, 2) have a low solubility in the aqueous phase, 3) have a high flash point and a low rate of evaporation, and 4) have a high chemical stability over the range of plant operating conditions.

The third point is especially important when the process runs at high temperature, but the choice of the diluent also affects the settling characteristics of the mixed phases. As it can be seen in Table VII, many different diluents may be considered. It should be realized that the commercial diluents are "cuts" obtained during the production of chemicals from petroleum "feedstocks" and as such are complex mixtures.

The Modifiers. Additional chemicals are sometimes added to solvents to prevent a third phase formation. In the past, long chain alcohols or tri-n-butyl phosphate (TBP) have been used. Certain modifiers enhance the rate of extraction and the final equilibirum position. It is known for example, that tributylphosphate acts synergistically with dialkylphosphoric acids.

The Extractants. The extractants are classified into different groups, according to their reaction type: solvating, salt forming (acidic agents) or ionic exchanging.

Solvating agents have the ability to solvate the hydrogen ion. TBP is the most useful since it extracts rare earths nitrates (Figure 16).

A variety of commercial organic acids are acidic extractants, they exchange the acidic hydrogen for the metal, and thus form a metal salt in the organic phase. A number of these acidic extractants are shown in Figure 16.

The ionic extractants are those chemicals that carry within an ion pair a labile cation or anion, which will exchange with the appropriate metal species in the aqueous phase. Their role may be regarded as a form of liquid ion exchange. Several commercially available amines belong to this class, are shown in Figure 17.

Rhone-Poulenc Rare Earths Separation Process

The ion exchange method previously described with resin columns has been completely abandoned by Rhone-Poulenc for industrial scale production of the individual rare earth elements. We still use it however in our laboratories and for

SOLVATING
Tributyl phosphate
(TBP)
C4 H9 O
C4 H9 O — P = O
C4 H9 O
ACIDIC
Naphthenic acids
R'
R
R''
R'''
CH2 CH2 COOH
Versatic acids
R
CH3
C
R'
COOH
Diethylhexylphosphoric acid
D 2 EHPA
CH3 (CH2)3 - CH - CH2O
C2H5
2
- P = O
OH

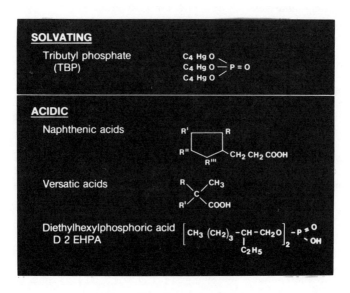

Figure 16. Extracting agents

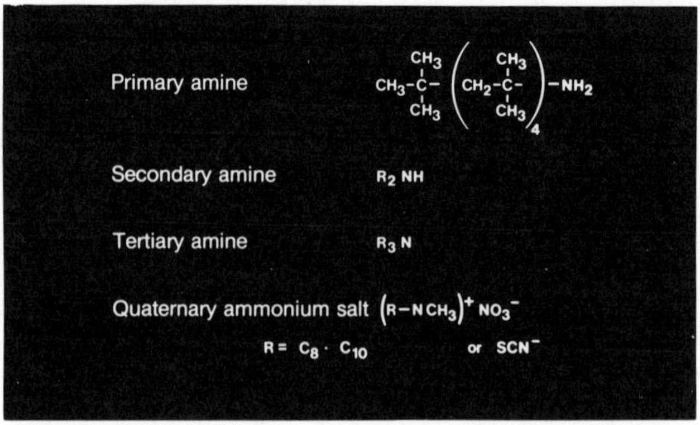

Primary amine
CH3
CH3-C-
CH3
CH3
CH2-C-
CH3
4
-NH2
Secondary amine
R2 NH
Tertiary amine
R3 N
Quaternary ammonium salt
(R-N CH3)+ NO3-
R = C8 · C10
or SCN-

Figure 17. Ionic extractant

pilot scale production. On the other hand, Rhone-Poulenc has developed the liquid-liquid extraction process to a high degree of sophistication for separating rare earths on a commercial basis.

This process offers a definite advantage in terms of economics, and is highly automated, thus requiring only a few skilled operators. In our LaRochelle plant, we operate more than one thousand extraction stages based on the mixing/settling principle. (Figure 18)   A typical mixer settler unit is shown in Figure 19.

The mixing and settling method is quite felxible and in particular, allows the operation to be stopped without disturbing the equilibrium between different phases. The fractionation is controlled on stream by means of continuous (Figure 20) analyzers located on reference stages. Such a continuous analytical control allows automatic regulation of the operation and provides high consistency in the production.

When studying a new separation, the separation factors applicable to the considered medium are first determined in our laboratories. Then the various parameters are fed into a computer which uses a program similar to the one used in fractional distillation. The data obtained are usually in excellent agreement with the results of commercial scale operations.

Figure 21 shows the flow of the different rare earths through the liquid-liquid extraction process at our LaRochelle plant. Several of the products shown in Figure 21 (Pr_6O_{11}, Nd_2O_3 and Sm_2O_3) have indicated purities of less than 99% since these are normal purities required by our customers. By proper choice of conditions, these oxides can be produced with purities 99.9%. In general the rare earths can be produced in our plant by liquid-liquid extraction at the same purity levels as achieved by ion extraction methods.

After being separated each rare earth is precipitated in the form of an organic salt, which is filtered and calcined. (See Figure 22.)

The LaRochelle capacity for ore cracking is over 5000 tons as rare earths oxides per year and in Table VIII we show the average production capabilities for the heavier rare earths. It should be noted that the above figures are average values as the rare earths composition of monazite varies somewhat depending on the source.

Conclusion

The information given in this paper describes the concepts and outlines the general separation techniques in use today. Details of the actual procedures, the sequence of various operations, yields and indentities of certain organic solvents remain trade secrets and cannot be discussed. In closing, I would also like to add a comment on a sensitive subject, the cost of the

Figure 18.   Principle of a mixing and settling unit

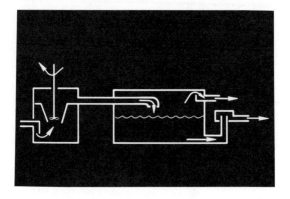

Figure 19.   Essential features of a mixer–settler

Figure 20.   On stream control analysis in one of the Rhone Poulenc liquid liquid extraction areas

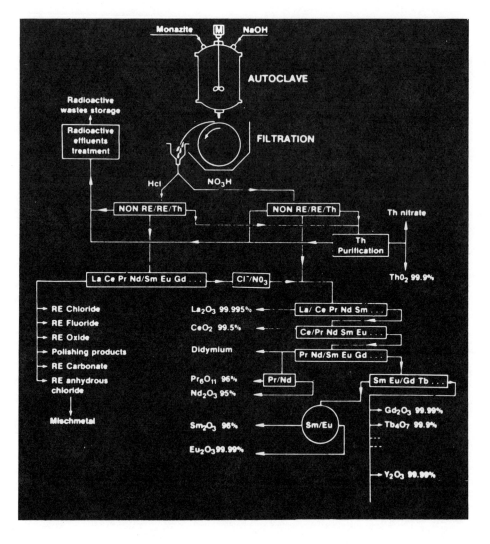

Figure 21.   Flowsheet of Rhone Poulenc separation facility, La Rochelle, France

Figure 22. One calcination furnace in the Rhone Poulenc plant

TABLE VIII

POTENTIAL/YEAR

for 5,000 tons of REO

Sm_2O_3	115	tons
Eu_2O_3	3.5	tons
Gd_2O_3	85	tons
Tb_4O_7	8	tons
Dy_2O_3	26	tons
Ho_2O_3	4.5	tons
Er_2O_3	6.5	tons
Tm_2O_3	0.65	tons
Yb_2O_3	3	tons
Lu_2O_3	0.3	tons
Y_2O_3	100	tons

separated rare earths, which occasionally discourages the
development of a potentially worthwhile application. All the
rare earths, when separated, are coproducts and since they occur
in relatively fixed ratios in the ores; the economics of the
industry depend in a large measure on how well the demand for
each rare earth can be matched with its availability. It is
important, therefore, for potential users to push forward because
as more applications are developed, the base usage of rare earths
becomes −roader and the overall economics become better. And it
is necessary for all of us to think in terms of overall economics
as there is no reasonable cost of extraction for one of a group
of coproducts. We now market at least 10 of the 14 lanthanides
commercially plus yttrium and thorium, as pure or separated products. This has taken place in the space of 15 years, starting
with the separation and commercial production of europium and
yttrium for the red phosphor which is used in television. More
recently a number of spectacular developments have occurred −
praseodymium replaced tin in yellow ceramic colors, gadolinium
is used in X−ray screen phosphors; monocrystalline GGG (gadolinium gallium garnets) substrates are used for bubble memory
chips; and samarium is used in high performance samarium cobalt
magnets. But new developments are still to come − the bottom of
the barrel is nowhere in sight. We hope that knowing that the
rare earths have become a viable industry will give those of
you who may have had doubts, the confidence to investigate ideas
for new uses for these most unusual and interesting materials.

RECEIVED March 3, 1981.

Industrial Applications of Pure Rare Earth Metals and Related Alloys

K. E. DAVIES

Rare Earth Products Limited, Widnes, Cheshire, England

In recent years researchers both in the U.S.A. and Europe have expended considerable time and effort in seeking to prepare rare earth metals of very high purity. For the most part their work has been successful and today it is possible to obtain several metals having an absolute purity of 99.99%. Understandably such metals tend to be available only in small quantities and their true cost of preparation is often discounted when set against a particular requirement.

By contrast, the industrial user must view any raw material purchase in terms of its cost effectiveness and in the case of rare earth metals this frequently requires the adoption of low purity specifications. Therefore, in the context of the industrial applications to which reference will be made, the term 'pure' will be taken to include all metals having a purity of not less than 95% — the balance being predominately other rare earths. But before considering the applications in detail it is perhaps of value to have some appreciation of the size of the market for these metals.

If we assume current world production of all rare earths to be of the order of 35,000 tons per year, expressed as rare earth oxide, then approximately 1% of this total, equating to about 230 tons, represents the current level of production of pure metals. While in itself this figure may appear insignificant, it is necessary to view it in the light of two other factors. First, expressed in monetary terms the 1% equates to nearer 7% of total value and secondly, over the past 3 years demand for pure metals has been increasing at a rate approaching 20% per year which, if sustained, could radically change the face of the industry within a short space of time.(1)

Of course it can be argued that the growth we are now seeing merely represents the logical development of the industry; once having achieved commercial success in high volume separation of pure oxides by solvent extraction it would seem only natural that the industry should then turn its attention to large scale production of the metals. But in practice it has not worked out that

0097-6156/81/0164-0167$05.00/0
© 1981 American Chemical Society

way – commercially viable applications for rare earth metals have
been slow to develop and the fact that it has taken almost 20
years to achieve the limited success we are now experiencing is a
measure of the difficulties that have been encountered and for the
most part overcome.

Of those factors that have proved a disincentive to the wider
application of the metals perhaps none has proved more formidable
than cost. Unquestionably some rare earth metals are expensive
when compared with many of the more common metals but then others,
such as the commercial grades of lanthanum and cerium produced by
electrolytic methods, are relatively inexpensive. Unfortunately,
for most rare earth metals one must use a metallothermic reduction
process that is inherently costly to operate. However, while there
is a wide variation in the price of the various metals, from $50 –
$7,000 per lb., the overall picture is one of relative price
stability when judged against the movements of many other metals.
To some extent this stability has been born out of the need to
encourage potential users to adopt a particular metal in the face
of a competitive product while in other cases it reflects more the
economy of scale that has been possible once production has passed
a given level.

Yttrium metal

The first rare earth metal to be produced on a large scale by
metallothermic reduction was yttrium in the early 1960's. At the
time researchers at General Electric discovered that stainless
steels containing both aluminium and yttrium possessed exceptional
resistance to corrosion. However, such steels as were then produced found only limited application in the nuclear industry and
it was not until 5 years ago that their potential for use in non-
nuclear applications was fully appreciated. The particular steel
that has since won widest acclaim is termed 'Fecralloy'; as the
name suggests its constituents are iron, chromium, aluminium and
yttrium. By comparison with existing stainless steels Fecralloy
possesses exceptional high temperature corrosion resistance – this
fact above all others has led to it being widely adopted for the
fabrication of furnace heating elements and, more importantly, it
is the number one contender to replace ceramic substrates in
emission control catalysts for the automobile and motor-cycle
industries.

The exceptional properties of the alloy are due in no small
way to the yttrium component which together with the aluminium
forms a stable and firmly bound oxide layer that exhibits excellent resistance to exhaust gas emissions at high temperatures over
prolonged periods.(2) At the same time, it provides an ideal
surface to receive another coating of metal or metal oxide which,
in the context of catalyst applications, is most essential. At the
present time most catalytic convertors utilise ceramic substrates
which are prone to damage by both mechanical and thermal shock.

Also in an industry where weight and space are at a premium ceramic substrates occupy a larger volume than would a unit of comparable catalytic activity manufactured using Fecralloy as the substrate. In the relatively short time that the alloy has been available for large scale evaluation it has already gained acceptance by many potential users in the automobile industry and, as a result, specialty steelmakers both in the U.S.A. and Britain are now able to offer tonnage quantities in various fabricated forms.

Yttrium is also used in other areas of metallurgy notably as a component of certain nickel-base and cobalt-base superalloys of the NiCrAlY and CoCrAlY type.(3) These alloys possess excellent corrosion and oxidation resistance, properties that have attracted the attention of the aero-engine industry where they are used as protective coatings on turbine blades. The alloys, when applied by vapour deposition, form an oxide coating that exhibits remarkable adhesion, a property attributed largely to the yttrium component acting to prevent the formation of voids at the oxide/substrate interface.(4)

Yttrium also finds application in titanium alloys where at concentrations of the order of 200 ppm it improves the ductility and ease of fabrication of vacuum arc-melted alloys. It is also used to improve the strength of magnesium castings and when used in combination with zirconium, as little as 100 ppm yttrium increases the conductivity of aluminium transmission lines by as much as 50%.

As one might expect, yttrium is not without its competitors; hafnium has been proposed as a replacement for it in certain iron-based alloys as have other elements, but in the context of the applications as described yttrium remains the preferred additive.

Lanthanum metal

All rare earth metals can be characterised as being electropositive with respect to most other metals; this fact, coupled with their large atomic radius and high reactivity towards non-metals, points the way to their widespread use as alloying constituents. However, in the manufacture of ductile iron and in steelmaking it is practice to use mischmetal or mixed rare earth silicides as the rare earth additive and from purely cost considerations this situation is unlikely to change significantly. But as one moves into the field of superalloys and other specialist alloys then this particular constraint tends to diminish and the cost of using a pure metal can well be justified. Such is the case with certain high strength nickel alloys which use cerium at the 100–300 ppm level to control sulphur and oxygen.

Of far greater significance, however, is the rapidly increasing use of lanthanum in high-temperature alloys. Developed originally to meet the demanding specifications for gas turbine manufacture, these alloys, which include both nickel-base and cobalt-base types, contain typically 200–400 ppm lanthanum.

Without it the alloys show significantly less resistance to cyclic oxidation which would suggest that, as with yttrium in Fecralloy, the lanthanum is acting to provide a firmly bound oxide barrier.

A more recent development that is attracting considerable attention is the use of lanthanum in high-temperature iron-base alloys. One such alloy manufactured in the U.S.A. (5) combines excellent oxidation resistance to 1100°C with good ductility and ease of fabrication. By comparison with other alloys possessing similar mechanical properties, the manufacturers attribute the alloys superior oxidation resistance to what they describe as a small (200 ppm) but effective addition of lanthanum.

Potentially one of the major applications for lanthanum is in the area of hydrogen storage alloys of the $LaNi_5$ type. These and related intermetallic compounds possess the ability to absorb and desorb large volumes of hydrogen at moderate temperatures and pressures. They have attracted the attention of many who regard them not only as an alternative to existing high pressure and cryogenic storage systems but more importantly as providing the means of achieving progress in the field of energy conservation. Although the subject is reviewed in detail elsewhere in the Proceedings, it is perhaps opportune to consider here the use of pure lanthanum metal as a component of these alloys.

The alloy $LaNi_5$ is generally considered as the classic storage compound in that it was the first rare earth intermetallic to be characterised and it remains one of the most efficient in terms of both capacity and kinetics but, unfortunately, it suffers from the disadvantage of being more expensive than the majority of its rivals. This fact has prompted its critics to dismiss compounds formulated on the basis of pure lanthanum as 'non-starters' in the context of commercial applications. While it is true that they are unlikely to find favour in large scale projects, there is ample evidence to suggest that they will be adopted for use in specialised applications where performance rather than cost is the determining factor. For example, within my own organisation consideration is being given to coupling a hydrogen generator direct to a $LiNi_5$ store; in the first instance this will be employed in a military context but already we see several applications that could benefit from the availability of such a system. In the U.S.A. one can now purchase small hydrogen storage units and one of the most versatile currently available employs $LaNi_5$ as the hydriding alloy. Other examples of systems employing $LaNi_5$ are in the pipe-line and while it would be true to say that industry has so far reacted cautiosly to this new technology, attitudes are changing and one may reasonably expect that their introduction will gain momentum in the period ahead.

Samarium metal

Next let us consider samarium, the fifth member of the lanthanide series. Twelve years ago it would have been difficult to name any applications involving its use in amounts greater than a few pounds per year. Today samarium is the industries brightest star accounting for nearly two-thirds of all metal usage. The reason for this transformation is due entirely to the discovery and subsequent development of rare earth-cobalt permanent magnets.

In the early 1970's when samarium-cobalt magnets were first being proposed as a replacement for platinum-cobalt in microwave tubes, few could have anticipated the success that was to follow. Notwithstanding the traumas brought about by a quadrupling of cobalt prices, their use has grown steadily to the point where they now command a vitally important position in the permanent magnet market.

Sintered magnets of the $SmCo_5$ type, the first to be manufactured commercially, possess specific magnetic properties that place them well above Ferrite and Alnico magnets in terms of performance, see Table I. In particular their maximum energy product is considerably greater, due principally to the extremely high coercivity of the alloy. This in turn can be attributed to the fact that $SmCo_5$, by virtue of its hexagonal structure, exhibits a high degree of uni-axial crystalline anisotropy.

TABLE I - COMPARATIVE PROPERTIES FOR VARIOUS TYPES OF MAGNET

Magnet Type	Maximum Energy Product $(BH)_{max}$ kJ/m^3	Remanence B_r T	Coercivity $_BH_c$ kA/m
Anisotropic Ferrite	26	0.37	240
Alnico 5	40	1.20	52
$SmCo_5$ – Sintered Polymer bonded	160 56	0.90 0.55	660 400

These properties have provided the design engineer with the means of achieving not only miniatturisation but performance characteristics hitherto unattainable. Today such magnets find application in a wide range of products including electronic watches, hi-fi equipment, high-power d.c. motors, magnetic bearings and they are even used in dentistry and surgery.

The first generation sintered magnets were based on the binary alloy $SmCo_5$ and such magnets still account for the bulk of those now manufactured. However, in order to meet certain cost criteria it was soon recognised that it would be to the benefit of all to provide a less expensive type of magnet based on a modofied composition and this was first achieved by partial substitution of the samarium by mischmetal. Today, alloys of this type offer the optimum energy product:cost ratio but more importantly they provide the magnet industry with the means of expanding production while conserving supplies of samarium oxide.

The oxide, the precursor to the metal/alloy, is currently available to the extent of about 150-200 tons per year and output may conceivably be doubled by 1985. Even so, when expressed in terms of samarium metal this quantity is relatively small, hence it is desirable to optimise the available resources by whatever means are possible. In Table II we illustrate one solution to the problem, namely the production of alloys containing much greater quantities of mischmetal.

TABLE II - WORLD PRODUCTION OF SAMARIUM OXIDE
EXPRESSED IN TERMS OF DERIVED ALLOYS

(metric tonnes per year)

Oxide	Metal	$SmCo_5$	$Sm_{.67}MM_{.33}Co_5$	$Sm_{.50}MM_{.50}Co_5$	$Sm_{.25}MM_{.75}Co_5$
150	116	336	500	665	1324
200	155	450	666	889	1769
400	310	900	1333	1778	3537

The above approach would almost certainly need to be adopted if, for example, the automobile industry was to decide to use RCo_5 magnets in the production of their accessory motors. Such an exercise has already been studied by at least two leading manufacturers and if pressures on weight and space become even more acute then the liklihood of them using such magnets must be greater.

Samarium is not the only rare earth metal used by the magnet industry. Several other RCo_5 systems have been studied and one in particular, namely $PrCo_5$, has attracted much attention. Unfortunately, its potentially very high energy product ($>200kJ/m^3$) is countered by what appears to be an inherent instability that so far has proved impossible to overcome. But praseodymium can be used to some extent as a partial replacement for samarium to provide magnets having marginally better performance characteristics than $SmCo_5$.

Bearing in mind the various constraints already referred to, it is perhaps fortuitous that a new generation of rare earth-cobalt magnets should recently have been developed that offer not only enhanced magnetic properties, as compared with $SmCo_5$, but also provide for savings on raw material costs. The new magnets are based on what are described as 2:17 alloys, the term relating to the Sm_2Co_{17} compound from which they are derived.

Of those 2:17 alloys currently in production the most widely employed are based on compositions of the type $Sm(Co,Cu,Fe,M)_x$ where M = Zr, Hf or Ti and x is within the range 7.0 - 8.5. Comparative data on this and other types of RCo_5 magnets are given in Table III.

TABLE III - COMPARATIVE DATA RCo_5 AND Sm_2Co_{17} TYPE MAGNETS

(Typical Magnetic Properties)

	Content%		$(BH)_{max}$	B_r	$_BH_c$	R.M. Cost
	Sm	Co	kJ/m^3	T	kA/m	$(SmCo_5=1)$
$SmCo_5$	33.5	66.5	160	0.90	660	1.00
$Sm_{.67}MM_{.33}Co_5$	22.8	66.5	110	0.75	520	0.85
$Sm_{.50}Pr_{.50}Co_5$	17.1	66.5	200	1.00	800	1 +
$Sm(Co,Cu,Fe,M)_x$	25.5	50.0	240	1.12	450	0.80

So far Japanese industry has been the most active in promoting the use of these newer magnets in such applications as stepping motors for quartz-analog watches and in high performance audio pick-ups and loudspeakers. However, there are signs that other countries are exolving their own 2:17 type magnets which one hopes will soon come into production.

Gadolinium and dysprosium metals

Of all the properties of the rare earths that contribute to their many and varied applications one that ranks of special interest is the extremely high thermal neutron capture cross-section associated with the elements gadolinium, samarium, europium and dysprosium, see Table IV.

TABLE IV - THERMAL NEUTRON ABSORPTION
CROSS-SECTION OF NATURAL ELEMENTS

(Barns per atom)

Gadolinium	40,000
Samarium	5,600
Europium	4,300
Dysprosium	1,100

As one might expect, the nuclear industry has not been slow to put
this property to good use and today gadolinium, in the form of its
oxide, is an essential component of certain fuel systems where it
is employed as a burnable poison, providing rapid core control
under emergency conditions.

By contrast, the metals have so far found only limited
application save for one important use in the field of non-
destructive testing. With the proliferation of research reactors
over the past decade, neutron radiography has become a practical
tool in the aerospace, nuclear and engineering industries, yet
without the availability of gadolinium and dysprosium in the form
of thin foils, the technique would be severely restricted.

Neutron radiography shares certain features in common with
X-radiography. In both systems an imaging beam is passed through
the specimen and the attenuated beam is then detected in such a
way as to produce an image of the internal detail of the specimen.
In neutron radiography the recording medium is standard X-ray film
but as the film is relatively insensitive to neutrons it is
necessary to use what are termed converter foils to produce the
image.

In the most widely employed method a gadolinium foil of
thickness 0.025mm is placed in direct contact with the X-ray film.
On exposure to the attenuated thermal neutron beam the gadolinium
converter foil absorbs neutrons and promptly emits beta radiation
thus activating the film. When required to examine irradiated
specimens, such as highly active fuel rods, it is neceassary to
adopt a somewhat different technique. The gadolinium is replaced
by a dysprosium foil generally of thickness 0.10mm which is
exposed to the attenuated neutron beam but in the absence of the
X-ray film. The activated foil is then removed from the beam and
its beta decay is used to produce an autoradiograph in contact
with X-ray film. As the gamma cross sections of the foil are both
small and lead to prompt interactions, this technique is uniquely
suited to the examination of highly radioactive materials.

Other rare earth metals

So far in this review reference has been made chiefly to the
elements that occur in the first half of the rare earth series.
Of the remaining elements such as holmium, erbium, thulium
ytterbium and lutetium it is unfortunately true that their
relatively low abundance coupled with high cost has tended to
preclude their use in applications outside of the laboratory.
Even so, demand for them is increasing year by year and in some
cases quite spectactularly. As an example, both thulium and erbium
are used as target materials in some sealed-tube neutron generators and erbium is also used in other generators designed
specifically for use in cancer therapy.

The final application to which reference will be made
concerns scandium. Although not a lanthanide its position

immediately above yttrium in Group III of the periodic table
qualifies it for inclusion in the rare earth series.

Despite it being a relatively rare metal, scandium is now
widely used by the lighting industry, albeit in small amounts, in
the manufacture of what are termed 'metal halide' lamps. For many
years it had been known that certain halides could be used to
change the spectral characteristics of mercury vapour lamps but it
was not until quite recently that it was discovered that mixed
halide systems based on scandium iodide could provide a near
perfect match to natural daylight. But scandium iodide is
extremely hygroscopic and it is difficult to use under normal
production conditions, therefore an alternative method had to be
found of incorporating it in the lamp. The method adopted was to
form the iodide in situ by reacting a small piece of scandium
metal with elemental iodine. Over the past few years the technique
has been refined considerably and today much of the scandium that
is used is supplied in the form of small discs of uniform size and
weight matched exactly to the lamp manufacturers requirements.

Metal halide lamps are without question one of the most
efficient forms of lighting available to us today. They deliver at
least 50% more light than conventional mercury lamps and by comparison with incandescent lamps of similar wattage their light
output is three times as great. Although at present they are used
mainly for outdoor and industrial lighting, low wattage lamps are
shortly to be introduced for home use so giving us all the
opportunity to effect some direct cost savings whilst at the same
time contributing to energy conservation.

In conclusion, it is particularly reassuring to know that
research involving rare earth metals and related alloys is as
active today as at any time during the past ten years. Additionally, many of the industrial applications to which reference has
been made are at a relatively early stage in their development.
Taken together these factors must point to an exciting future for
rare earth metals.

Literature Cited

1. Moore, Christine M. Rare-earth elements and yttrium.
   U.S. Dept. of the Interior, Bureau of Mines, 1979.
2. Fecralloy Steels. Trade publication. The Metals and
   Chemical Technology Centre, A.E.R.E. Harwell, England.
3. Talboom F.P.Jr and Grafwallner,J., U.S. Patent 3,542,530,
   November 24, 1970.
4. Metal Progress 106, (5) 7,10 (October 1974)
5. Trade publication. Haynes Development Alloy.
   Stellite Division, Cabot Corporation, Kokomo, Ind.46901, U.S.A.

RECEIVED March 3, 1981.

Use of Rare Earths in Television and Cathode Ray Phosphors

JAMES R. McCOLL and FRANK C. PALILLA

GTE Laboratories, Incorporated, 40 Sylvan Road, Waltham, MA 02254

Rare earth elements have earned an important role in the CRT (cathode ray tube) phosphor industry - a highly significant one for both the color TV and the rare earth businesses. This paper will review how rare earths earned this role, and will attempt to build a framework for discussion of future use of rare earths in CRT phosphors. Color TV phosphors will be emphasized since color TV is the largest market for CRT phosphors both generally, and in particular, those which contain rare earth elements.

Initially, an historical review will provide convincing evidence that the spectral properties of Eu^{3+} emission are so uniquely matched (1-4) to the human eye response that Eu^{3+}-activated phosphors will almost certainly remain as the red primary in color TV. We shall then discuss the prospects for adopting rare earth-activated phosphors that emit other colors. Finally, we will consider other factors that do have or may have a changing impact on the use of rare earths in the CRT phosphor industry.

Review of Color TV Principles

The way colored images are produced in a color TV picture tube (5,6) is illustrated in Figure 1. Electron beams from three separate guns impinge from slightly different angles onto a triad arrangement of phosphors. In this illustration, a shadow mask causes the beams to be directed to a triad of phosphor dots, but an arrangement of slots is also possible, whereby sequential stripes of phosphors are used instead. In either case, electrons that pass through the apertures from different guns strike different phosphors, each of which emits one of the three primary colors: red, green, or blue. The size of the phosphor dots is small enough that they are not visually resolved at normal viewing distances; instead the viewer has the impression of a single, blended color. Figure 2 is a chromaticity diagram (7) in which all visible colors are assigned numerical values

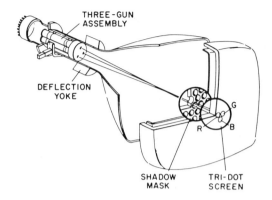

Transactions of the New York Academy of Sciences

Figure 1.   Principal components of color picture tube (5)

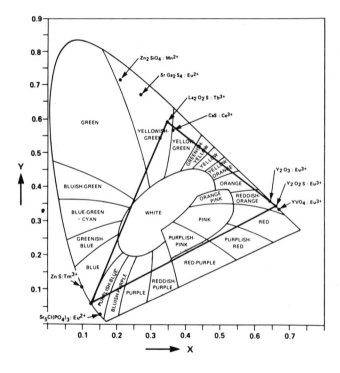

Figure 2.   CIE chromaticity diagram.   The triangle encompasses the gamut of colors obtainable in a typical TV screen.   A shift in the apices of this triangle to the points indicated would result from changes in primary phosphors shown in the diagram.

according to a system established by the Commission Internationale
de l'Eclairage (CIE) in 1931. A blend of two colors has chromaticity coordinates, and color value, lying on a line between end
points representing the two components on the diagram. All the
colors viewable on a color TV screen are formed by a blend of the
three colors emitted from the screen. The point which represents
the color of the blend lies within a triangle in the diagram, the
apices of which represent the three primary colors that comprise
the screen. The triangle shown in Figure 2 illustrates the color
gamut available in typical modern color TV screens.

It is obviously crucial then that the three color TV primary
phosphors be chosen with two factors in mind: first the colors
must be highly saturated so that the gamut of achievable blended
colors can be as large as possible. Secondly, the phosphors have
to do this efficiently by creating a maximum visual impression
with minimum excitation energy.

The CIE chromaticity system was based on a careful study of
a large number of experimental investigations of eye response.
To use this system a phosphor's emission energy $E(\lambda)$ is measured
as a function of wavelength λ and the following computations are
carried out.

$$E = \int E(\lambda) d\lambda \tag{1}$$

$$X = \int E(\lambda) \bar{x}(\lambda) d\lambda \tag{2}$$

$$Y = \int E(\lambda) \bar{y}(\lambda) d\lambda \tag{3}$$

$$Z = \int E(\lambda) \bar{z}(\lambda) d\lambda \tag{4}$$

Then E is the total radiant energy of the light, while X,Y, and Z
are, respectively, the magnitudes of hypothetical (not actually
realizable) red, green, and blue primaries as defined by the CIE
that would have to be blended to yield the same eye response, both
in color and intensity, as the phosphor emission under consideration. Although not strictly correct, it can be useful to regard X, Y, and Z as the response of red, green, and blue receptors
in the eye.

Several more formulae yield the luminosity, L, which is the
overall brightness response, and the chromaticity coordinates x
and y, as used in Figure 2:

$$L = 683Y = 683\bar{\bar{y}}E, \tag{5}$$

where $\bar{\bar{y}}$ is the lumen equivalent of the emission, and

$$x = X/(X+Y+Z), \tag{6}$$

$$y = Y/(X+Y+Z). \tag{7}$$

The units of L are lumens if E is expressed in watts. The product
$\bar{\bar{y}}E$ thus represents a figure of merit for phosphors: $\bar{\bar{y}}$ is

determined by the phosphor's emission spectrum, while E is determined by the phosphor's electrical to radiant energy conversion
efficiency.

Color TV Reds

The values of $\bar{x}$, $\bar{y}$, and $\bar{z}$ published by the CIE are presented
in Figure 3; $\bar{y}(\lambda)$ is also the luminosity response function. As
discussed above, these curves can loosely be regarded as the eye
response curves of red, green, and blue color receptors in the
eye. For greatest effectiveness, a phosphor's emission spectrum
has to match these curves well to yield both the proper color and
maximum brightness. Of the two components of rare earth phosphors,
the host largely determines efficiency while the activator determines the emission spectrum.

We will examine the example of red-emitting phosphor in some
detail, since Eu^{3+}-activated phosphors provide the best example
of the practical realization of these principles. First consider
the effect of the spectral width. Figure 4, taken from Levine
and Palilla (5), shows a series of hypothetical spectra, of different widths, which yield the same overall red color, namely,
the same ratio X/Y. (Blue response Z can be ignored in this
example because of the remoteness of the $\bar{z}$ curve; see Figure 3.)
We see that as spectral width is increased, the spectra have to
be shifted to longer wavelengths to maintain the proper X/Y ratio,
otherwise the short wavelength wing would yield an orange color
shift. This has the disastrous consequence, however, of drastically reducing the values of X and Y, since the broadened, shifted
spectra make increasingly poorer matches to the $\bar{x}$ and $\bar{y}$ curves.
It is extremely important, then, that an efficient red emitter
should have an emission spectrum that is narrow as well as
properly located with regard to its visibility.

We illustrate this principle with the phosphor spectra shown
in Figure 5, taken from ref (8). The Mn^{2+} activated phosphate,
a broad band emitter, was the original red color TV phosphor. It
was superseded in 1960 when RCA introduced the all sulfide screen
utilizing (Zn,Cd)S:Ag as the red primary. The spectrum of the
sulfide is also broad and actually makes an even poorer match to
the eye than that of the phosphate, but this is more than compensated for by a threefold increase in efficiency (integrated area
under the curve). The spectrum of $YVO_4:Eu^{3+}$, which was introduced as a color TV phosphor in 1964 by Sylvania as a result of
pioneering work by Levine and Palilla (9), is qualitatively different and beautifully illustrates the eye response principle.
The narrow line spectrum is dominated by strong lines peaking
near 620 nm. Even though the vanadate is only slightly more
energetically efficient than the phosphate, its brightness
exceeds even that of the sulfide. The vanadate has been largely
superseded in the U.S. for color TV by two other Eu^{3+}-activated
phosphors: $Y_2O_3:Eu^{3+}$ (10) and $Y_2O_2S:Eu^{3+}$ (11). Both phosphors

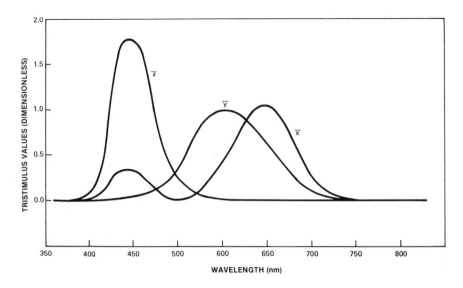

Figure 3.   Spectral tristimulus values according to the 1931 CIE standard observer. These values are dimensionless.

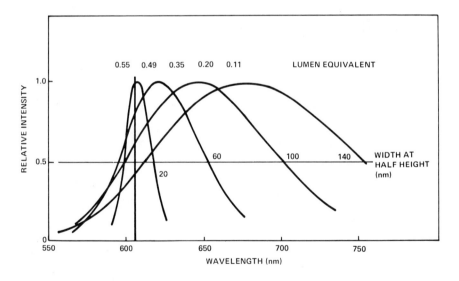

Figure 4.   Lumen equivalent values of several spectral distributions having the color coordinates x = 0.65, y = 0.35 *(1–5)*

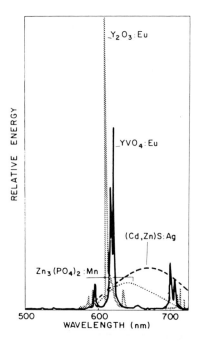

*Figure 5. Spectral energy distributions
of red-emitting cathode ray phosphors (8)*

Electrochemical Technology

Table I. Red Emitting Phosphors

MATERIAL	RELATIVE BRIGHTNESS	COLOR COORDINATES			RELATIVE ENERGY EFFICIENCY	RELATIVE COLOR GAMUT	COMMENT
		X	Y	$\overline{\overline{Y}}$			
$Zn_{.2}Cd_{.8}S{:}Ag$	48%	0.66	0.33	0.12	180%	112%	• SATURATES EASILY • COLOR SHIFTS • DARK BODY COLOR
$YVO_4Eu^{3+}(4.5\%)$	57%	0.66	0.33	0.30	86%	112%	•DEEPEST RED
$Y_2O_3{:}Eu^{3+}(3.5\%)$	100%	0.64	0.35	0.45	100%	100%	•ORANGISH EMISSION •MOST SALVAGEABLE • USED IN DUSTING PROCESS
$Y_2O_2S{:}Eu^{3+}(3.65\%)$	100%	0.65	0.34	0.375	120%	106%	•USED IN SLURRY PROCESS

are brighter than the vanadate for two reasons: their energy conversion efficiency is somewhat greater, and their emission is a bit more orange. This is illustrated by the spectra in Figure 5, and by the data in Table I. Relative brightnesses were measured photoelectrically. The emission spectra treated according to Eq. (1-7) yield chromaticity coordinates which then permit calculation of relative energy efficiency and color gamut, i.e. the range of colors encompassed within the triangle as described in the previous section. Some of the possible tradeoffs in brightness, color, etc. in color TV tube design can be gleaned from this table; another variable not shown here is Eu concentration, which can influence color and brightness. The concentration of Eu in Y_2O_2S produces drastic color changes while having a relatively small effect in Y_2O_3 and YVO_4. The main point, though, is that the Eu^{3+}-activated phosphors are twice as bright even though they are half to two-thirds as efficient as $(Zn,Cd)S:Ag$, a phosphor which is probably at the theoretical limit of cathode ray efficiency. No other activator system produces anything like this favorably located narrow band emission, so it is highly unlikely that Eu^{3+} would be replaced.

Rare earth consumption could, however, be affected by a change in host lattice system, with Eu^{3+} still being retained as activator. Either cost or luminescence efficiency could drive such a change. Costs could be decreased either by eliminating rare earth host lattice cations or by a decrease in the required concentration of Eu. However, in spite of considerable research effort, new host systems that accomplish these objectives have not been found.

Color TV Greens

The situation for greens is very different than for reds. Narrowness of spectral emission has some importance in the green spectral region, but it is not the dominant concern that it is in the red system. This is because the green response and luminosity curves coincide, so that green light intrinsically has high luminosity. Consequently, the dominant factor for improvements in the green would be the CR (cathode ray) electrical energy to radiant energy efficiency rather than radiant energy to luminous response efficacy.

Spectral and numerical data on the presently most-used U.S. color TV green, $(Zn,Cd)S:Cu,Al$, and its best competitors are given in Figure 6 and Table II. Three of these competitors are rare earth phosphors, $La_2O_2S:Tb^{3+}$ (12), $CaS:Ce^{3+}$ (13) and $SrGa_2S_4:Eu^{2+}$ (14), and illustrate the three most important green-emitting rare earth activators: Tb^{3+}, Ce^{3+}, and Eu^{2+}. Of these only Tb^{3+} has the characteristic rare earth narrow line emission due to transitions within 4f electron levels. The broad emission spectra of the other two, Ce^{3+} and Eu^{2+}, are due to 5d-4f electronic transitions. These transitions yield broad spectra whose

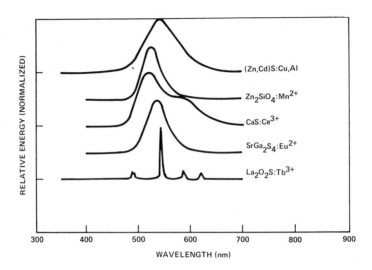

Figure 6. Spectral energy distributions of several green-emitting cathode ray phosphors

Table II. Green Emitting Phosphors

MATERIAL	RELATIVE BRIGHTNESS	COLOR COORDINATES			RELATIVE ENERGY EFFICIENCY	RELATIVE COLOR GAMUT	COMMENT
		X	Y	$\overline{Y}$			
$Zn_{.93}Cd_{.07}S:Cu,Al$	100%	0.34	0.59	0.76	$\equiv$100%	$\equiv$100%	• STANDARD TV PHOSPHOR • SATURATES EASILY
$Zn_2SiO_4:Mn$	42%	0.21	0.71	0.76	42%	125%	• NTSC STANDARD
$La_2O_2S:Tb^{3+}$	66%	0.34	0.60	0.76	66%	102%	
$CaS:Ce^{3+}$	85%	0.36	0.57	0.68	95%	97%	• DESATURATED COLOR • INCOMPATIBLE WITH TV TUBE PROCESSING
$SrGa_2S_4:Eu^{2+}$	50%	0.27	0.67	0.82	47%	116%	• USED IN SOME PROJECTION TV

dominant wavelength can vary enormously from host to host [uv to yellow for Ce^{3+} and uv to red for Eu^{2+} (15).]

In the green system, none of the rare earth phosphors have significantly more favorable emission spectra than the standard sulfide and they all have lower energy efficiency. Nevertheless, there is one factor that could lead to adoption of rare earth based green emitters, namely the nonlinear response of the sulfide. As shown in Figure 7, the efficiency of the standard sulfide relative to $La_2O_2S:Tb$ decreases rapidly as electron beam current density is increased (16). At high enough current density, rare earth phosphors can actually become brighter than the sulfide (17). This saturation can be a 15% to 35% effect in conventional color TV picture tubes. Both brightness and maintenance of desired overall blended color are adversely affected by the nonlinearity of the sulfide green. While the effect is tolerable in picture tubes manufactured today, it would be worse in tubes with higher current densities, like tubes with improved spot size performance or projection TV tubes. Thus the possibility of adoption of rare earth greens is real, but dependent on changes in picture tube technology.

Color TV Blues

The prospects for use of rare earth based blue emitters in color TV is by far the least likely. Here some leeway is possible in shifting emission peak positions and spectral widths but still other considerations become important.

Blue is a unique color in that the z curve of Figure 3, related to the eye's blue sensitivity, is much more remote from the $\bar{x}$ and $\bar{y}$ curves than the $\bar{x}$ and $\bar{y}$ curves are from each other. The consequence of this is that statements about the brightness of a blue phosphor can be highly misleading. This is because the really meaningful figure of merit for a color TV screen is its white field brightness (WFB). This is defined as lumen output divided by total excitation power (P) incident on all three phosphors while they are excited so as to yield a specified white color. That is,

$$WFB = 683 \frac{Y_{blue} + Y_{green} + Y_{red}}{P_{blue} + P_{green} + P_{red}} \qquad (8)$$

Approximately equal excitation of the eye's blue, green, and red centers is needed to yield white. We especially note that for white,

$$Z_{blue} + Z_{green} + Z_{red} \sim Y_{blue} + Y_{green} + Y_{red} \qquad (9)$$

The term Y_{blue} in the numerator of Eq. (8) is inevitably small, so that the major impact of the blue phosphor on white field brightness is through the term P_{blue} in the denominator. The

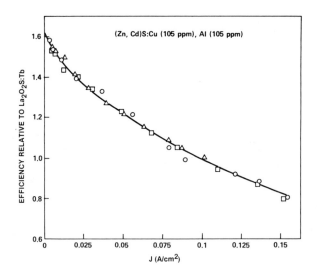

Figure 7. Efficiency of green-emitting (Zn,Cd)S:Cu,Al relative to $La_2O_2S:Tb^{3+}$ as a function of electron beam current density: (○) 30 kV, (□) 25 kV, (△) 20 kV. Electron beam dwell is 0.5 μs and pulse repetition rate is 60 pps.

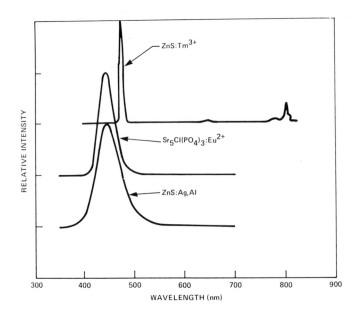

Figure 8. Spectral energy distributions of several blue-emitting cathode ray phosphors

value of P_{blue} is determined by the necessity to have an adequate value for Z_{blue} as required by Eq. (9). A measure of the quality of the spectrum of a blue phosphor for this purpose may be defined as $\bar{z} = Z/E$.

Spectra and numerical data to illustrate this point are presented in Figure 8 and Table III. The best rare earth blue line emitter is Tm^{3+}, but its emission, as typified by $ZnS:Tm^{3+}$ (18) emission, peaks at ~ 475 nm, a wavelength that poorly matches the $\bar{z}$ curve; thus $\bar{z}$ is low and Tm^{3+} emission contributes ineffectively to a white field.

The standard color TV blue, $ZnS:Ag,Al$, has a broad emission spectrum, but its peak at 445 nm matches the $\bar{z}$ curve well. The emission of Eu^{2+} in $Sr_5Cl(PO_4)_3:Eu^{2+}$ (19) while broad, is narrower than that of the sulfide, so the match is even better and $\bar{z}$ is larger. Unfortunately, the CRT energy efficiency (unlike that for uv excitation, which is exceptionally good) is so low that the spectral virtues of this phosphor cannot be used to advantage.

Rare Earth Host Lattices

Most of the successful rare earth activated phosphors comprise host lattices in which the host cation is also a rare earth. A principal reason for this relates to the optical inertness of La, Gd, Y, and Lu; this is essential to avoid interference with activator emission spectra. Close chemical compatibility including amenability to substitutional incorporation of rare earth activators are also essential features. Rare earth hosts such as oxides, oxysulfides, phosphates, vanadates and silicates also tend to be rugged materials compatible with high temperature tube processing operations and salvage.

The exceptions to the rule that rare earth hosts are best for rare earth activators are special cases. For example, some anions such as sulfide yield compounds in combination with non-rare earth cations (e.g. Zn) which show higher luminescent efficiency than with rare earths. Additionally, divalent rare earth activators like Eu^{2+} substitute readily for non-rare earth divalent cations.

Factors Affecting Rare Earth Consumption in TV Phosphors

The consumption of rare earths in color TV is dictated in the first instance by the choice to use rare earth phosphors and the number of picture tubes produced. Within these constraints, several other factors tend to exert a downward influence on rare earth consumption. Reclaim, that is, reuse of phosphor coated on but not retained by the picture tube screen, is now universally practiced in the U.S. TV industry. Reclaim was not practiced at the time of the introduction of Eu-based reds. The high cost and uncertain availability of rare earth phosphors

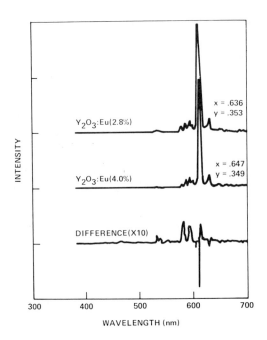

Figure 9.   Dependence of emission spectrum of Y_2O_3:Eu^{3+} on europium concentration. The difference spectrum is defined as the normalized Y_2O_3:Eu (2.8%) spectrum minus that for Y_2O_3:Su (4.0%). This enhances perceptibility of the increased $^5D_1$ emission (yellow and green lines) in the low Eu concentration phosphor.

Table III. Blue Emitting Phosphors

MATERIAL	RELATIVE BRIGHTNESS	COLOR COORDINATES				RELATIVE ENERGY EFFICIENCY	RELATIVE WHITE FIELD EFFECTIVENESS	RELATIVE COLOR GAMUT	COMMENT
		X	Y	$\bar{Y}$	$\bar{\bar{Z}}$				
ZnS:Ag,Al	≡100%	0.148	0.060	0.094	1.23	≡100%	≡100%	≡100%	• STD TV PHOSPHOR • SATURATES
$Sr_5Cl(PO_4)_3$:Eu^{2+}	14.9	0.154	0.028	0.052	1.53	27	32	118%	• ENLARGED COLOR GAMUT
ZnS:Tm^{3+}	74%	0.115	0.107	0.092	0.67	76	41	82%	• REDUCED COLOR GAMUT

dictated conservation measures, while their ruggedness made reclaim possible.   The ability to reclaim, on the other hand, has
the positive effect of providing a strong case for the continued
use of rare earths.

The introduction of pigmented phosphors by RCA (20), followed
by some but not all other manufacturers, indirectly reduces Eu
consumption.   Pigmented phosphors are coated with compatibly
colored inorganic pigments, whose purpose is to improve contrast
by reducing reflected ambient light (red pigment is used with red-
emitting phosphor, etc.).   We shall show how this permits reduction
of Eu concentration in the red phosphor.   The spectra of $Y_2O_3:Eu^{3+}$
at two Eu levels, in Figure 9, help to show why relatively large
Eu concentrations have to be used in these phosphors.   The difference spectrum brings out the fact that at lower Eu^{3+} concentration, emission from $^5D_1$ levels, lying in the green-yellow
regions of the spectrum, is enhanced at the expense of the red
$^5D_0$ emission.   The high Eu concentration (3–5 m/o) found in TV
reds is needed not so much for efficiency (which typically peaks
for Eu at about 2 m/o in these materials) but rather to yield the
required saturated red emission color.   The red pigment used in
tinted red-emitting phosphor preferentially absorbs in the green-
yellow; this restores the color of low Eu phosphor to the desired
redness.   The impact on Eu consumption is small but not negligible.

Data Display Phosphors

An already substantial and rapidly growing market for CRT
phosphors and tubes is in the area of data displays, both alpha-
numeric and graphic, e.g., computer terminals and word processors.
In spite of dramatic advances in other technologies, CRT's are
still the most cost effective way to present information, and very
likely always will be.   Most data display tubes do not use rare
earth phosphors; because of their high cost, rare earth phosphors
find use only when there is a compelling need for their special
properties.   At the present time, this is limited to the use of
Eu^{3+} reds in tricolor tubes that use the same shadow mask
principle as conventional color TV.

There are several demonstrated, but not as yet commercialized,
schemes for two color, non-shadow mask, high resolution display
tubes which could use rare earth phosphors.   The voltage penetration (21) scheme uses a two layer phosphor and exploits the
principle that electron beam penetration into a phosphor increases
as beam voltage is increased.   At low voltage, only the surface
layer emitting one color is excited, while at higher voltage,
excitation reaches a deeper phosphor layer emitting a different
color.

A second scheme (22) utilizes a blend of sublinear and superlinear phosphors.   At low current, the sublinear phosphor domi-
nates the emission.   As the beam current is increased, the
emission of the superlinear phosphor begins to surpass that of the

sublinear, yielding a color shift. Displays using either of these principles would not be capable of the full color gamut of tricolor tubes, yet would be simple and yield both high resolution and the contrast enrichment provided by the added dimension of color.

A final comment in the data display area concerns an unfulfilled need that might conceivably be met by rare earth materials. Some data displays utilize low frame rates that can lead to the perception of flicker when conventional short or medium persistence phosphors are used. Long persistence, i.e., long decay time, can reduce flicker, but until very recently, only one color has been commercially available - the green emission of Zn_2SiO_4:Mn,As. The need for other colors and higher efficiency is so great that new long persistence phosphors could be put to use immediately. Rare earth phosphors have a potential for fulfilling this need, but useful long persistence rare earth phosphors have not yet been discovered. In response to this need, GTE Sylvania has recently introduced nonflickering red, yellow and white emitting phosphors.

Recent Research Activity in Rare Earth CRT Phosphors

Several areas of recent research activity that have an impact on rare earth usage in CRT phosphors have already been mentioned--pigmented phosphors for color TV, and voltage penetration and current saturable phosphors for two-color displays.

There has been a continuing emphasis on development of rare earth activated sulfides; examples of such materials are $ZnS:Tm^{3+}$ (18), $ZnS: Cu,Er$ (23), $SrGa_2S_4:Eu^{2+}$ (14) and $SrGa_2S_4Ce^{3+}$ (14). The motivation for choosing sulfides for development is, in part, simply that the most efficient families of CRT phosphors are sulfides: ZnS, CdS, and the alkaline earth sulfides. However, rare earth based sulfides have not achieved the CR efficiency of the conventional sulfides.

The story is somewhat different when one is interested in absolute light output rather than efficiency; $YAG:Ce^{3+}$ (24) can be used when light outputs in excess of 10,000 ftL are required. Even though its efficiency is low, $YAG:Ce^{3+}$ can withstand the enormous energy input necessary for the generation of this amount of light. A related phosphor, the perovskite $YAlO_3:Ce^{3+}$, has recently (25) been developed as an effective uv-emitting beam index phosphor. Beam index tubes are an alternative form of tricolor picture tube that have only one electron gun and no shadow mask. The gun is modulated so that an appropriate current flows as the beam strikes each colored phosphor during scanning. The additional uv-emitting phosphor, in conjunction with a uv sensor within the tube, is required to maintain proper synchronization.

The "golden" period of the 1960's when several important new rare earth phosphors were developed each year appears to be over. Nevertheless, useful new CRT phosphors are still being developed, some examples of which have been discussed above. Additionally, we have pointed out areas where unfulfilled needs have yet to be met.

Finally, the impact of efficient rare earth phosphors on stimulating basic research should be noted. This aspect of rare earth phosphors has not been widely recognized because it has been overshadowed by the practical merits of these materials. Essentially, the rare earth phosphors have provided a tool in the form of unique optical spectra which are conveniently amenable to theoretical interpretation. Because of the discreteness of the optical adsorption and emission features of rare earth ions, subtle changes in their environment can be associated with distinct and measurable changes in their spectra. Analyses of these changes therefore give insights into host-activator interactions. These analyses have not been available in easily interpretable form with non-rare earth phosphors. Consequently, considerable effort has since gone into improving our theoretical understanding of energy transfer mechanisms in phosphors as well as in understanding the efficiency of radiative (and nonradiative) mechanisms in phosohors (26,27,28). Such research ultimately should permit a more rational selection of host activator combinations for further investigation thereby minimizing the historical, more empirical, approaches to the development of phosphors for specific applications.

Economic Impact of CRT Phosphors On The Rare Earth Industry

Phosphor manufacture is still a dominant factor for suppliers of rare earth chemicals. According to industry sources (29), approximately 1/3 of the monetary volume of rare earth chemicals is used by the electronics industry. Included in this figure is Sm_2O_3 for samarium-cobalt magnets. The remainder includes Gd_2O_3, La_2O_3 and Tb_3O_4 for x-ray and lighting phosphors, and Y_2O_3 and Eu_2O_3 for CRT and lighting phosphors. Essentially all of the Eu_2O_3 consumed, totaling 6-7 tons in the U.S., is used for phosphor manufacture--80% to 90% of this for CRT's, the remainder for lighting. About 2/3 of the Y_2O_3 consumed ($\sim$ 100 tons U.S.) is used for phosphors. This fraction might decrease if some other envisioned uses for yttria-based ceramics, e.g., automotive emission sensors, reach fruition.

Overall, the total monetary volume of rare earths used for U.S. CRT phosphor manufacture is $20-25M. The volume by weight is only roughly 1% of total rare earth production, but the monetary volume is large because of the high value of Eu_2O_3 and Y_2O_3 compared to other rare earth oxides, and the high purity required of phosphor grade chemicals.

Summary

We have reviewed some of the factors governing selection of

phosphors for color TV and other CRT applications from the point
of view of rare earth usage. The dominant use for rare earths
for CRT phosphors is, and will very likely continue to be, yttria-
based europium-activated, red-emitting phosphors for tricolor TV
and data display. A big decrease in use of these red phosphors
would be desirable from the picture tube makers' viewpoint, because of cost, but is highly unlikely.

New use of rare earth phosphors in color TV would most
likely result from choice of Tb^{3+} or Eu^{2+} based green emitters.
While selection of these phosphors could result from changes in
picture tube design, prospects for this are slim.

As we will no doubt learn in the following two companion
papers, the new developments in phosphors that will have the
greatest changing impact on the rare earth industry will almost
surely occur in the areas of lighting and radiography.

Acknowledgements

The authors are honored by the invitation of Karl A.
Gschneidner, Jr. to present this paper at the Second Chemical
Congress of the North American Continent. They are also indebted
to Joseph G. Cannon of Molycorp, Inc. and H. Holt Apgar of Rhone-
Poulenc, Inc. for discussions relating to the market for rare
earths. We acknowledge with thanks Wayne Person of GTE Sylvania,
Towanda, PA, who provided the brightness and color coordinate
data in Table I.

Literature Cited

1. Palilla, F.C., Keynote Address - Electrochem. Soc. Spring
    Meeting, Dallas, 1967, Abstract No. 68; Electrochem. Tech.
    1968, 6, 39.
2. Palilla, F.C., Award Address, Electrochem. Soc. Spring
    Meeting, Washington, DC, 1971.
3. Larach, S., Hardy, A.E., Proc. IEEE, 1973, 61, 915.
4. Stevels, A.L.N., J. Luminescence, 1976, 12/13, 97.
5. Levine, A.K., Palilla, F.C., Trans. N.Y. Acad. Sci. Ser. II,
    1965, 27, 517.
6. Nimeroff, I., "Colorimetry", NBS Monograph 104, US Gov.
    Printing Office: Washington, 1968,
7. Kelly, K.L., Bull. Natl. Formulary Comm., 1940, 8, 459
8. Levine, A.K., Palilla, F.C., Electrochem. Tech., 1966, 4, 16.
9. Levine, A.K., Palilla, F.C., Appl. Phys. Lett., 1964, 5, 118.
10. Wickersheim, K.A, Lefever, R.A., J. Electrochem. Soc., 1964,
    111, 47.
11. Hardy, A.E., IEEE Trans. Electron Devices ED15, 1968, 868;
    Royce, M.R., Smith, A.L. Electrochem. Soc. Spring Meeting,
    Boston, Abstract No. 34, 1968.
12. Wang, S.P., Landi, O., Lucks, H., Wickersheim, K.A.,
    Buchanan, R.A., IEEE Trans. Nucl. Sci. NS17, 1970, 49.

13. Lehman, W., Ryan, F.M., J. Electrochem Soc., 1972, 119, 275; 1971, 118, 477.
14. Peters, T.E. Baglio, J.A., J. Electrochem. Soc. 1972, 119,230.
15. Avella, F.J., J. Electrochem. Soc., 1971, 118, 1862.
16. McColl, J.R., Dodds, R.E., Electrochem. Soc. Spring Meeting, Seattle, Abstract No. 325, 1978.
17. Meyer, V.D., Palilla, F.C., J. Electrochem. Soc., 1969, 116, 535.
18. Shrader, R.E., Larach, S., Yocom, P.N., J. Appl. Phys., 1971, 42, 4529.
19. Palilla, F.C., O'Reilly, B.E., J. Electrochem. Soc., 1968, 115, 1076.
20. Trond, S.S., Electrochem Soc. Spring Meeting, Seattle, Abstract No. 329, 1978.
21. Hallett, J., Rhodes, C., Proc. SID, 1969, 10, 9.
22. Sisneros, T.E., Faeth, P.A., Danis, J.A., NASA Report Cr-1228, 1969; Avella, F.J., IEEE Trans. Electron Devices, 1971, 18, 719.
23. Schlam, E., Pucilowski, J.J., Reingold, I., J. Electrochem. Soc., 1975, 122, 655.
24. Blasse, G, Bril, A., Appl. Physics Lett., 1967, 11, 53; J. Chem. Phys., 1967, 47, 5139; Bril, A., Blasse, G., DePoorter, J.A., J. Electrochm. Soc., 1970, 117, 346.
25. Taked, T., Miyata, T., Tomiki, T., Electrochem. Soc. Spring Meeting, Boston, Abstract No. 222, 1979.
26. Struck, C., Fonger, W.H., J. Luminescence, 1975, 10, 1.
27. Riseberg, L.A., Weber, M.J., "Progress in Optics", Wolf, E., Ed.,North Holland, Amsterdam, 1975, vol.14.
28. Alig, R.C., Bloom, S., Struck, C.W., Electrochem. Soc., Spring Meeting, St. Louis, Abstract No. 206, 1980; Alig, R.C. Bloom, S., J.Appl. Phys., 1978, 49, 3476; Robbins, D.J., Electrochem. Soc. Spring Meeting, St. Louis, Abstract No.207, 1980.
29. Cannon, J., Personal Communication; Apgar, H., Personal Communication.

RECEIVED March 3, 1981.

Lamp Phosphors

W. A. THORNTON

Westinghouse Electric Corporation, Bloomfield, N.J. 07003

This Symposium gives a fine overview of the contributions of the rare earth elements to human need and activity. Their applicability to iron and steel, to other alloys, glasses, abrasives, refineries, electronic parts is most impressive in its scope. But I note, with wry satisfaction, that the lampmaker's use of rare earths is visually the most spectacular of all -- that of generating brilliant colored lights to see by. The rare earth ion being a sheltered place, inside, safe from disrupting influences of its environment, it can take a bit of absorbed energy, shape it, and spit it out in one of the purest forms of visible light we know. These pure, brilliant, colored lights (termed spectral colors or spectral lights)show enormous promise for general illumination. What I would like to do is to extend the description of phosphors, of the previous paper, to modern lighting.

Not long after the turn of the century, one of the magnificent red-emitting luminescent materials, activated by the rare earth europium, was discovered(1). Its brilliant red-orange light has a spectral power distribution as in Figure 1A. From that day to this, no more efficient rare earth material for generating commercial lamplight has ever been produced, and europium has recently begun to play a major role in lighting human activities all over the world.

Generating brilliant colored lights is essential to the lampmaker, because the white light he sells is composed of a mixture of brilliant colored lights, and because he is beginning to understand which colored lights are most important to human vision. Some hundred and fifty spectral lights are distinguishable by the normal human observer. They are, of course, far from equally effective in aiding the human visual system to function with maximum efficiency. The visual system has three independent inputs, allowing it to sort incoming lights in three dimensions. There must be three independent spectral responses, associated with these inputs, each spectral response sampling a different region of the visible spectrum, although there may be a great deal of overlap between pairs of responses. Each spectral response may be characterized by

0097-6156/81/0164-0195$05.00/0

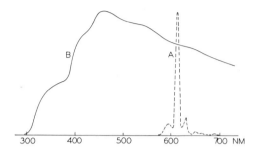

Figure 1.   The brilliant orange–red emission of Eu^{3+} (A), contrasted to the bluish-
white spectral power distribution of average daylight (B)

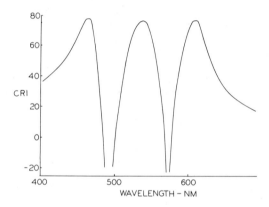

Figure 2.   The color-rendering index (CRI), of similarity to daylight-rendering,
dependence upon choice of triad of spectral lights to form white light of daylight-
color. Wavelengths of two components are fixed at their peaks, and the wavelength
of the third component is varied. Optimum combination appears in Figure 3.

Figure 3.   The three pure spectral colors,
the "prime-colors," uniquely related to
normal human vision. Combined, as
shown here, they form a white-light mixture the color of sunlight.

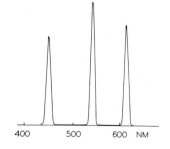

a single wavelength(2,3)marking its peak, or mean, sensitivity;the
resulting three wavelengths expectably play a unique role in human
vision, and the spectral lights corresponding to them may do the
same in illumination.

    We name these wavelengths the "prime-colors" of human vision
(4), and ask where in the visible spectrum they lie. If artificial
white light of daylight color is composed of triads of spectral
lights, one soon finds that the color-rendering of such mixtures
varies from very poor to very good. Eventually it is found how
critical the choice is, that three specific wavelengths are necessary for greatest similarity to real-daylight-rendering, that the
color-rendering of this unique triad is very good indeed (better
than that of most commercial lamps marketed), and that deviation
in wavelength from any one of the three optimum spectral lights
results in rapid deterioration of color-rendering of the white-
light mixture(2,5). The final iteration is shown in Figure 2,where
two of the wavelengths are set at optimum values and the third
wavelength is varied. For each triad, the color-rendering index
(CRI, an index of similarity to daylight-rendering)is computed(6).

    I see no explanation of Figure 2 other than that the unique
wavelengths mark the mean sensitivities of the three visual responses, and can be thought of as the "sampling points" of the visual system. In any case, the white-light mixture of Figure 3, which
is about the color of sunlight, renders the color of complexions,
foods, clothing, furnishings, plants, animals, and minerals aston-
ishingly well,i.e. pleasantly and expectably. The widths of the
components can be narrowed without limit, until almost all of the
visible spectrum is empty. Yet moving one of the components fif-
teen nanometers can be disastrous. The color of such prime-color
light may be varied by altering the ratio of power in the three
components, taking care not to alter the mean wavelength of any
component.

    In addition to similarity to daylight-rendering, prime-color
white light yields an illuminated scene which is peculiarly attrac-
tive(7), shows peculiar "visual clarity"(8,9,10),and high perceivd
brightness per footcandle(11). Other psychophysical evidence(2,3,
12,13)suggests that the spectral response of the human visual system is approximated by the dashed envelope of Figure 4; the three
peaked responses are independent although overlapping. The solid
curve is the traditional luminous efficiency function, allowing
only one-dimensional vision, operative only under uncommon visual
conditions, yet wrongly presiding over lamp development for more
than sixty years.

    A modern objective is to feed lighting power into the visual
system at its peaks of response, as does the white light of Figure
3, for example. This a revolutionary turnabout from traditional
views of how commercial lamplight should be designed; the daylight
in which we presumably evolved is a continuum(Figure 1B) as are
firelight and light from the oil lamp and the incandescent lamp.
The primary use of lamplight is to light human activities, and it
is high time the lamplight is designed for the human visual system.

Generating brilliant colored lights like the components of Figure 3 is something rare earths can often do as no other materials can. Ideally, the components of lamplight should comprise very narrow bands centered near 450nm, 535nm, and 615 nm. Variation of mean wavelength of one of the components by +5nm has little deleterious effect, but more than that results in rather rapid degradation of the visual efficiency of the lamplight. Particularly to be scrupulously avoided, in the ideal case, are the "antiprime" colors, violet, blue-green, yellow and deep-red.

Europium 3+ is made to order for the red-orange prime-color. The crystal playing host to the europium impurity must, however, strongly favor the $^5D_0$--$^7F_2$ electric dipole transition, which yields strong emission in the wavelength range 612-618nm. Some crystals hosting Eu 3+ allow magnetic dipole transitions and thus strong yellow-orange emission near 590nm, and are unsuitable(14,15). The useful electric dipole transitions are favored by oxygen-dominated lattices(small ion, large charge). Perhaps the best luminescent material of this type, at least for use in fluorescent lamps, is $Y_2O_3:Eu^{3+}$(Figure 1A).

Achieving a prime-color spectral power distribution like that of Figure 3 requires good control of the emitting species in the commercial lamp. At present, the fluorescent lamp offers the best control. The visible contribution of its arc is so far intractable but amounts to only a few percent of visible output. The rest derives of course from luminescent materials which convert 254nm radiation from the mercury arc, to useful light. The problem is therefore to provide efficient luminescent materials which emit the prime-colors, preferably one phosphor per prime-color for ease in color adjustment of the resulting lamplight. Quantum efficiency (visible photons emitted per 254nm photon absorbed)must be 0.8-0.9 in order to stay in the fiercely competitive fluorescent lamp market.

So $Y_2O_3:Eu^{3+}$ is, except for its high cost, not far from ideal as a photoluminescent orange-red prime-color generator. What about the blue-violet, and the green, prime-colors? The writer knows of no rare earth ion, in any host crystal, which is strongly photoluminescent and emits a narrow band in the blue-violet centered at 450+5nm. Thulium 3+, in YVO_4 for example, emits near 475nm, which is too greenish. Praseodymium, even given an appropriate host crystal, would probably be too green in its emission also. However, divalent rare earth ions can emit strong bands of rather pure visible light, although interaction with the crystal environment broadens the emission band far more than is characteristic of trivalent rare earth emission. There are a number of host crystals, perhaps the best of which is strontium chlorapatite(16), for divalent europium. Its emission spectrum appears in Figure 5A. Quantum efficiency is close to 0.9, and fortunately the emission band, while not ideal, feeds into the human system with great visual efficiency. It is the best we have, at any rate. If a rare

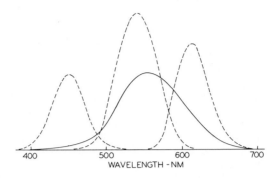

Figure 4.   The three-peaked spectral response of the human visual system, the peak responses being marked by the prime-colors: (――――) the luminous efficiecy curve upon which much of modern lighting is wrongly based.

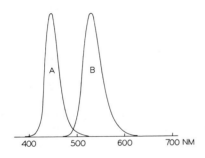

Figure 5.   The brilliant blue–violet emission of Eu^{2+} (A), and the green emission of zinc silicate activated by Mn^{2+} (B).

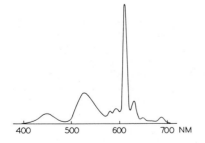

Figure 6.   The spectral power distribution of a fluorescent lamp containing two rare earth phosphors, those of Figures 1 (Curve A) and 5 (Curve A), and green-emitting zinc silicate:Mn. A closer approximation to Figure 3 is desirable.

earth-host crystal combination could be found, which concentrates
its emission more closely around 450nm, it would be welcome indeed.
    The situation in regard to the green prime-color is not as
satisfactory. Trivalent terbium, holmium and erbium have transitions in the desirable wavelength regions, but the last two have
not yet been developed in efficient photoluminescent materials,
and terbium has special problems. We need a narrow emission near
530nm or 540nm, uncontaminated with satellite emission in unwanted
regions, particularly the yellow. Terbium ions in certain crystals
make very fine phosphors(17), possibly unmatched in efficiency and
ruggedness. (The mercury arc is a small inferno, and these inorganic materials have to be robust.) But terbium always, or at
least so far, brings with it sidebands in the yellow and blue-
green. These rapidly degrade the clarity and coloration of a scene
if they are present in the white light illuminating the scene. So
we have had to stick with an old and trustworthy phosphor, zinc
silicate:Mn^{2+}, to provide our green emission(Figure 5B). It is
not, however, quite narrow enough, nor rugged enough. I would like
to take this opportunity to ask, very seriously, for any help
readers can give toward identifying an efficient pure-green-
emitting luminescent material. A new phosphor of that sort could
have a profound effect on the quality of lighting around the world.
Hopefully some one of the rare earths could help to bring this about.
    The spectral power distribution of Figure 6 is as close as
we can presently get to the ideal prime-color mixture.
    In summary, lamplight illuminates human activities, so lamp
phosphors should feed their light into the human visual system
with high visual efficiency. Rare-earth-activated phosphors tend
to produce narrow, strongly saturated, brilliantly colored lights.
It begins to appear that rare earth emission is not only useful,
but made-to-order, for the requirements of the human visual system for optimum seeing. The visual system has three well-defined
peaks of response, placed at three wavelengths unique to human
vision. When white lamplight is composed as nearly as possible of
these three pure spectral colors, and the remainder of the visible
spectrum is left as nearly empty as possible, at least four strong
positive visual effects result: The perceived brightness per watt
of lamplight exceeds that of normal illuminants by tens of percent.
The visibility of a scene per watt of lamplight increases by larger factors still. Clarity, in the sense of sharpness of detail in
a scene, is enhanced. Attractiveness of coloration, measured in
terms of what Judd called "preferred coloration", exceeds that of
daylight, which itself excels normal illuminants. The three spectral colors so important to human vision are: blue-violet near
450nm, green near 535nm, and orange-red near 615nm. The first and
last of these colored lights are fairly satisfactorily supplied
by lamp phosphors activated by europium 2+ and europium 3+,
respectively. The need for a better pure green emission is acute.

Literature Cited

1. Urbain,G.,<u>Ann.Chim.Phys.</u>,1909,<u>18</u>,294.
2. Thornton,W.A.,<u>J.Opt.Soc.Amer.</u>,1971,<u>61</u>,1155.
3. Thornton,W.A.,<u>J.Opt.Soc.Amer.</u>,1972,<u>62</u>,457.
4. Thornton,W.A.,Westinghouse <u>Engineer</u>,1972,<u>32</u>,170.
5. Thornton,W.A.,<u>J.Ill.Eng.Soc.</u>,1979,<u>8</u>,78.
6. CIE Pub.#13,E-1.3.2,1965,1st Ed.
7. Thornton,W.A.,<u>J.Ill.Eng.Soc.</u>,1974,<u>4</u>,48.
8. Aston,S.N.,Bellchambers,H.E.,<u>Lighting Res.Tech.</u>,1969,<u>1</u>,259.
9. Bellchambers,H.E.,Godby,A.C.,<u>Lighting Res.Tech.</u>,1972,<u>4</u>,104.
10. Thornton,W.A.,Chen,E.,<u>J.Ill.Eng.Soc.</u>,1978,<u>7</u>,85.
11. Thornton,W.A.,Chen,E.,Morton,E.W.,Rachko,D.,<u>J.Ill.Eng.Soc.</u>,
    (in press).
12. Thornton,W.A.,<u>J.Color Appearance</u>,1973,<u>II</u>,23.
13. Thornton,W.A.,<u>Lighting Des.Appl.</u>,1975,<u>5</u>,35.
14. Palilla,F.C.,<u>Electrochem.Tech.</u>,1968,<u>6</u>,39.
15. Blasse,G.,Bril,A.,<u>Philips Tech.Rev.</u>,1970,<u>31</u>,304.
16. Wachtel,A.,Netherlands Patent 6906724,1969.
17. McAllister,W.A.,<u>J.Electrochem.Soc.</u>,1966,<u>113</u>,226.

RECEIVED January 8, 1981.

Rare Earth X-Ray Phosphors for Medical Radiography

JACOB G. RABATIN

Quartz and Chemical Products Department, General Electric Company,
1099 Ivanhoe Road, Cleveland, OH 44110

When a uniform flux of x-ray photons passes through an object, a radiologic image is formed of the object parts. In order to be viewed, this radiologic image must be converted into an optical image by means of inorganic crystalline phosphors which are disperesed in polymeric screens. The optical image can be viewed directly by means of fluoroscopic screens. However, in general radiological practices, the optical images are recorded on films which are subsequently viewed by radiologist. Without these x-ray intensifying screens, modern radiology would be impossible. The general physical aspects of diagnostic radiology have been thoroughly covered by M. Ter-Pogossian (1).

For many years, most intensifying screens contained $CaW\bar{O}$ phosphors. After numerous improvements in $CaWO_4$ efficiencies and particle shapes, a plateau was reached for the speed of these screens in recording satisfactory radiologic images. In recent years, several new phosphors were discovered which contain rare earth elements and are considerably more efficient under x-ray excitations. These new rare earth phosphors include: $La_2O_2S:Tb$ (2), $Gd_2O_2S:Tb$ (2,3), $BaFCl:Eu$ (4,5), $LaOBr:Tm$ (7). Several physical properties of these x-ray phosphors have important effects on the final image quality as viewed by the radiologist. These physical properties include x-ray absorption, conversion efficiency, emission characteristics, absolute density, particle size and shape and refractive index. The purpose of this paper is to describe and compare these properties for several phosphors and to indicate desireable properties needed in future more ideal x-ray phosphors.

Experimental

Materials. All phosphors used in this study were prepared by solid state methods previously reported. LaOBr:Tb and LaOBr:Tm phosphors were prepared by a molten KBr flux recrystallization method (8) which gives clear, single crystal

0097-6156/81/0164-0203$05.00/0

particles that have plate-like crystal habits. Divalent europium
activated BaFCl phosphors were prepared in reducing atmospheres (4). The resulting particles are irregular in shape but
can be prepared as plates when an alkali chloride flux is used.
La_2O_2S:Tb and Gd_2O_2S:Tb were prepared by a high temperature
method involving alkali polysulfides, Na_2CO_3 and sulfer as recrystallization media. These phosphor crystals have polyhedral
shapes.

        Screen Preparations. 100 micron thick x-ray intensi-
fying screens were prepared using standard doctor blade coating
techniques. The final phosphor volume was 50% when the coatings were dried. In most instances, the phosphor suspensions
were prepared using polyvinyl butyral binders with viscosities
adjusted to 2000 centipoise for the doctor blade operation and
care was taken to avoid convection cell formation (9). A cross
section of the screen construction is shown in Figure I. The
completed screens consist of polyester (Mylar) base about 10 mil.
thick, a 50 micron thick (TiO_2 (rutile) reflector layer, a 100
micron thick phosphor layer, a 10 micron thick clear cellulose
acetate butyrate top protective layer.

        Measurements.

                Emission Spectra. High resolution emission spectra
were obtained using cathode ray excitation. For this purpose,
phosphor powders were uniformly settled on conductive glass.
The samples were excited in a demountable cathode ray apparatus with 10 kilovolts and 7 microampere energetic electrons. The
demountable apparatus was coupled to a Cary 14 spectrophoto-
meter for recording of the emission spectra.

                X-Ray Absorption Data. The x-ray absorption
data shown in Figure 2 were obtained using a computer program
based on the mass absorption coefficients, μ, total energy, as
found in the paper of Storm and Israel (10) and using the
fundamental absorption equation for x-rays (11).

$$I/I_0 = e^{-\mu\rho x} \quad (1)$$

where I_0 is the incident x-ray bean, I is the transmitted beam,
ρ is the phosphor density and x is its thickness. The computer
program includes appropriate changes in the energies of the x-
ray spectra after passage of 80 KV peak x-rays through a 10
inch human body equivalent absorption before impinging on the
x-ray screens. The thickness x was set equal to 100 microns
(typical of x-ray screens). Not included are corrections for the
escape of some secondary radiation. These corrections are difficult to make accurately (12).

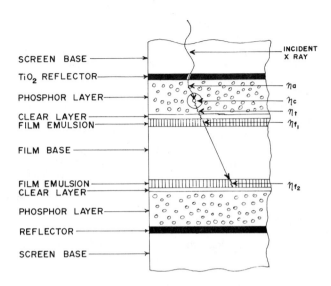

Figure 1. Cross section of x-ray screens and film assembly

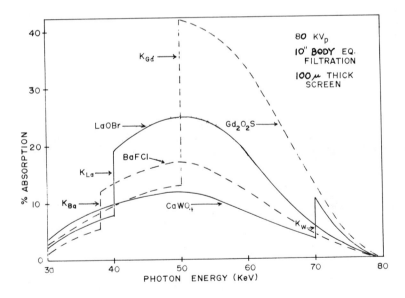

Figure 2. Relative x-ray absorptions of 100-micron thick x-ray screens using a filtered 80 KV peak x-ray beam

Relative Screen Speeds. All screen speed measurements were made at 80 KV peak x-ray beam settings using
a Faxitron x-ray apparatus for exposures. One inch aluminum
filters were used to simulate a 10 inch human body equivalent
absorption. All speed measurements were compared to commercial DuPont Par $CaWO_4$ screens whose speeds were set equal to
one using Kodak BB-54 blue medical film. For phosphors with
green emissions, green sensitive films were used including 3M
Co. brand XM green film and Kodak Co. Ortho G green film.
Relative log sensitivity curves for typical medical films are shown
in Figure 3. It should be noted that blue emitting phosphors
will expose efficiently either green or blue sensitive films. On
the other hand, green emitting phosphors with emissions above
about 480 nm have practically no effect on blue sensitive films
most commonly used in medical radiography.

Image Quality. Resolution of screens were measured at 50 KV peak x-ray exposures at film densities of 1.0
using standard lead resolution grids with sets of etched lines
about 1 line pair per mm up to 15 line pairs per mm. The
results are reported as the maximum set of line pairs resolved
per mm.

Other Measurements. Particle size distributions
were measured by the Coulter Counter method. Absolute density
measurements were made using the well known pycnometer
method.

Results and Discussions

At first glance, x-ray intensifying screens appear to perform a simple function of converting x-ray photons to light
photons which expose the film sandwiched between two screens
(See Figure 1). However, x-ray screens serve a much more
important function of faithfully converting radiologic images into
optical images which are subsequently recorded as photographic
images. These several complex processes are graphically illustrated in Figure 1 and can be described as follows. After
passing through a body part, a beam of x-ray photons contains
useful information. A small fraction, η_a, of this beam is
absorbed by the phosphor particles in the x-ray screens producing a radiologic image. A fraction of this absorbed energy
is converted into an optical image of ultraviolet – visible light
with an energy efficiency given by η_c. After multiple scattering and absorption events, a fraction, η_t, of this light reaches
the first emulsion of the double emulsion film used in medical
radiography. A major fraction, η_{f1}, of this light is absorbed
by the first silver halide emulsion which on development produces a photographic image. A significant fraction, η_{f2}, of
this light crosses over to the second emulsion and is absorbed.

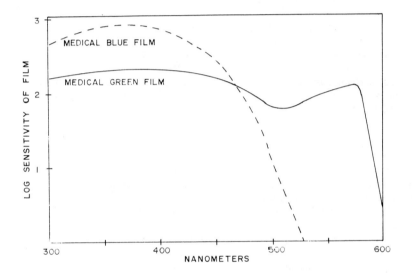

Figure 3.   Blue and green x-ray film sensitivities to ultraviolet and visible light

This cross-over phenomenon degrades the image due to spreading of the light. Other processes which significantly degrade the radiologic image include: η_c, η_t, η_{fl}, and η_{f2}.

Several attempts have been made to quantitatively account for various aspects of x-ray screen performances including; phosphor efficiencies (13, 14, 15), x-ray absorption and quantum noise (12,16,17,18), screen performance (14,16,17,18,19) and image quality (20, 21). None of these studies adequately covers the complete performance of x-ray screens or is sufficiently quantitative so that simple comparative analyses can be made of the phosphors used. In this study, primary emphasis is given to evaluation of measurable phosphor properties which contribute significantly to final screen performance regarding speed and image quality characteristics.

Intrinsic X-Ray Absorption. The maximum amount of information coded in a radiologic image is limited, in part, by the statistical fluctuations of the x-ray photons that form the radiologic image (1). These fluctuations are often referred to as "quantum noise" and as "quantum mottle" when viewed on films since the films have a grainy appearance (17). These fluctuations can be expressed as a signal to noise ratios (12).

$$\sigma = \sqrt{N} \qquad (2)$$

where N is the number of absorbed x-ray photons. According to Cleare et al (18) about 400 x-ray photons of ~70 KeV energies must be absorbed by a $CaWO_4$ screen to produce a film density of 0.6 for a 0.1 mm^2 area. Thus the signal to noise ratio is about 20. To increase the signal to noise ratio for a given screen thickness and speed, the relative x-ray absorption must be increased.

Shown in Figure 2 are the calculated absorption curves for several 100 micron thick screens using an 80 KV peak x-ray beam which has been filtered by one inch aluminum to simulate a 10 inch human body absorption. In the incident beam profile, most of the x-ray photon energies are between 40 and 50 KeV. Since these photons are more readily absorbed by body parts, more desireable contrasts result. In this regard, the K_α absorption edges of La and Ba are more useful since a greater fraction of these x-ray photons are absorbed as compared to Gd. Also for a good x-ray phosphor with high μ in this region, the phosphor should contain elements with K-edge absorption energies between about 35 and 50 KeV (Z from 55 to 65). The phosphor should have a high density of at least 6.0 which can be only achieved with cations having small ionic radii such as La and Gd. Only a small number of useful x-ray phosphors have been discovered which meet most of these criteria.

Listed in Table I are the absolute densities, relative x-ray absorptions of 80 KV peak x-rays at equal thickness, and signal to noise ratios for the radiologic images for several x-ray phosphors. The signal to noise ratios were calculated using the data of Cleare et al (18) and equation 2. As will be discussed later, these ratios will decrease as screen speeds, etc. are included.

TABLE I

Absolute Densities, Relative X-Ray Absorptions and

Radiologic Image Signal to Noise

Ratios of Several X-Ray Phosphors

Phosphor	Density	Relative X-Ray Abs.	Signal to Noise Ratio
$CaWO_4$	6.1	1.0	20
BaFCl:Eu	4.7	1.1	21
Gd_2O_2S:Tb	7.3	1.7	26
LaOBr.002Tb	6.3	1.9	28
LaOBr.003Tm	6.3	1.9	28
La_2O_2S:Tb	5.9	1.7	26

The results in Table I indicate that the radiologic image will be significantly improved by the use of rare earth phosphors as compared to $CaWO_4$. Because of its lower density, BaFCl:Eu must be used in thicker screens in order to increase x-ray absorption. In general, thicker screens have poorer resolution.

Emission Spectra. Before comparing the emission spectra of several important x-ray phosphors, it is useful to examine briefly the interaction of the phosphor emission with x-ray films. For many years, blue sensitive x-ray films have been developed to be most sensitive to the ultraviolet-blue emissions of phosphors such as $CaWO_4$. Since AgBr has high intrinsic absorption in this region, no special efforts were needed to improve light absorption. Film speeds were adjusted primarily by such parameters as grain size of AgBr and other emulsion properties. In order to use Gd_2O_2S:Tb and La_2O_2S:Tb phosphors, green sensitive x-ray films were developed using a dye-AgBr coupled system. Figure 3 shows typical relative sensitivities of blue and green x-ray films. Green films have no advantages over blue film in speed or resolution. Green films require special safe lights in the dark rooms. It should be noted that blue emitting phosphors will also expose green film.

The emission spectra shown in Figures 4 through 7 were

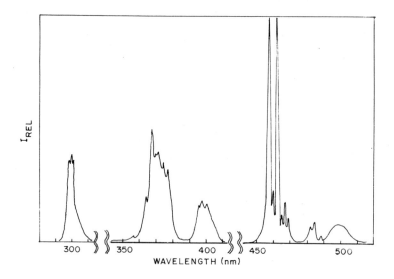

Figure 4.   Emission spectrum of LaOBr.003Tm under CR excitation

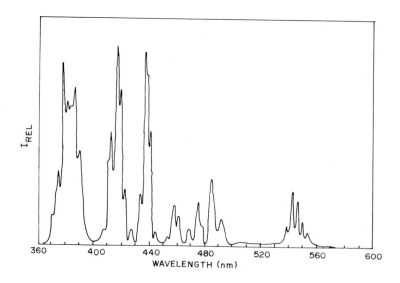

Figure 5.   Emission spectrum of LaOBr.002Tb under CR excitation

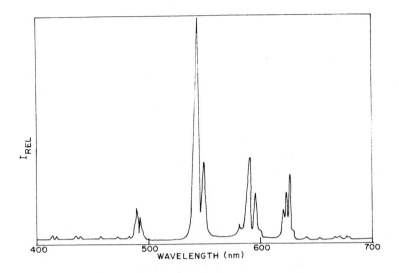

Figure 6.   Emission spectrum of GD$_2$O$_2$S.005Tb under CR excitation

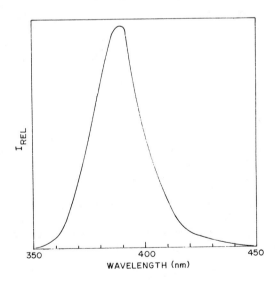

Figure 7.   Emission spectrum of BaFCl.05Eu under CR excitation

obtained using cathode ray excitations which give emission spectra practically identical to those when x-ray excitations are used (15). Figure 4 shows a typical emission spectrum for LaOBr.003Tm (22). The principal emissions are below 400 nm where the intrinsic film absorptions are greatest, less unsharpness occurs due to less cross over (η_{f2} in Figure I). Since significant emissions also occur at 460 and 500 nm, this phosphor is also useful with green sensitive films with speeds comparable to Gd_2O_2S:Tb green screens such as Kodak Lanex. LaOBr.003Tm phosphors are currently being used in DuPont Co. Quanta III screens and Ilford Ltd. Rapide screens.

Shown in Figure 5 is the emission spectrum for LaOBr.002Tb (23). At these terbium concentrations, the principal emissions occur at 380, 415 and 440 nm which can be used with blue sensitive films. This phosphor is being used in Agfa-Gevaert Co. MR screens, in Picker Spectra screens and in the General Electric Co. Blue Max screens. At higher terbium concentrations, the emission spectra emit predominantly green at 542 nm with efficiencies of about 20% comparable to ZnCdS:Ag phosphors (24). These green emitting phosphors are suitable for green sensitive films.

Figure 6 shows the emission spectrum for Gd_2O_2S.005Tb. The principal emissions are at 542 nm. At lower Tb concentrations, some emissions will occur at 380, 415 and 440 nm. However, the phosphor efficiency decreases. This phosphor is useful with green sensitive films and is being used in Kodak Co. Lanex green screens and in 3 M Co. Trimax green screens.

Shown in Figure 7 is the emission spectrum for BaFCl.05Eu. The divalent europium emission is a broad band peaking at about 380 nm. This phosphor is used in DuPont Co. Quanta II blue screens and is useful with blue film only.

To be used in x-ray intensifying screens, rare earth phosphors must also have high conversion efficiencies (η_c in Figure 1) in addition to high intrinsic absorptions of x-rays and suitable emission characteristics. The several rare earth phosphors listed in Table I have conversion efficiencies from about 10% for La_2O_2S:Tb to about 20% for LaOBr:Tb (5, 26, 24) as compared to about 6% for $CaWO_4$.

Screen-Film Systems. According to Ludwig (5), crucial to the application of x-ray phosphors for intensifying screens is the efficiency with which the incident x-ray energy is converted to useful light energy as given by the expression:

$$\eta = \eta_a \, \eta_c \, \eta_t \qquad (3)$$

where η_t is the efficiency with which the light energy is transmitted through the screen to the film. The processes η_a and η_c have been discussed. The transmission, scattering and absorption processes, η_t, are extremely complex involving such parameters as particle size, particle shape, refractive index, particle dispersion and structure mottle (18, 25). As indicated earlier, these processes degrade the quality of the original radiographic image. Presently no measurements can be made which account for these processes individually. Comparisons using modulation transfer function measurements involve all image degrading processes (1, 21).

Table II lists several physical properties of various phosphors as compared to those for an ideal phosphor. The refractive index should be fairly low so that in a polymeric system (polymer RI $\sim$ 1.5) the number of scattering phenomena are decreased. In this respect, BaFCl:Eu is best. To reduce structure mottle and improve phosphor packing, spherical or polyhedral shaped particles are most desireable. Further, to improve phosphor packing, narrow particle distributions are best. Finally, average particle sizes between 5 and 10μ give best image quality. Clearly none of the phosphors meet all of these criteria. In addition to the above, other factors also affect image quality including coating operations (25).

TABLE II

Physical Properties of Various X-Ray Phosphors

Phosphor	Refractive Index	Particle Shape	Avg Particle Diameter	Particle Distribution
Ideal	1.6 1.7	Polyhedral, Spheres	5–10μ	Narrow
BaFCl:Eu	1.7	Irregular- Plates	10–15μ	Broad
Gd_2O_2S:Tb	1.8	Polyhedral	8–15μ	Broad
LaOBr:Tb	2.0	Plates	3–10μ	Narrow
LaOBr:Tm	2.0	Plates	3–10μ	Narrow
$CaWO_4$	1.9	Polyhedral	5–10μ	Broad

The overall efficiency of given x-ray screen is given by equation 3. Screen speed, however, also depends on the film interaction steps n_{t1} and n_{t2} shown in Figure 1. In practice it is best to determine the overall speed, S, of the screen-film system (26) using the expression:

$$S = S_s \cdot S_f \cdot R \qquad (4)$$

where S_s is relative screen speed, S_f is relative film speed, and R is a correction factor.

In Table III, for comparative purposes, DuPont Par screen speeds were set equal to 1 and Kodak Blue Brand BB-54 film was set equal to 1.   Table III also lists the resolution of various experimental 100 micron thick screen pairs when the indicated average particle diameter (APD) were used.   The radiologic signal to noise ratios were calculated using the following expression which takes in to account the reduced x-ray absorption required because of the screen speed for equal thickness screens.

$$\sigma = \sqrt{400 \; \eta_a \; \frac{S}{S_1}} \qquad (5)$$

where η_a is the relative x-ray absorption (Table I), S is speed of Par screen set equal to one, S_1 is speed of experimental screen.

The results in Table III indicate that for screens of equal thickness, LaOBr:Tb screens have the highest speed.   The LaOBr screens have the best resolution partly due to the smaller particle size of the phosphors.   It was not possible to prepare all phosphors with about the same particle size.   Clearly, at the speeds indicated, all rare earth phosphors have lower signal to noise ratios since fewer x-ray photons are required to obtain the same film exposures as compared to $CaWO_4$ Par screens.

TABLE III

Speed, Resolution and Radiologic

Noise of Various Experimental Screens

	Particle Size APD	Relative Blue Film	Speeds Green Film	Resolution, Line Pairs Per mm	Signal to Noise Ratio
$CaWO_4$(Par)	5	1.0	–	7.2	20
BaFCl:Eu	12	3.4	2.5	5.4	11
Gd_2O_2S:Tb	7	–	4.2	5.6	13
La_2O_2S:Tb	9	–	3.0	5.8	15
LaOBr:Tm	4	4.0	4.2	7.0	14
LaOBr:Tb	4	5.0	4.0	7.0	12

No easy comparisons can be made of commercial screens regarding quantum mottle, resolution and speed since different screen constructions are used and particle sizes differ. Other factors cannot be easily compared. The intent of the previous discussions was to compare several physical properties of rare earth x-ray phosphors which have an important effect on final image quality. Other benefits of rare earth screens include:

1. Reduced patient exposure.
2. Reduced motion unsharpness (27).
3. Reduced focal spot size of x-ray generators.
4. Longer life of x-ray tubes (28).
5. Better use of lower powered generators (29).
6. Fewer retakes (28).

The potential market for rare earth phosphor is at least 100,000 kilo annually.

Rare Earth Phosphors for Color Contrast Radiography. At present all radiological examinations use black and white films to record the images. Studies by Prins and coworkers (30) have clearly demonstrated that colored radiographs contain more information than conventional black and white radiographs. The underlying reasons for these advantages are that black and white image contrasts are limited to differences in shades of grey. On the other hand, colored images can have variations in hue, brightness and color saturation allowing for greater image contrasts. The main problems regarding the use of color radiography center on development of suitable fast color films with associated development techniques and on the availability of efficient x-ray phosphors which have different emission colors. For such developments to take place requires additional studies.

A recent study by the author (31) indicates that by the appropriate choice of two or more x-ray phosphors mixed in suitable ratios will give a desired color when excited by x-rays. If one of these phosphors had Gd and the others contain La, Ba or lower Z elements (See Figure 2), then, due to the presence of different absorption edges, unbalancing of the color will occur as the x-rays are differentially absorbed by body parts. As the x-ray energy profile is hardened the Gd containing phosphor will emit a greater proportion of light compared to the phosphors containing lower Z elements. This unbalancing of color can be further enhanced by use of body contrast media such as $BaSO_4$ and potassium iodide solutions. When suitably coupled with appropriate x-ray color films, these color unbalancings will show changes in hue, color saturation and brightness. Table IV lists several rare earth x-ray phosphors suitable for this purpose. Color points and emission colors under 90 KVp x-ray excitation are also listed. It should be noted that for blue colors ultraviolet emitting phosphors are suitable and will expose the blue emulsion of color film.

TABLE IV

Colors and Color Points of
Rare Earth X-Ray Phosphors
Under 90 KV Peak X-Ray Excitations

Phosphor	Colors	Color Prints	
		X	Y
Y_2O_3:Eu	Red	.655	.355
Y_2O_2S:Tb	Green	.336	.536
LaOBr.05Tb	Green	.350	.533
LaOBr.005Dy	Yellow	.430	.466
LaOBr.005Sm	Orange	.546	.384
Gd_2O_3:Eu	Red	.655	.355
Gd_2O_2S:Tb	Green	.336	.536
BaFCl:Eu	for Blue	Near UV	Near UV
LaOBr.003Tm	for Blue	Near UV	Near UV

Summary and Conclusions

The desireable phosphor properties which contribute significantly to final speed and image quality include the following (Using Figure 1 as reference).

Intrinsic X-Ray Absorption, η_a.

The desireable characteristics are high absolute densities and atomic numbers from about 55-65 to reduce quantum noise.

Emission Characteristics.

The conversion efficiencies, η_c, should be at least 15%. The preferred emission spectra are in the near ultraviolet to match the spectral sensitivity of silver halide emulsions, η_{f1}, and to reduce cross over, η_{f2}.

Scattering and Transmission Characteristics, η_t.

The phosphors should possess low refractive indices to reduce scattering. Polyhedral shapes promote better packing and reduced structure mottle.

At present only rare earth x-ray phosphors meet most of these characteristics. Rare earth phosphors are also useful for color contrast radiography.

Acknowledgments

The author is especially grateful to Robert Evans for making numerous preparations, measurements and related studies.

References

1. Ter-Pogossian, M.M. "The Physical Aspects of Diagnostic Radiology". Harper and Row Publishers: New York, 1967.

2. Alves, R.V.; Buchanan, R.A. IEEE Trans. Nuc. Sci., 1972, 19, 415.

3. Buchanan, R.A., Finkelstein, S.I., Wickersheim, K.A., Radiology, 1972, 105, 185-190.

4. Chenot, D.F. Canadian Pat. 896453, 1972.

5. Stevels, A.L.N., Pingault, F., Phillips Res. Repts., 1975, 30, 277.

6. Rabatin, J.G., U.S. Pat. 3,617,743, 1971.

7. Rabatin, J.G., U.S. Pat. 3,795,814, 1974.

8. Rabatin, J.G., U.S. Pat. 3,591,516, 1971.

9. Rabatin, J.G., Extended Abstract, #220, Electrochemical Meeting, May 1979.

10. Storm, E., Irael, H.I., Report LA3753 Los Alamos Scientific Lab., Univ. of Calif., 1967.

11. Clark, G. "The Encyclopedia of X-Rays and Gamma Rays", Reinhold Publishing Corp., New York, 1963, 9.

12.   Swank, R.B., J. Appl. Phys. 1973, 44, 4199.

13.   Coltman., J.W., Ebbighausen, E.G., Altar, W.J.,
J. Appl. Phys., 1947, 18, 530.

14.   Grum, F., Costa, L.F., Donavan, J.L. J. Opt. Soc. Am.,
1969, 59, 848.

15.   Ludwig, G.W., J. Electrochem. So., 1971, 118, 1152.

16.   Venema, H.W., Radiology, 1979, 130, 765.

17.   Lubberts, G., J. Opt. Soc. Am., 1968, 58, 1475.

18.   Cleare, H.M., Splettstosser, H.R., Seemann, H.E.,
Am. J. Roent. And Radium, 1962, 88, 168.

19.   Herz, R.H., Bri. J. Appl. Phys., 1956, 7, 182.

20.   Klasens, H.A., Philips Res. Rep., 1947, 2, 68.

21.   Morlotti, R., J. Photo. Sci., 1975, 23, 181.

22.   Rabatin, J.G., Extended Abstract #198, The Electro-
chemical Society Meeting, May 1975.

23.   Rabatin, J.G., Extended Abstract #102, The Electro-
chemical Society Meeting, May 1974.

24.   Ludwig, G.W., Kingsley, J.D., J. Electrochem. Soc.,
1970, 117, 348.

25.   Rabatin, J.G., Extended Abstract #220, The Electro-
chemical Society Meeting, May 1979.

26.   Moser, E.S., Holland, R.S., SPIE, 1975, 56, 26.

27.   Prasad, S., Marc Edwards, F., Hendel, W.R., Radiology,
1977, 123, 763.

28.   Thompson, T.T, Radford, E.L., Kirby, C.C., Applied
Radiology, 1977 6, 71.

29.   Rucker, J.L., Applied Radiology, 1980, 9, 57.

30.   Prins, H.R., Katz, J.L., Billmeyer, F.W., Am. J. of
Roent., 1966, 98, 966.

31.   Rabatin, J.G., Extended Abstract #332, The Electro-
chemical Society Meeting, May 1978.

RECEIVED December 29, 1980.

Bubble Domain Memory Materials

J. W. NIELSEN

Bell Laboratories, Murray Hill, NJ 07974

The use of cylindrical domains to store information in a
sheet of magnetized material was first reported by Bobeck in
1967 (1). He observed that cylindrical domains in a magnetized
plate of material were stable over a convenient range of bias
field and could be readily moved about in the plate under the
influence of a field gradient. Bobeck called the domains "bubble"
domains because their motion in a perturbing field looked much
like the motion of bubbles on the surface of a liquid. Since
Bobeck's discovery, development of bubble domain memories has
been carried on in many laboratories all over the world, and
production of bubble domain memories is underway at a few
companies. As a result of all the work on bubble domain memories,
and materials for them, a voluminous literature has been
generated (2-10). Here we have space only to outline briefly
the present state of bubble domain memory materials development.
The reader may use the references to obtain a more detailed
account of memory design and materials selection.

Material Requirements

A bubble domain is most stable under bias when its diameter
is approximately equal to, or slightly more than, the thickness
of the magnetic sheet in which it is situated. Since economical
packing densities require domain diameters of three micrometers
or less, it is clear that the magnetic medium in a bubble domain
memory must be a thin film supported by a substrate. A major
breakthrough in memory development was the discovery by Bobeck
et al (11) that many rare earth garnet crystals grown from fluxes
possess sufficient uniaxial anisotropy to maintain bubble domain
stability. This was surprising since rare earth magnetic garnets,
like the parent compound yttrium-iron-garnet, $Y_3Fe_5O_{12}$, are
cubic, and it was soon established that the anisotropy was
induced during growth of the crystals.

Following the important discovery of anisotropy, Shick et al (12), and Levinstein et al (13), showed that films of magnetic garnets could be readily deposited by liquid phase epitaxy from molten PbO-B$_2$O$_3$ solutions onto gadolinium gallium garnet, Gd$_3$Ga$_5$O$_{12}$, (GGG) substrates.

There followed many studies on a large number of garnet compositions in the search for the optimum bubble domain material (14). It soon became apparent that properties desired in the garnet for best device performance, i.e., high domain mobility, low coercivity, high anisotropy and high bubble stability required a carefully designed compromise in the selection of garnet substituents. For example, spherical ions in the garnet lead to high domain mobility and low coercivity, but low anisotropy and stability. Non-spherical ions, on the other hand, lead to high anisotropy and stability but at the same time yield low mobility and high coercivity. It is testimony to the great versatility of the garnet system that substituted garnets could be designed that not only met the magnetic requirements for bubble domain memories but matched the lattice parameter of the most useful substrate, GGG, as well (15). A typical film composition for 3µm diameter bubble is:

$$Y_{1.25} \, Lu_{0.45} \, Sm_{0.4} \, Ca_{0.9} \, Fe_{4.1} \, Ge_{0.9} \, O_{12}.$$

Substrate Preparation

It is fortunate that the non magnetic garnet, GGG, with a lattice parameter (12.383A) most nearly matching those of useful magnetic garnets, is also one of the easiest garnet crystals to grow. GGG melts congruently at 1740°C and is grown by the well known Czochralski, or pulling technique. The crystals are grown from melts contained in iridium crucibles under an atmosphere of N$_2$ containing 2% O$_2$ (16,17). Crystals weighing up to 10 kg. with diameters of 75 mm are grown routinely (18).

Substrates are prepared for film deposition from the crystals by sawing, lapping and polishing using techniques similar to those used in the semiconductor industry.

Liquid Phase Epitaxy (LPE) Garnets

Magnetic garnet films are deposited on GGG substrates from solutions of the garnet oxides dissolved in PbO-B$_2$O$_3$ melts. The dipping technique is used (13), and because of the great stability of the solutions in the supersaturated state, large numbers of substrates, up to 30 at a time (19), can be dipped simultaneously under nearly isothermal conditions.

Although the molten salt solutions are extremely complex in that they may contain up to nine components, they behave in a straightforward manner almost exactly like the pseudo-ternary Y$_2$O$_3$ - Fe$_2$O$_3$ - PbO (20). This simplification permits great flexibility in adjusting melt compositions to yield garnet films meeting varied device specifications. Temperatures for garnet LPE may range from 750° to 1100°C, but most experiments, and production runs, are carried out near 950°C at supercoolings of 10° - 40°C.

Rare Earth Use in Bubble Domain Memories

Although the garnet compositions used in memories contain rare earths, the total rare earth use in magnetic films is not sufficient to make much impact on the rare earth market. The use of gadolinium oxide in substrate crystals is another matter. It has been estimated that by 1990 the annual use of Gd_2O_3 for GGG substrates will reach 40 metric tons, about twice the present rate (21).

Conclusion

The development of the bubble domain memory has been remarkable in that since the discovery of the growth induced anisotropy in garnets, problems connected with materials have been relatively few and not too difficult to solve. A major reason is that the different sizes and magnetic properties of the rare earths offer a wide range of choices for the materials designer.

The major problem still to be solved is development of a high speed material with bubble diameters of the order one micrometer. In view of the success in developing garnet materials so far, we can be optimistic about the solution of the small bubble problem (22, 23, 24, 25).

Literature Cited

1. Bobeck, A. H. Bell Syst. Tech. J., 1967, 46, 1901-25.
2. Smith, A. B. "Bubble Domain Memory Devices"; Artech House: Denham, Mass., 1973; p. 258.
3. O'Dell, T. H. "Magnetic Bubbles"; Macmillan: London, 1974; p. 159.
4. Bobeck, A. H.; Della Torre, E. "Magnetic Bubbles"; North-Holland: Amsterdam, 1975; p. 222.
5. Chang, H. "Magnetic Bubble Technology"; IEEE Press: New York, 1975; p. 699.
6. Bobeck, A. H.; Scovil, H. E. D. Sci. Am., 1971, 224(6), 78-90.
7. Bobeck, A. H.; Bonyhard, P. I.; Geusic, J. E. Proc. IEEE, 1975, 63, 1176.
8. Van Uitert, L. G.; Bonner, W. A.; Grodkiewicz, W. H.; Pictroski, L.; Zydzik, G. J. Mater. Res. Bull., 1970, 5, 825-35.
9. Nielsen, J. W. IEEE Trans. Magnetics, 1976, MAG-12, 327-45.

10. Nielsen, J. W. Am. Rev. Mater. Sci., 1979, 9, 87–121.
11. Bobeck, A. H.; Spencer, E. G.; Van Uitert, L. G.; Abrahams, S. C.; Barns, R. L.; Grodkiewicz, W. H.; Sherwood, R. C.; Schmidt, P. H.; Smith, D. H.; Walters, E. M. Appl. Phys. Lett., 1970, 17, 131–34.
12. Shick, L. K.; Nielsen, J. W.; Bobeck, A. H.; Kurtzig, A. J.; Michaelis, P. C.; Reekstin, J. P. Appl. Phys. Lett., 1971, 18, 89–91.
13. Levinstein, H. J.; Licht, S. J.; Landorf, R. W.; Blank, S. L. Appl. Phys. Lett., 1972, 19, 486–88.
14. See in particular references 9 and 10.
15. Nielsen, J. W.; Blank, S. L.; Smith, D. H.; Vella-Colerio, G. P.; Hagedorn, F. B.; Barns, R. L.; Biolsi, W. A. J. Electron Mater., 1974, 3, 693–707.
16. Brandle, C. D.; Valentino, A. J. J. Cryst. Growth, 1972, 12, 3–8.
17. Brandle, C. D.; Miller, D. C.; Nielsen, J. W. See Ref. 16, 1972, 195–200.
18. Brandle, C. D. "Crystal Growth, a Tutorial Approach"; Bardsley, W.; Hurle, D. T. J.; Mullin, J. B., Eds. North Holland: Amsterdam, 1979; p. 189–214.
19. Blank, S. L.; Licht, S. J. presented at INTERMAG, Boston, MA, March, 1980.
20. Blank, S. L.; Nielsen, J. W. J. Cryst. Growth, 1972, 17, 302–11.
21. Arai, Shigeru presented at the First International Conference on Magnetic Bubble Materials, Santa Barbara, CA, January, 1980.
22. Hu, H. L.; Hatzakis, M.; Geiss, E. A.; Plaskett, T. S. Shift Registers with Submicron Magnetic Bubbles on Epitaxial Garnet Films. Presented at Intermag, Washington, D.C. See also Abstr. 26.5 in Abstr. Dig. for the same conference, 1973.
23. Giess, E. A.; Davies, J. W.; Guerci, C. F.; Hu, H. L. Mater. Res. Bull., 1975, 10, 355–62.
24. Carlo, J. T.; Bullock, D. C.; Johnson, R. E.; Parker, S. G. AIP Conf. Proc., 1976, 29, 105–7.
25. Yamaguchi, K.; Inoue, H.; Asama, K. AIP Conf. Proc., 1976, 34, 160–62.

RECEIVED May 7, 1981.

Applications for Rechargeable Metal Hydrides

E. L. HUSTON
Ergenics Division MPD Technology, 681 Lawlins Road, Wyckoff, NJ 07481

J. J. SHERIDAN III
Air Products and Chemicals, Incorporated, Corporate Research and Development
Department, Allentown, PA 18105

Traditionally, hydrogen has been stored, transported and
used in the form of compressed gas or cryogenic liquid. Rechargeable metal hydrides have been proposed as an alternative solid
state storage method. A dynamic research community has assembled
to explore the scientific basis and evaluate the technology of
this hydrogen-metal reaction (1-4). Metal hydride topics have
been discussed at each of the World Hydrogen Energy Conferences
(1976 Miami, 1978 Zurich, 1980 Tokyo) and last year's ACS meeting
in Hawaii. The International Symposium on Hydrides for Energy
Storage - Geilo, Norway, August 1977 was attended by over 70
researchers. It's successor, the International Symposium on the
Properties and Applications of Metal Hydrides - Colorado Springs,
April 1980, had over 225 attendees. Approximately 35% of these
participants represented industrial organizations. A third
meeting of the metal hydride community is scheduled for Japan in
1982.
    Although the fundamental properties of metal hydride systems
are still under intensive study, increased emphasis is being
placed on developing the known applications for reversible metal
hydrides, while the search for new applications continues. In
this paper, we will summarize the current development status of
a few selected applications.

Chemical and Thermodynamic Fundamentals

Many metals, alloys and intermetallic compounds (Me) react
reversibly with gaseous H_2 to form a metal hydride, MeH_x, at
practical temperatures and pressures. This simple reaction,
neglecting the solid solution phase, may be written as:

$$Me + \frac{x}{2} H_2 \rightleftarrows MeH_x. \qquad (Eq. 1)$$

Absorption (→) and desorption (←) properties of these
reversible metal hydrides are determined from pressure composition isotherms (P-C-T)—a schematic of which is shown in Figure 1.

0097-6156/81/0164-0223$07.25/0

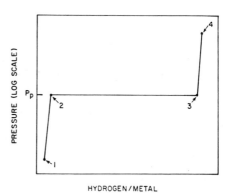

Figure 1. Ideal absorption and desorp-
tion isotherm for a metal–hydrogen sys-
tem (1)

American Chemical Society

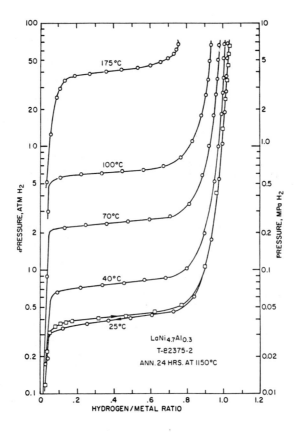

Journal of Less-Common Metals

Figure 2. Static hydrogen absorption/desorption isotherms for HY-STOR Alloy
207 (LaNi$_{4.7}$Al$_{0.3}$) (2)

Starting from point 1, a small amount of hydrogen goes into solution in the metal phase as the H_2 pressure increases. At point 2, the hydriding reaction begins (Eq. 1) and H_2 is absorbed at nearly constant pressure. This pressure P_p is termed the "plateau pressure" and corresponds to a two-phase mixture of metal, Me, and metal hydride, MeH_x. At point 3, the metal has been completely converted to the hydride phase. Further increases in H_2 pressure (point 4) result in only a small addition of hydrogen in solution in the hydride phase. In principle this curve is reversible. Extraction of H_2 from the gas phase results in the dissociation of the hydride phase in an attempt to maintain the equilibrium plateau pressure.

Isotherms for an actual system are shown in Figure 2. The alloy has the chemical composition $LaNi_{4.7}Al_{0.3}$ and is manufactured and marketed by Ergenics as HY-STOR Alloy 207. Compared to the ideal curve (Figure 1), the plateau is slightly sloped, the plateau limits are not as clearly defined and there is a measurable pressure hysteresis between absorption and desorption.

Figure 2 also shows a strong temperature dependence for the plateau pressure. This is an important consequence of the heat of reaction, ΔH, associated with Eq. 1. Hydrogen absorption ($\rightarrow$) is exothermic and desorption ($\leftarrow$) endothermic. The plateau pressure is related to the absolute temperature, T, by the familiar Van't Hoff equation:

$$\ln P_p = \frac{2}{x}\frac{\Delta H}{RT} + B \qquad\qquad (\text{Eq. 2})$$

where x is defined in Eq. 1, ΔH is the enthalpy change of the reaction, R is the gas constant, and B is a constant related to the entropy change of the reaction. Thus, from a series of experimental isotherms (Figure 2) a plot of $\ln P_p$ vs 1/T can be constructed and the value of ΔH is determined from the slope.

Van't Hoff plots for a number of reversible metal hydrides are given in Figure 3. The chemical symbol M denotes mischmetal which is a mixture of rare earth metals. The usual mischmetal contains 48-50% Ce, 32-34% La, 13-14% Nd, 4-5% Pr, and 1.5% other rare earth metals. The chemical formula labeling each curve specifies the hydrogen/metal atom ratio for each P_p value. The heat of reaction for the $LaNi_{4.7}Al_{0.3}$ alloy shown in Figure 2 is -8.1kcal/mole H_2. This is the heat generated during the hydriding reaction (absorption) and must be supplied during desorption. The magnitude of this heat is only 15% of the lower heating value of the contained hydrogen and can be supplied from "low grade" sources. Waste heat at 70 °C would dissociate $LaNi_{4.7}Al_{0.3}H_6$ and provide H_2 at approximately 2 atm absolute.

There are a number of engineering properties relating to practical applications of hydrides; hysteresis, reversible capacity, decrepitation, activation, reaction kinetics, impurity tolerances, chemical stability, heat transfer, safety, cost and

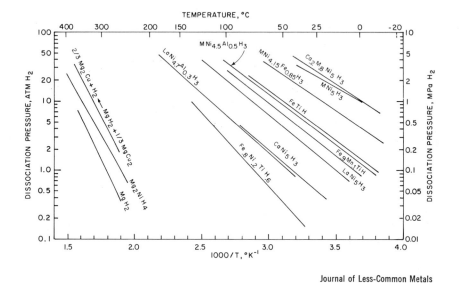

Figure 3.   Van't Hoff plots (desorption) for various hydrides (2)

availability. These properties have been discussed extensively
by others (1, 2, 5, 6, 7) and will not be mentioned further
unless critical to the understanding of a particular application.

Hydrogen Storage

Virtually all applications for reversible metal hydrides
involve the storage, at least temporarily, of hydrogen as a
metal hydride. As it turns out, solid-state storage of hydrogen
offers advantages in volume, weight, pressure, energy savings
and safety over cryogenic and compressed gas storage. Small hydride storage units are commercially available and their wide-
spread use depends upon identification of applications where
these advantages can be translated into cost/performance benefits.

A comparison of hydrogen storage parameters for cryogenic,
compressed gas (200 atm) and several hydrides is made in Table I.
Storage pressure is much lower for metal hydrides and liquid
hydrogen. Thus these storage vessels can be of lighter construction. In practice, hydride storage systems should be designed
for gas pressures several times (perhaps 2-5) the plateau pressure to allow for rapid charging and ambient temperature changes.

The high volumetric packing density for the hydrides is
evident in Table I. Over three times as much hydrogen can be
stored per unit volume with hydrides than for compressed gas at
200 atm. The volumetric density of the hydrides shown approaches
that of liquid hydrogen. This is particularly striking since the
density calculation includes a 50% void volume for the hydride
storage container and, therefore, represents the volumetric
density for practical hydride storage devices. Void spaces are
required because of the particulate nature of the metal hydride
and also to accommodate the volume expansion accompanying hydride
formation.

Reversible metal hydrides are comparable with conventional
storage methods on a weight basis. Cryogenic containers for
liquid hydrogen reduce the hydrogen capacity to about 5% of the
system weight. A standard 1A Mathieson hydrogen cylinder, weighs
135 lbs and contains only 0.83% hydrogen by weight. For tube-
trailer cylinders, hydrogen capacity is increased to about 1.3%
by weight. The values quoted in Table I for hydride storage include an allowance (25% of the hydride weight) for the container.
Thus the FeTi and LaNi5 type storage systems are comparable to
200 atm compressed gas storage while the Mg systems compare with
liquid H_2 but must be heated to about 300 $^{\circ}C$ to increase the
hydrogen pressure to one atmosphere for convenient desorption.

The fact that the hydride storage can be done at modest
pressure is an obvious safety advantage. In the event of container rupture, only a modest amount of gaseous hydrogen is
released. The bulk of the hydrogen is contained as an endothermic reactant. Rupture tests of hydride cylinders (8, 9) have
shown an initial flash followed by a low flame as frost forms on
the container walls.

TABLE I – COMPARISON OF STORAGE PARAMETERS FOR SEVERAL MODES OF HYDROGEN STORAGE

		Storage Parameters	
H_2 Storage Mode	Plateau Pressure (atm @ 25°C)	Reversible* (wt %)	Volumetric** SCF H_2 ft3 container
Liquid H_2	(~1)	5.3	850
Compressed H_2	(200)	1.3	205
FeTi	4.7	1.4	550
LaNi5	1.7	1.1	755
V	2.5	0.9	620
Mg	0.01	5.6	670
Mg2.4Ni	0.01	3.1	600

  * Assumes container is 25% of hydride weight

 ** Assumes 50% void space in hydride containers

A hydride storage unit manufactured by Laboratory Data Control under the trade name H_2YCELL is shown in Figure 4. This unit contains 8 ft^3 of hydrogen as $LaNi_5H_6$. It is electrically heated and regulated to deliver hydrogen at 215 psia at a rate of 1 SCFH. The H_2YCELL can be recharged from a low pressure electrolyzer. It is being marketed for use with gas chromatography equipment in analytic laboratories and hospitals.

A larger unit manufactured by Ergenics is shown in Figure 5. This unit contains 90 SCF of hydrogen and is available with a variety of reversible metal hydrides depending upon the pressure requirements of the application. The hydride is contained in 1" diameter capsules to reduce the tendancy for hydride packing. Hydrogen charging curves for a unit containing HY-STOR 209 $MNi_{4.15}Fe_{0.85}$ are shown in Figure 6. The heat transfer media has a pronounced influence on the charging rate. With forced air cooling, the unit can be fully recharged in about 100 minutes. Discharge curves are shown for a flow rate of 28 liter per minute (1SCFM) in Figure 7. Heat transfer by still air limits desorption after about 20% of the hydrogen is discharged. However, with forced air across the container tubes, a constant desorption rate is maintained until the hydride is exhausted. The pressure inside the container during desorption is shown in Figure 8. The poor heat transfer properties of still air allows the heat of desorption to cool the metal hydrides and hence reduce the hydride plateau pressure so that only very low hydrogen flow rates can be maintained. In fact, an ice film formed on the container during this test to further aggrevate the heat transfer.

The Ergenics unit is modular in construction and portable. Applications include storage for fuel cells and electrolyzers as well as hydride modules for compressors and heat pumps.

Two factors currently limit reversible metal hydride storage applications: cost and weight. The relatively high cost of the elemental constituents for the hydriding alloys (Ni, $3.45/lb; Ti, $8-10/lb; mischmetal, $5/lb) set a cost which cannot be reduced by existing metallurgical practices. Magnesium-based hydriding alloys are less expensive but are presently limited to high temperature (~300 $^{\circ}C$) operation. Because of the materials costs, small storage units or systems that are cycled rapidly to increase utilization are favored. Weight is also a factor for most mobile storage applications. Although many demonstration vehicles have been fielded with hydrogen internal combustion engines fueled by hydride storage systems, the fuel system weight relative to liquid fuels is not impressive. Comparisons with electrics are much more favorable. Development work today is focused on fleet vehicles with specialized applications (e.g. forklifts, mine vehicles, downtown buses, etc.).

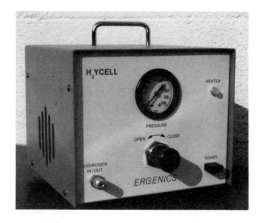

Figure 4. H₂YCELL hydride storage unit manufactured by Laboratory Data Control

Figure 5.   Hydride storage unit (90 SCF) manufactured by Ergenics

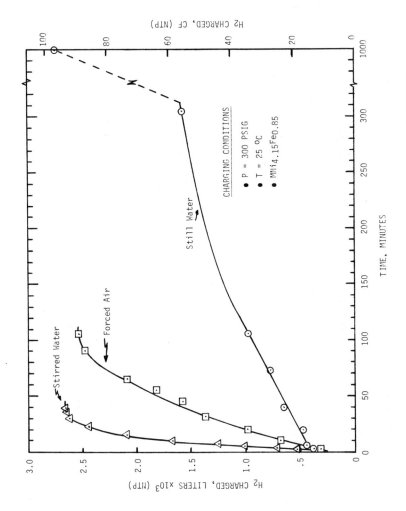

Figure 6. Hydrogen charging curve for Ergenics storage unit (90 SCF)

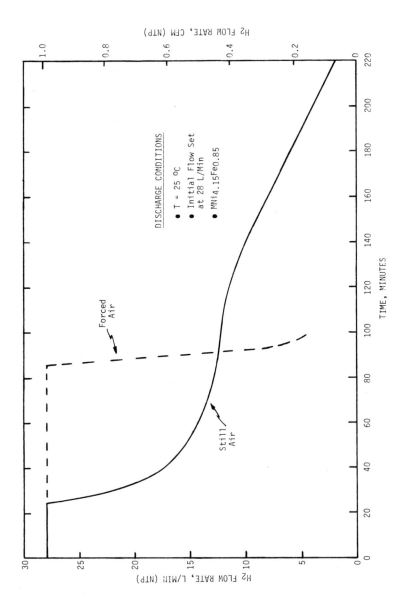

Figure 7. Hydrogen discharge curves (1 SCFM) for Ergenics storage unit (90 SCF)

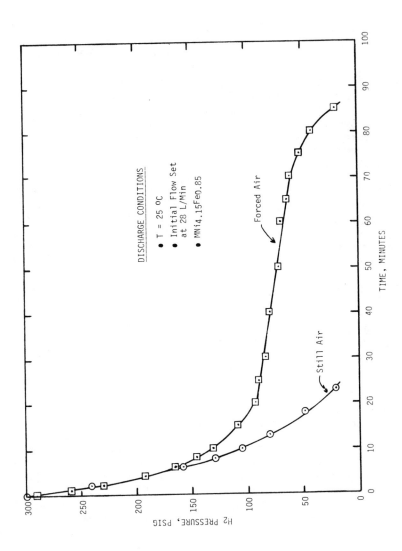

Figure 8.   Hydrogen discharge pressure for Ergenics storage unit (90 SCF)

Hydrogen Separations

During the past two years, the Ergenics Division of MPD Technology and Air Products have been engaged in a joint venture R&D program to develop hydrogen recovery processes for treating industrial off-gas streams based on the unique hydrogen absorption properties of metal hydrides.

Currently, large volumes of off-gas hydrogen are either flared, burned as fuel, or routed to secondary operations within the chemical and petroleum refining industries. Such off-gas streams represent a potentially significant source of hydrogen that, if economically recoverable, could partially satisfy the near term (1988-1990) hydrogen supply problems in the U.S.

Metal Hydride Absorption Process. Basically, the metal hydride process consists of two steps: (1) hydrogen absorption, and (2) hydrogen desorption. The process is carried out in a packed-bed containing the hydride former (absorbent). During absorption, the hydrogen partial pressure of the feed stream must be higher than the hydrogen plateau pressure for the hydride former to enable absorption of the hydrogen by the bed. The absorbed hydrogen is then recovered by desorbing the hydrogen from the bed via either increasing the bed temperature or lowering the system pressure. Hydrogen recovery depends on the ratio of the hydrogen partial pressure of the feed stream and the plateau pressure of the selected hydride former. Hydrogen delivery pressure depends upon the bed temperature during desorption. Successful operation of this process depends upon the proper design of the hydride bed (absorber column).

Our approach to the design of the absorber column is to develop H_2 breakthrough data for a variety of system configurations and stream conditions. Figure 9A shows a typical hydrogen breakthrough curve for a hydride former in a packed-bed. A feed stream containing hydrogen of concentration C_F is fed into the absorber. The breakthrough data are obtained by monitoring the hydrogen concentration in the outlet stream of the absorber column. The exit hydrogen concentration is reduced to a value C_O which is dependent upon the hydride P-C-T properties. The ideal breakthrough curve is also shown on Figure 9A and represents the case of instantaneous H_2 absorption.

The breakthrough data can be employed to construct a wave- or reaction-front plot as shown in Figure 9B. This curve represents a stable reaction front of length, L_f, moving through the absorber column at velocity, V_f. Along the reaction front, the hydrogen loading of the absorbent varies. Upstream of the front, the hydrogen capacity of the absorbent is at saturation (full capacity). To the right of the front (downstream) the hydrogen partial pressure of the stream is less than the plateau pressure and absorption does not occur.

In operation, the flow to an absorber column is stopped and sent to another column once the breakthrough point (Figure 9A) is

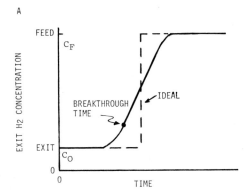

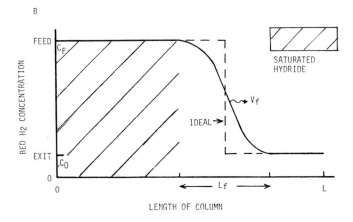

Figure 9.   Schematic (A) hydrogen breakthrough and (B) absorption wavefront curves for a hydride absorber column

encountered. Therefore, the shape of the reaction front (or
breakthrough curve) dictates the hydrogen recovery and bed utilization (i.e., lbs H_2/lb absorbent) for the process. A shallow
reaction front leads to poor bed utilization and hydrogen recovery; whereas, a steep reaction front yields a higher bed utilization and recovery.

For hydride absorbents, the shape of the reaction front
depends on many factors, for instance:

> pressure drop through the packed-bed,
>
> hydrogen absorption kinetics of the alloy,
>
> gas blanketing,
>
> equilibrium P-C-T properties of the alloy,
>
> hydrogen partial pressure of the stream,
>
> presence of interferring or inhibiting gaseous
> components.

Hydrogen separations with metal hydrides can be viewed as
complementary technology to cryogenic and adsorption (PSA)
processes. Attributes of this new process are listed in Table
II.

TABLE II. ADVANTAGEOUS FEATURES OF HYDRIDE-
           HYDROGEN SEPARATION PROCESSES

REACTION SPECIFICITY	- Only H_2 reacts, useful for dilute streams
HIGH RECOVERY	- Determined by H_2 partial pressure and hydride former
PRODUCT PURITY	-> 99.9% if required
ENERGY EFFICIENT	- Heat of reaction typically 10-15% of the lower heating value of H_2 and can be partially recovered

Metal Hydride Process for Ammonia Purge Gas. The metal
hydride process will be illustrated using the case of hydrogen
recovery from an ammonia purge gas stream generated during
ammonia manufacture.

Figure 10 is a block diagram for ammonia synthesis from
steam reforming gas. As shown in the figure, inert gases such
as argon and methane from the secondary reformer accumulate in
the synthesis loop and decrease the partial pressures of hydrogen
and nitrogen which react to form ammonia. Therefore, it becomes
necessary to continuously remove (purge) these inerts from the

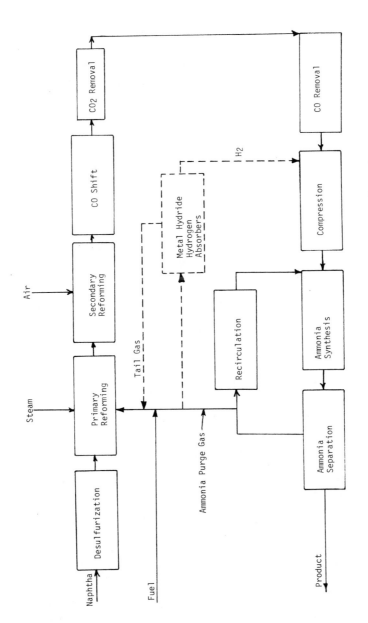

Figure 10.   Block diagram for ammonia synthesis by steam reformation

recycle gas in order to maintain a steady rate of ammonia synthesis. The typical composition of the ammonia purge gas stream is shown in Table III.

TABLE III

TYPICAL COMPOSITION OF AMMONIA PURGE GAS STREAM

Component	Mole Percent
H_2	63
N_2	21
CH_4	12
Ar	2
NH_3	2
Pressure	50-60 atm
Temperature	40 °C

Characteristic breakthrough curves for synthetic ammonia purge gas streams have been measured as a function of system parameters in a bench scale reactor. A Ni-containing AB_5 hydride former was used. Data for a stream containing 0.92% NH_3 is given in Figure 11. A steep breakthrough curve is observed at a superficial gas velocity of approximately 3 feet per minute. For a constant ammonia concentration, the length of the reaction front, L_f, varies approximately as the square root of the gas velocity, Figure 12. The length of the reaction front also shows a weak dependence on ammonia concentration. Figure 13 shows $L_f \propto (NH_3)^{\frac{1}{4}}$ over the range 0-5% NH_3. For typical purge gas streams containing 1.5 to 2.5% NH_3 (see band in Figure 13) the front varies from 1.5 to 3.5 feet at superficial gas velocities of 3.5 to 10.5 feet per minute.

These results are not unlike those reported by others for separation of gases with molecular sieves. For example, when H_2S is stripped from natural gas with a Davison 5A molecular sieve, the reaction front is typically 1 to 5 feet at superficial gas velocities of 15 to 30 feet per minute (10). From this perspective, the operation of a hydride-hydrogen separation system is similar to conventional units.

Our data indicate that ammonia acts as a mild inhibitor for hydrogen absorption in Ni-containing AB_5 alloys. The measured heat of adsorption of NH_3 on Ni is about -11 kcal/mol NH_3, suggesting weak, physical adsorption. Since Ni is viewed to be a catalyst for the hydriding reaction, weak physical adsorption of NH_3 at these Ni sites would retard the reaction and promote a broadening of the reaction front as shown in Figures 12 and 13. We have shown that the adsorbed NH_3 is easily desorbed from the Ni sites during hydrogen desorption and, therefore, acts only as a mild inhibitor for the absorption step.

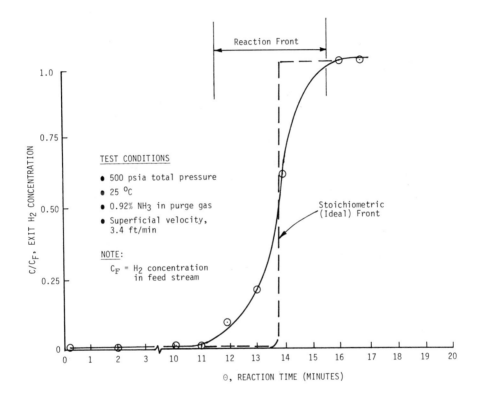

Figure 11.   Hydrogen breakthrough curve for a 0.93% NH₃ stream

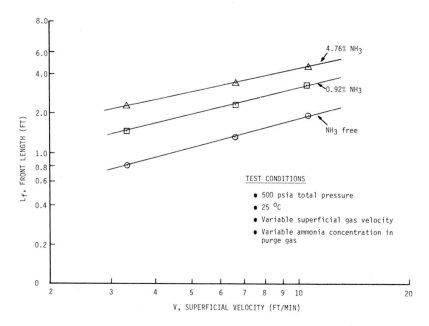

Figure 12. Effect of gas velocity on reaction front length

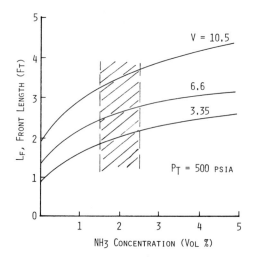

Figure 13. Effect of ammonia on length of breakthrough front

Process Economics. Preliminary process economics for recovering hydrogen from the ammonia purge gas stream have been prepared. The H_2 recovery costs depend on many factors and are in the range 0.30-0.80 \$/MSCF H_2. These costs compare favorably with those figures reported for cryogenic and molecular sieve (absorption) processes. The process can be scaled to produce units capable of treating 10 MMSCFD of H_2. Currently, the developed process is being readied for pilot plant testing at an ammonia manufacturer's installation.

A typical hydride hydrogen separation unit sized to process 10 MMSCFD of H_2 would require 50 to 100,000 lbs of hydride forming alloy. Approximately 1/3 of the alloy weight would be a rare earth(s) if AB_5 alloys are utilized. A range of alloy compositions is likely to be required to optimize separation costs for different streams.

Other Applications. Metal hydrides are unique in that they are one of the few compounds that selectively and reversibly absorb large quantities of hydrogen at practical temperatures and pressures. This property enables one to treat dilute hydrogen streams that cannot be otherwise economically treated.

Figure 14 shows the qualitative effect of hydrogen concentration of the stream on the processing costs to recover hydrogen by the metal hydride, cryogenic and molecular sieve processes. Clearly, the metal hydride process is preferred for treating dilute streams and is a direct consequence of the high degree of reaction specificity of hydride formers for hydrogen. Coupled with this is the property that hydride formers can absorb hydrogen at relatively low partial pressures while retaining good kinetics and recovery. These two properties can be employed to develop an applications map for the metal hydride process as shown in Figure 15. The regions of the figure indicate preferred operating parameters for the various processes. It is evident that the metal hydride option is superior in terms of its ability to economically treat typical off-gas streams.

We are currently involved in a three phase developmental program to extend the process to other hydrogen containing streams. The program involves: screening candidate streams to identify poisonous species for the metal hydrides, developing poison resistant processes for each stream, and demonstrating the process(es) on a pilot scale to establish process economics.

Hydrogen Purification

The specificity of the hydriding reaction (Eq. 1) also provides a method for the purification of high purity hydrogen. The technology is similar to that previously described for hydrogen separations and is capable of producing purity levels exceeding 99.999%. If the impure hydrogen is already 99[+]% H_2, single ended reactors can be employed. Residual gases (impurities) are

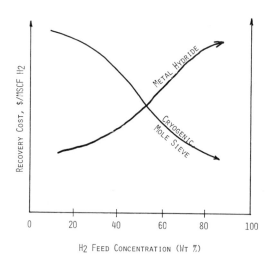

Figure 14. *Qualitative effect of hydrogen concentration on processing costs for various recovery methods*

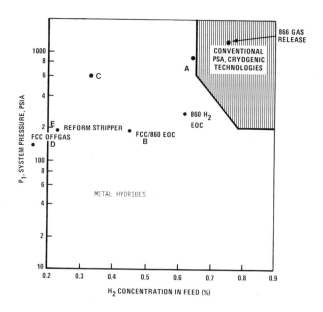

Figure 15. *Applications map for hydrogen recovery process: A, ammonia purge gas; B, refinery stream; C, coal conversion recycle gas; D, ethylene plant cracked gas; E, FCC C₄ minus gas*

expelled immediately after charging by simply desorbing a portion of the hydride. The principal application for ultra high purity hydrogen is for heat treating atmospheres in the semiconductor industry. Palladium purifiers are the current industry standard.

Experiments at KFA Julich have shown that hydrogen can be purified to greater than 99.9999% using special FeTi hydride tanks (11). The Laboratory Data Control H2YCELL unit shown in Figure 4 claims even higher purity levels based on atomic absorption analysis (12). Additional surface poisoning studies similar to the work sponsored by Brookhaven National Laboratory (6) will be required to delineate the types of hydrogen streams that can be processed by this technology.

Thermal Compression

Hydrogen compression is a vital step for most industrial uses of hydrogen. Conventional markets for hydrogen are growing rapidly and the synthetic fuels programs will multiply the quantities of hydrogen processed each year. This assures increased demand for compression equipment. Existing mechanical compressors, although well engineered, are high maintenance, high operating cost items. Is there a better way?

The ability of reversible metal hydrides to absorb hydrogen at low pressures and temperatures, then when heated to a higher temperature, desorbs the hydrogen at a higher pressure, is the basis for the hydride chemical compressor. The pressure-temperature characteristics are governed by the Van't Hoff equation (Eq. 2). Compression ratios for several hydrides operating between 25 and 85 °C are given in Table IV. These data are taken directly from Figure 3 and range from 6 to 9. The compression ratio varies directly with the heat of formation, ΔH, as required by Eq. 2.

Hydride chemical compressors have two attractive features. Only low grade (low temperature) energy sources are required. The example cited required 85 °C—typically a waste heat temperature for most industrial environments or a temperature readily delivered by solar heating installations. There are no rotating parts requiring maintenance. Check valves regulate the hydrogen flow. Continuous operation is achieved by using multiple hydride beds operated in a staggered sequence.

A preprototype ("proof of concept") unit has been assembled and tested by Ergenics and Denver Research Institute with DOE funding through Brookhaven National Laboratory. One half of the unit is shown in Figure 16. A LaNi4.5Al0.5 alloy was selected to permit absorption of hydrogen at ambient temperature and a pressure of 1 atmosphere absolute. Thus, the unit could be operated in conjunction with a low pressure electrolyzer. The hydride was contained in capsules in stainless steel tubes which were electrically heated and cooled by fans. A peak pressure of 75 atm (1100 psig) was attained at 300 °C. In continuous operation, the unit delivered 43 SCFH of hydrogen at 42 atm (650 psig).

TABLE IV - COMPARISON OF THERMAL COMPRESSION RATIOS FOR
SEVERAL REVERSIBLE METAL HYDRIDES BETWEEN 25 AND 85°C

Alloy	P_p (atm,25°C)	P_p (atm,85°C)	Ratio	H (k cal/mole H_2)
FeTi	4.8	28	5.8	-6.7
MNi$_{4.5}$Al$_{0.5}$	3.9	24	6.2	-6.7
Fe$_{0.9}$Mn$_{0.1}$Ti	2.8	19	6.8	-7.0
LaNi$_5$	1.7	13	7.6	-7.4
CaNi$_5$	0.50	4.4	8.8	-7.6
LaNi$_{4.7}$Al$_{0.3}$	0.45	4.0	8.9	-8.1
Thermal	1.0	1.20	1.20	--

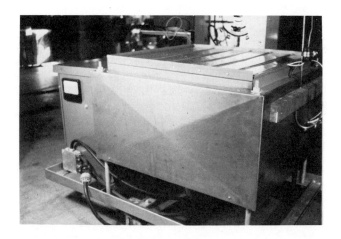

Figure 16.   Prototype hydride chemical compressor constructed by Ergenics and Denver Research Institute: (top) front view; (bottom) topview showing metal hydride tube bundle

During cooling, the fans rapidly cool the tubes to ambient conditions at which time a second check valve opens allowing reabsorption of the compressed hydrogen. Some degradation of performance was noted during cycling. As the cycle number increased, time required to compress the same quantity of hydrogen increased. This degradation is believed to reflect an instability in the hydride aggrevated by the 300 °C temperature excursion.

The efficiency of this preprototype device was low due principally to the thermal mass of the copper buss bars, convection losses associated with the air cooled design and radiation losses at the high operating temperatures. Current work is directed at staged compressors (more than one alloy) operating over smaller temperature ranges supplied by a liquid heat transfer media.

Sandia Laboratories (Albuquerque) has recently completed a study on closed-cycle hydride engines based on the hydride chemical compression cycle (13). A practical demonstration unit was constructed to operate a water pump (14). The down-hole bladder pump is capable of pumping against large hydrostatic heads. Coupled with a solar collection, this concept should find applications in arid third world countries.

Heat Pumps and Refrigeration

The reversibility of the metal-hydrogen reaction (Eq. 1) and the heat of chemical reaction (Eq. 2) provides the basis for hydride heat pumps. These devices are closed units in which hydrogen serves as an energy carrier between two or more hydride beds. By selecting appropriate hydriding alloys, heat sources and heat sinks, heat can be pumped over wide temperature differentials with no moving parts except possibly check valves.

There are two basic cycles for heat pump operation: conventional (15) and temperature upgrading (16, 17). It is convenient to visualize the operation of these cycles by following the changes in pressure and temperature of each alloy on a Van't Hoff plot. For ease of narration, these curves are idealized. Many engineering properties of metal hydrides must be considered in a detailed explanation (e.g., hysteresis, plateau slope, cyclic stability, etc.). The two cycles are shown in Figure 17.

In the conventional cycle, hydride B at, say 40 °C, is heated to about 90 °C. Heat is absorbed (Q_B) from the high temperature bed to dissociate hydrogen. This hydrogen in turn reacts with hydride former A, releasing heat (Q_A) at the intermediate temperature. When the reaction is complete, alloy B is cooled to the intermediate temperature. Hydride A desorbs hydrogen and cools, thereby absorbing heat (Q_A refrigeration) at a low temperature. The hydrogen reacts with alloy B releasing additional heat (Q_B) at the intermediate temperature and completing the cycle. The net result is heat $Q_A + Q_B$ delivered to the intermediate temperature with Q_B taken from a high temperature

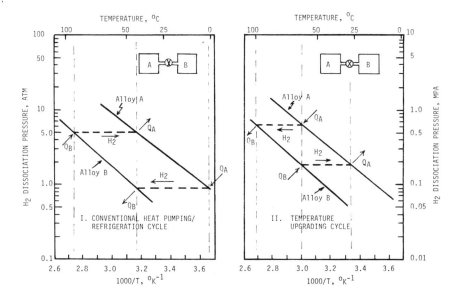

Figure 17.   Schematic hydride heat pump cycles

Figure 18.   Prototype 3.5 Kw heat pump constructed by Ergenics for New York State Energy Research and Development Administration

source and Q_A a low temperature source (refrigeration). The cycle operates continuously requiring only switching of heat transfer fluids from the heat sinks and sources. A demonstration of this cycle has been in operation for several years at Argonne National Laboratories.

The temperature upgrading cycle has the hydrogen flow in the opposite direction. This results in the removal of heat from the intermediate temperature bed and delivery to higher (Q_B) and lower (Q_A) temperature sinks. The temperature range (0-100 ^{O}C) in Figure 17 illustrates that the hydride heat pumps can operate with low grade heat. Much larger temperature ranges can be achieved by selecting different alloy pairs (e.g., Mg_2Ni-$LaNi_5$).

A 3.5kw demonstration unit has been constructed by Ergenics for New York State ERDA. The unit is shown in Figure 18. $LaNi_5$ and $LaNi_{4.7}Al_{0.3}$ were selected to generate 95-100 ^{O}C water from 60 ^{O}C waste water and 20 ^{O}C cooling water. These values were selected as representative of applications in the food processing industry. Initial tests show that the desired thermal upgrading has been achieved and detailed testing and evaluation are now in progress.

DOE, through Brookhaven National Laboratories, has recently issued a contract for an industrial team to design, build, and test a prototype metal hydride heat pump for residential, commercial or industrial applications. This three-year program is intended to assess the commercial viability of this technology.

Concluding Remarks

We have provided an introduction to the technology of reversible metal hydrides and reviewed the applications which are currently being commercially developed. These include mobile and stationary hydrogen storage, hydrogen separation and purification, thermal hydrogen compression and heat pumping. Other applications in earlier stages of development include catalysis (hydrogenation, Fischer-Tropsch synthesis) and hydrogen battery electrodes. To capitalize on the technology developed so far, further advances are needed in the following areas: 1) hydrides with greater hydrogen storage capacity, 2) hydrides with improved poison resistance and thermal stability, and 3) methods for enhancing the heat transfer characteristics of hydride systems.

Acknowledgment

The authors are indebted to G.D. Sandrock (Inco Research and Development Center, Inc), F.E. Lynch (Hydrogen Consultants Inc), F. G. Eisenberg (Air Products and Chemicals Inc) and P.P. Turillon (Ergenics) for many helpful discussions and original research materials used in the preparation of this manuscript.

List of Symbols

B	constant, see Eq. 2	dimensionless
C	hydrogen concentration	volume (or mole) percent
CF	gas volume	cubic feet
CFM	volumetric gas flow	cubic feet per minute
ΔH	heat of reaction	k cal/mole H_2
L_f	reaction front length	feet
M	misch metal (48–50% Ce, 32–34% La, 13–14% Nd, 4–5% Pr, 1.5% other rare earths)	--
psia	pressure absolute	lb. force/square inch
psig	pressure gauge	lb. force/square inch
SCF	gas volume at standard conditions, 1 atm pressure and 0°C	cubic feet
SCFM	volumetric gas flow	cubic feet per minute (M)
SCFH	at standard conditions	cubic feet per hour (H)
SCFD		cubic feet per day (D)
MSCF	gas volume at standard conditions	10^3 cubic feet
MMSCFD	volumetric gas flow at standard conditions	10^6 cubic feet per day (D)
R	universal gas constant	appropriate units
T	temperature	°K (or °C)
V_f	reaction front velocity	feet per minute
X	stoichiometric coefficient for Eq. 1	dimensionless
Subscripts F and O	feed and outlet conditions, respectively	dimensionless

References

1. Sandrock, G.D.; Snape, E. "Rechargeable Metal Hydrides. A
    New Concept in Hydrogen Storage, Processing and Handling".
    ACS Symposium Series No. 116, Hydrogen Production and
    Marketing 1980, 293.
2. Huston, E.L.; Sandrock, G.D. "Engineering Properties of
    Metal Hydrides" to be published in J. Less-Common Metals,
    1980.
3. Reilly, J.J.; Hydrogen It's Technology and Implications
    Vol. II, Chapter 2, Cox, K.E. and Williamson, K.D., editors,
    CRC Press, Boca Raton, Fl. 1977.
4. Reilly, J.J. and Sandrock, G.D. "Hydrogen Storage in Metal
    Hydrides", Scientific American, 242 No. 2, 1980, 118.
5. Goodell, P.D. "Thermal Conductivity of Hydriding Alloy
    Powders and Comparisons of Reactor Systems", to be published
    in J. Less Common Metals, 1980.
6. Sandrock, G.D. and Goodell, P.D. "Surface Poisoning of LaNi5,
    FeTi and (Fe,Mn) Ti by O2, CO and H2O," ibid.
7. Goodell, P.D.; Sandrock, G.D. and Huston, E.L. "Kinetic and
    Dynamic Aspects of Rechargeable Metal Hydrides", ibid.
8. Howe, L.M. "Fire in the Water" ABC-TV Channel 7, Denver, Co.
    1979.
9. Lynch, F.E. Hydrogen Consultants, Inc. Denver Co., Private
    Communication.
10. Chi, C.W. and Lee, H. "Natural Gas Purification by 5A
    Molecular Sieves and It's Design Method", AIChE, Symposium
    Series, Gas Purification by Absorption, Zwiebel, I.;
    Broughton, D.B. and Camp, D.T. editors. Vol. 69, 1973, 95.
11. Klatt, K.H.; Wenzl, H.; Carl, A. and Pick, M. "Hydrogen in
    Metals, Hydrogen Storage, Hydrogen Purification". Technische
    Information No. 6, Kernforschungsanlage Julich GMBH, 1976.
12. McCue, J.C. "The Commercial Development of H2YCELL; Rare
    Earth Metal Hydride Storage Device", to be published in
    J. Less Common Metals, 1980.
13. Hinkebein, T.E.; Northrup, C.J. and Heckes, A.A. "Closed
    Cycle Hydride Engines" Sandia Laboratories Report, SAND78-
    2228, Dec. 1978.
14. Heckes, A.A.; Hinkebein, T.E. and Northrup, C.J. "Hydride
    Engines" Hydrogen, Proc. 14th Intersociety Energy Conversion
    Engineering Conference, Boston, MA. American Chemical Soc. 1
    743 (1979).
15. Sheft, I.; Gruen, D.M. and Lamich, G. "HYCSOS:A Chemical Heat
    Pump and Energy Conversion System Based on Metal Hydrides"
    1979 Status Report, Angonne National Laboratory Report
    ANL-79-8.
16. Terry, L.E. "Hydrogen-Hydride Absorption Systems and Methods
    for Refrigeration and Heat Pump Cycles" US Patent 4,055,962
    Nov. 1, 1972.
17. Sirovich, B.E. "Hydride Heat Pump" US Patent 4,200,144
    April 29, 1980.

RECEIVED February 18, 1981.

Oxygen Sensors

FREDERICK L. KENNARD III

AC Spark Plug Division of General Motors Corporation,
1300 North Dort Highway, Flint, MI 48556

Recent emission control system development in the automotive industry has been directed mainly towards the use of three-way or dual bed catalytic converters. This type of converter system not only oxidizes the hydrocarbons (HC) and carbon monoxide (CO) in the exhaust gas but will also reduce the nitrous oxides (NO_x). An integral part of this type of system is the exhaust oxygen sensor which is used to provide feedback for closed loop control of the air-fuel ratio. This is necessary since this type of catalytic converter system operates efficiently only when the composition of the exhaust gas is very near the stoichiometric point. This type of emission control system has been in use in limited volumes in California since the 1977 model year, on nearly all California cars in the 1980 model year, and will apparently be on a majority of cars in this country in the 1981 model year. No other method has been nearly as effective in meeting the federally mandated emission requirements without severe penalties in performance and/or fuel economy.

While this paper will concentrate on oxygen sensors as used in automotive applications, there is increasing interest in their use in the measurement and control of industrial and other furnaces in order to reduce fuel costs by maximizing the combustion efficiency. They have also been used for many years to measure the oxygen content of molten glass, of molten steel and other metals and for numerous other applications where a measurement of the oxygen partial pressure is desired.

While several types of oxygen sensors have been investigated for automotive use, the most common type in commercial use consists of a galvanic cell with a fully or partially stabilized zirconium oxide electrolyte.

Stabilized zirconia refers to a solid solution of zirconium oxide with one or more of a number of stabilizing oxides (CaO, MgO, Y_2O_3, or others) to form a cubic fluorite structure. This reduces or eliminates the destructive monoclinic-tetragonal phase transition encountered with pure zirconia during thermal cycling and also greatly increases the oxygen ion conductivity. The zirconium and stabilizer cations fill the cation sites and the difference in valence between the stabilizing cations (Mg^{2+}, Ca^{2+}, Y^{3+}, Yb^{3+}) and the zirconium cations (Zr^{4+}) is compensated for by oxygen vacancies. This defect structure leads to a high electrical conductivity which is essentially completely due to oxygen ion transport (1).

When a zirconia electrolyte is exposed on different sides to gases with different oxygen partial pressures a relationship such as shown in Figure 1 is obtained. The voltage, E, developed with this type of galvanic cell is given by the Nernst equation as shown below:

$$E = \frac{RT}{4F} \ln\left(\frac{p'_{O_2}}{p''_{O_2}}\right)$$

where R is the gas constant, T is the absolute temperature, F is the Faraday constant and p'_{O_2} and p''_{O_2} are the partial pressures of oxygen in the two gases.

While a number of designs have been used, most oxygen sensors for automotive applications consist of a hollow, closed end tube, a schematic of which is shown in Figure 2. As shown, the interior of the closed end tube is open to the atmosphere which serves as a constant or reference oxygen partial pressure while the exterior is exposed to the exhaust gas. The voltage signal produced by the electrolyte is sensed by electrodes on the inner and outer surface of the sensor. These, in turn, are connected to the electronics package of the closed loop system.

The equilibrium oxygen content of an exhaust gas as a function of the air-fuel ratio is shown in Figure 3. It must be emphasized that, while the transient oxygen content can be affected by many factors, the equilibrium oxygen content depends solely on the gas composition, air-fuel ratio, and temperature. It should also be noted that at the stoichiometric point, a change in oxygen partial pressure of many orders of magnitude occurs. In order that the equilibrium and not the transient oxygen content is sensed, the exhaust side of the sensor generally has catalytic electrodes although other means are possible to achieve this end.

Figure 4 shows the theoretical output of a sensor calculated using the Nernst equation and the oxygen partial pressures of Figure 3. Again note the step change at the stoichiometric air-fuel ratio. Many commercially available sensors have outputs that closely approach this theoretical relationship.

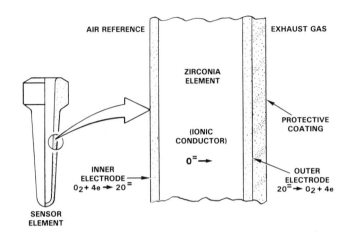

Figure 1. Schematic of oxygen sensor solid electrolyte galvanic cell

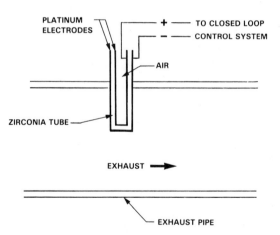

Figure 2. Schematic of exhaust oxygen sensor

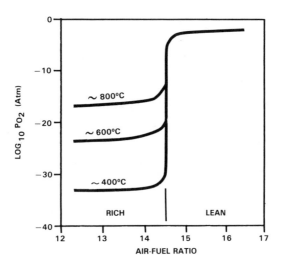

Figure 3.   Exhaust gas equilibrium oxygen partial pressure as a function of the
air–fuel ratio

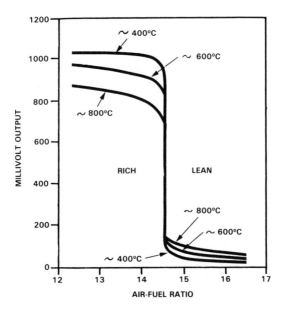

Figure 4.   Theoretical sensor output as a function of the air–fuel ratio

Because of this type of behavior, a sharp transition at stoichiometry but low sensitivity and temperature effects either rich or lean of this point, the oxygen sensor is most useful in controlling at the stoichiometric point. It is of limited usefulness at other exhaust compositions. However, as shown in Figure 5, this is exactly the point at which a three-way or dual bed catalytic converter is most efficient. Only when the exhaust composition is near the stoichiometric point will both the oxidation of the HC and CO and the reduction of the NO_x occur satisfactorily.

Figure 6 is a schematic of a closed loop system. It consists basically of an oxygen sensor to monitor the exhaust air-fuel ratio, a "black box" electronic control system, a carburetor or fuel injector which is controlled and adjusted by the "black box" and, finally, a three-way or dual bed converter. The signal from the oxygen sensor is monitored continuously by the electronics package which then adjusts the carburetor or fuel injector to control the air-fuel ratio at stoichiometric.

Electrodes and Electrode Protective Coating

The electrodes and electrode protective coating of the oxygen sensor play a crucial role in determining the performance characteristics and durability (2). The electrodes used are the inner or air-reference electrode and the outer or exhaust gas electrode. The protective coating goes over the outer or exhaust electrode. While a complete discussion of the requirements and properties of the electrodes and electrode protective coating is beyond the scope of this paper, a brief description will be given.

The inner electrode must be oxidation resistant at temperatures up to $1000^\circ C$, porous, and exhibit good adhesion to the electrolyte. The inner electrode used for automotive applications has typically been a thick film platinum material. Figure 7 is a SEM micrograph of a typical inner electrode.

The outer or exhaust electrode must survive under both oxidizing and reducing conditions at temperatures up to $1000^\circ C$, must also be porous and have good adhesion to the electrolyte and, in addition, must be able to catalyze reactions in the exhaust gas in order that the equilibrium oxygen content is measured. Again, platinum is a good choice for this electrode because of its stability under both oxidizing and reducing conditions and because of its excellent catalytic properties. Figure 8 shows a typical thin film outer electrode.

Finally, the protective coating over the outer electrode must resist abrasion by particulates in the exhaust gas, must be porous to allow access of the exhaust to the outer electrode, must adhere to the outer electrode, must have expansion characteristics compatible with the electrolyte, and must be stable under oxidizing and reducing conditions at temperatures up to $1000^\circ C$. A flame sprayed spinel ($MgAl_2O_4$) coating as shown in Figure 9 meets these requirements.

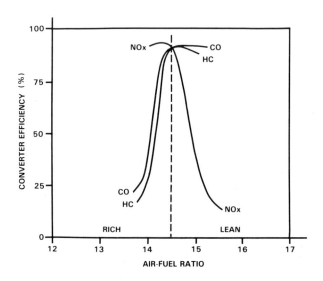

Figure 5.   Converter efficiency as a function of air–fuel ratio

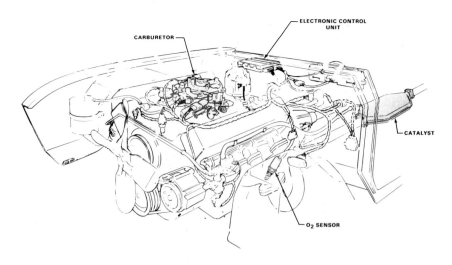

Figure 6.   Schematic of closed loop system

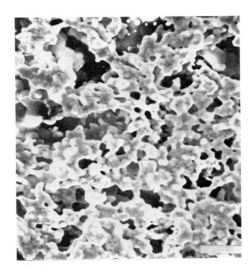

Figure 7.   SEM micrograph of platinum thick film air electrode (bar = 75 microns)

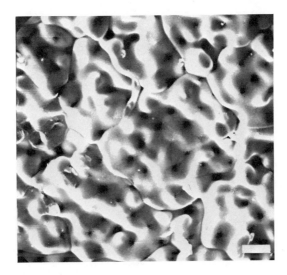

Figure 8.   SEM micrograph of platinum thin film exhaust electrode (bar = 7.5 microns)

Figure 9.   SEM micrograph of flame sprayed spinel protective coating (bar = 75 microns)

Electrolytes

Many oxygen ion conducting electrolytes are available for sensor applications. These include mainly solid solutions of ZrO_2, HFO_2, ThO_2, or CeO_2. Of these, stabilized zirconia has been found to have the best combination of cost, mechanical, chemical, and electrical properties for this type of application and has been the most widely used. Various stabilizers are available and have a strong effect on the properties obtained, particularly the electrical conductivity.

The conditions under which the sensor must perform satisfactorily are quite severe. This includes a temperature range of -40 to $1000^\circ C$, oxidizing and reducing atmospheres, severe thermal shock conditions and high thermal and mechanical stress imposed due to temperature gradients, vibration, etc. The sensor must function electrically at temperatures as low as $316^\circ C$ and preferably lower. This requires that the electrolyte have good mechanical properties, high resistance to thermal shock, good ionic conductivity at low temperatures, and good chemical stability over the temperature range of use. It must also be available at a reasonable cost. While this requires some trade-off in properties, one electrolyte that has had the most success in meeting the above requirements is a partially stabilized zirconia body with Y_2O_3 as a stabilizer. A partially stabilized body is a body containing some percentage of the unstabilized monoclinic zirconia phase with the remainder the stabilized cubic phase. A typical body for this application contains 20% of the monoclinic phase. The partially stabilized body gives greatly improved mechanical properties and thermal shock resistance although at a sacrifice in electrical conductivity while the use of Y_2O_3 as a stabilizer achieves a balance between cost, ionic conductivity, and chemical stability.

The following table contrasts the properties of a typical partially stabilized zirconia (PSZ) body as used in this application with a typical fully stabilized (Y_2O_3) body.

	FULLY STABILIZED	PARTIALLY STABILIZED
Transverse Bend Strength (psi)	20-30,000	45-55,000
Linear Thermal Expansion ($X10^{-6}$ in./in./$^\circ C$)	11	7-8
Thermal Shock Resistance	Poor	Good
Ionic Conductivity (at 700°C) ($ohm^{-1} cm^{-1}$)	1×10^{-2}	4×10^{-3}

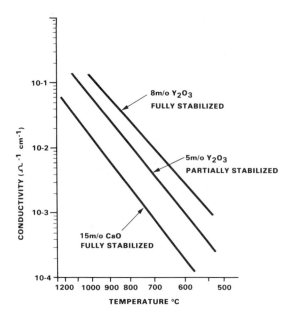

Figure 10. Ionic conductivity of fully and partially stabilized zirconia bodies

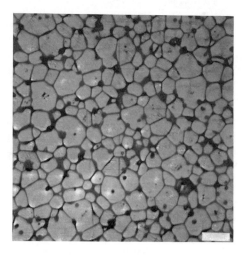

*Figure 11. Optical micrograph of high silica content (> 1%) yttria fully sta-
bilized zirconia body (bar = 37 microns)*

As can be seen, the mechanical strength of the partially stabilized body is approximately twice that of the fully stabilized and the thermal expansion is approximately 30% lower. Because of this, the thermal shock resistance of the PSZ body is greatly improved. The ionic conductivity of the PSZ body is lower but is still adequate for automotive applications. Figure 10 compares the conductivity of a yttria partially stabilized zirconia body with several fully stabilized bodies.

Figure 11 shows the microstructure of a typical fully stabilized body with a high silica content (approximately 1% or greater) while Figure 12 is for a low silica (less than 0.25%) fully stabilized body. All of the fully stabilized property data listed has been for a low silica compositions. The higher silica composition exhibits a much lower ionic conductivity without any significant improvements in other properties. Figure 13 shows the microstructure of a partially stabilized body. Note the two phase structure and very fine grain size of this body when compared with the fully stabilized bodies. The improved mechanical properties of this type of partially stabilized body are due mainly to the fine grain size obtained while the reduction in the ionic conductivity is caused by the presence of the lower conductivity monoclinic phase.

It should be noted that it is possible to produce fully stabilized bodies with much higher fracture strengths than listed here but this requires the use of fine particle size, chemically prepared powders (3). The use of this type of material involves a number of penalties both in cost and processability that may be prohibitive for a high volume automotive application. In addition to the type of partially stabilized body described here, two other basic types of partially stabilized bodies have been reported (4, 5). Both are classified as transformation toughened partially stabilized zirconias and involve different processing techniques to obtain a body with various amounts of a metastable tetragonal phase. While the mechanical properties of these materials have been studied extensively, little has been reported about their electrical properties or their stability under the thermal, mechanical and chemical conditions of an automotive exhaust system.

CaO has been used to some degree as a stabilizer and is attractive due to its low cost. Its ionic conductivity, however, is approximately an order of magnitude less than an equivalent yttria stabilized body. There has also been some question about the chemical stability of a CaO stabilized body, although this may be more of a factor with a partially stabilized body than a fully stabilized body. Calcia fully stabilized ZrO_2 has been and may still be used in commercial production of oxygen sensors.

Yb_2O_3 stabilized electrolytes have somewhat better ionic conductivity than Y_2O_3 stabilized materials but are unattractive due to the high cost of Yb_2O_3.

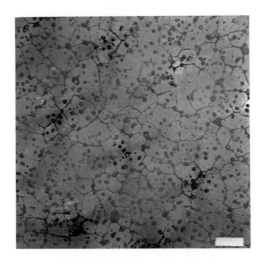

*Figure 12.   Optical micrograph of low silica content (< 0.25%) yttria fully sta-
bilized zirconia body (bar = 75 microns)*

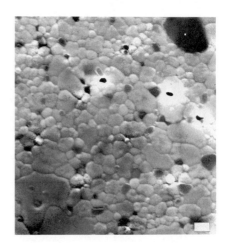

*Figure 13.   SEM micrograph of yttria
partially stabilized zirconia body (bar =
0.75 micron)*

Other fairly common stabilizers for zirconia include MgO (low cost but poor ionic conductivity and stability) and Sc_2O_3 (good ionic conductivity but high cost).

Other oxygen ion conducting electrolytes, CeO_2, HfO_2, and ThO_2 doped with various oxides, generally are found to have poorer ionic conductivity, may be unstable under certain conditions and have other unsuitable properties.

Alternative Types of Oxygen Sensors

One other type of oxygen sensor has received considerable attention as an alternative to the galvanic type of sensor. This is the resistive type of sensor which uses a metal oxide whose resistance is dependent on the oxygen partial pressure [6]. While a number of different oxides have been used, titanium oxide appears to have the best combination of properties for automotive applications [7].

Summary

Oxygen sensors, in low volume use as part of a closed loop emission control system for automotive applications since 1977, have seen wide-spread use starting with the 1981 model year. At the present time, a partially stabilized zirconia electrolyte using yttrium oxide as the stabilizer appears to be the most common choice for this application.

References

1.   Kingery, W. D.;   Pappis, J.;   Doty, M. E.;   Hill, D. C. J. Amer. Ceramic Society, 1959, 42 (8), 393398.

2.   Fleming, W. J. SAE Congress, 1977, Paper 770400.

3.   Scott, C. E.; Reed, J. S. Amer. Ceram. Soc. Bull., 1979, 58 (6) 587-90.

4.   Porter, D. L.; Heuer, A. H.; J. Amer. Ceram. Soc., 1977, 60 (34), 18384.

5.   Gupta, T. K.;   Lange, F. F.;   Bechtold, J. H.   J. Mat. Sc., 1978, 13, 14641470.

6.   Logothetis, E. M., Ceram. Eng. & Sci. Proc. 1980, 1, 281301.

7.   Tien, T. Y.;   Stadler, H. L.;   Gibbons, E. F.; Zacmanidis, P. J.; Amer. Ceram. Soc. Bull., 1975, 54 (3), 280-282.

RECEIVED March 30, 1981.

PLZT Electrooptic Ceramics and Devices

GENE H. HAERTLING

Ceramic Products, Motorola Incorporated, 3434 Vassar NE, Albuquerque, NM 87107

Approximately ten years ago, it was first reported by Haertling and Land (1) that optical transparency was achieved in a ferroelectric ceramic material. This material was, in reality, not just one composition but consisted of a series of compositions in the lanthanum modified lead zirconate-lead titanate (PLZT) solid solution region. The multiplicity of compositions, each with different mechanical, electrical and electrooptic properties; has led to a decade of study in defining the chemical and structural nature of these materials; in understanding the phenomena underlying their optical and electrooptic properties and in evaluating the practicality of the large number of possible applications (2-12).

The purpose of this paper is to review the status of the PLZT materials, dealing particularly with specific compositions, processing and fabrication; and to demonstrate the application of these materials to practical devices. To date, these devices are largely confined to applications involving shutters and modulators, but PLZT ceramics also offer a promising solid state answer to display applications of the future. Specific examples of military and industrial devices cited in this paper include (1) the Air Force sponsored Thermal/Flash Protective Device, (2) Bell and Howell's Data Recorder, (3) a stereo-viewing system manufactured by Megatek Corporation and (4) eye safety viewing devices (welding helmet, inspection goggles) by Motorola.

Materials

PLZT Compositional System. The solid solution region which forms the basis of the PLZT materials is a series of compositions resulting from the complete miscibility of lead zirconate and lead titanate (commonly designated at PZT) in each other. Modifications to the PZT system by the addition of lanthanum oxide has a marked beneficial effect upon several of the basic properties of the material such as decreased coercive field and increased dielectric constant, electromechanical coupling coef-

0097-6156/81/0164-0265$05.00/0

ficient, mechanical compliance and optical transparency. The
latter of these properties, optical transparency, was only discovered in recent years but came about as the result of an in-
depth study of various additives to the PLZT system. Results
from this work indicate that La^{+3}, as a chemical modifier, is
unique among the off-valent (chemical valency of the modifier is
different or "off-valent" from that of the ion it replaces in the
lattice; e.g., La^{+3} replacing Pb^{+2}) additives in producing transparency. The reason for this behavior is still not fully understood; however, it is known that lanthanum is, to a large extent,
effective because of its high solubility in the PZT oxygen octa-
hedral structure, thus producing an extensive series of single
phase solid solution compositions. The mechanism is believed to
be one of lowering the distortion of the unit cell, thereby reducing the optical anisotropy of the crystalline lattice and at
the same time promoting uniform grain growth and densification of
a single phase, pore-free structure.

A generalized formula for all compositions in the PLZT
system is:

$$Pb_{1-x}La_x(Zr_y\ Ti_{1-y})_{1-\frac{x}{4}}O_3$$

where lanthanum ions replace lead ions in the A site of the perovskite ABO_3 ionic structure shown in Figure 1. Since La^{+3}
(added as La_2O_3) substitutes for Pb^{+2}, electrical neutrality is
maintained by the creation of lattice site vacancies. The
location of these vacancies in either the A(+2) sites or B(+4)
sites of the unit cell has not yet been completely resolved
despite numerous studies on the subject; however, it is most
probable that both A and B site vacancies exist as pointed out by
Hardtl and Hennings (13). If both A and B site vacancies are
present in the lattice, it is to be expected that the above for-
mulation would provide excess Pb^{+2} ions which are expelled from
the lattice (as PbO vapor) during the densification process at
elevated temperatures. This behavior does, indeed, occur; and in
fact, it has been reported by Snow (14) that this excess PbO contributes to achieving full density by forming a liquid phase at
the grain boundaries and by inhibiting grain growth during the
initial stages of densification. Both of these effects are beneficial to the attainment of theoretically dense material by eliminating residual porosity before it becomes entrapped within the
grains.

The PLZT phase diagram is given in Figure 2. As can be seen,
the overall effect of adding lanthanum to the PZT system is one of
decreasing the stability of the ferroelectric (FE) phases (a ferroelectric material possesses spontaneous internal polarization,
P, which can be switched by an electric field, E, as illustrated
in the P vs. E hysteresis loops in Figure 2) in favor of the non-
ferroelectric cubic and antiferroelectric (AFE) phases. At a
65/35 ratio of $PbZrO_3$ to $PbTiO_3$, a concentration of 9.5% lanthanum is sufficient to reduce the rhombohedral-cubic phase transi-

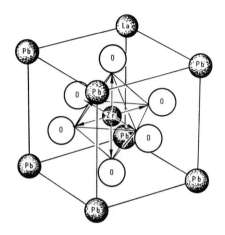

Figure 1.   Configuration of the ABO$_3$ unit cell shown with sites occupied by Pb, La, Zr, Ti and O atoms as in the para-electric cubic phase of PLZT

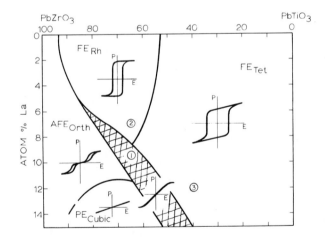

Figure 2.   Room temperature phase diagram of the PLZT system illustrating phases present and typical hysteresis loops associated with each phase: compositions 1, 2 and 3 are 9565, 7065 and 12040, respectively

tion (Curie temperature) to below room temperature. Thus, a
material of this composition (designated as 9.5/65/35 or simply,
9565) is non-ferroelectric and cubic in its virgin condition. It
is identified as composition 1 on the phase diagram and will be
discussed later in relation to its optical and electrooptic properties. It should be noted that this composition is also located in the cross hatched portion of the diagram which indicates
a region of metastable ferroelectric phases that can be electrically induced with a sufficiently high field.
     The phase diagram is only given to 15 atom percent La since
all of the compositions of interest lie within this range. Although not shown, compositions with La concentrations higher than
approximately 30% possess mixed phases and are optically opaque.

     Processing and Fabrication. Ceramics are traditionally
prepared from powders formulated from the individual oxides;
however, early attempts to produce the PLZT powders by this
method proved to be inadequate from the standpoint of chemical
and optical uniformity. As a result, a chemical co-precipitation
method designed specifically for the PLZT materials which utilized
liquid precursor materials was developed and successfully imple-
mented as a production process (15).
     Figure 3 shows in pictorial form the various steps involved
in the powder processing and fabrication of the PLZT materials.
The high purity, liquid organometallics, tetrabutyl zirconate
and tetrabutyl titanate, are first intimately mixed together in a
high speed blender along with the appropriate amount of lead
oxide powder and then precipitated by adding the lanthanum acetate
solution while blending. As the lanthanum acetate is introduced,
the zirconium and titanium butoxides are hydrolyzed by the water
from the lanthanum acetate solution producing a precipitate of
mixed hydroxides. At the same time, lead oxide and lanthanum
acetate react with the freshly hydrolyzed precipitate to produce
a final product consisting of mixed oxides and hydroxides in a
thin slurry form. The slurry is dried, resulting in the white
precipitated powder shown in Figure 3. This powder is then calcined or chemically reacted at an elevated temperature (500°C
for 16 hours) in order to produce the desired PLZT crystalline
phase. After calcining, the powder is wet milled for several
hours in order to promote additional chemical homogeneity, dried
and prepressed into a slug of proper size and shape for hot
pressing.
     A typical hot pressing setup is given in Figure 4. Ex-
perience has shown that a simple uniaxial, single-ended hot
pressing arrangement is both reliable and economical in producing
consistent, optical quality material. The prepressed slug is
placed into a silicon carbide mold resting on an alumina plate
and surrounded completely with a refractory grain such as magnesia or zirconia in order to prevent reaction with the mold at
high temperature. An alumina plate and push rod are located

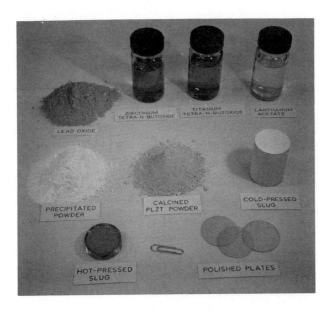

Figure 3.   Various stages in the processing of PLZT ceramics

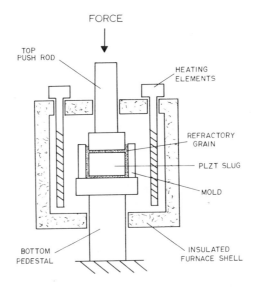

Figure 4.   A typical setup for hot pressing PLZT ceramics

on top of the slug and a modest amount of pressure is applied to
the slug for alignment purposes. Heat-up of the furnace is
started, while at the same time a vacuum is drawn on the slug via
a water-cooled vacuum chamber surrounding the furnace. Oxygen is
back-filled into the chamber at $700^{\circ}C$, full pressure is applied
and the furnace temperature is raised to its final value. Typical hot pressing conditions are $1250^{\circ}C$ for 18 hours at 2000 psi.
After hot pressing, the slug is extracted from the mold, its surfaces are cleaned, and it is then polished for optical evaluation.
This method of vacuum/oxygen hot pressing was successfully used
by Dungan and Snow (16) for fabricating optical quality PLZT slugs
up to five inches in diameter. An alternate method of hot
pressing in flowing oxygen rather than vacuum/oxygen is also known
to produce optical quality material, but it is generally limited
to slug sizes less than two inches in diameter. Typical examples
of hot pressed ceramics are given in Figure 5.

Microstructure. Ceramic compositions in the PLZT system
characteristically exhibit a highly uniform microstructure consisting of randomly oriented, equiaxed grains (crystallites)
intimately bonded together. An example of such a microstructure
is shown in Figure 6 for PLZT 9565 thermally etched at $1100^{\circ}C$.
The average grain size of a given material may vary from about
two microns to 15 microns depending on the temperature and time
of hot pressing, with a typical size being approximately eight
microns average diameter. A uniform grain size is a highly desirable feature from the standpoint of performance.
     Another distinctive characteristic of the PLZT materials is
their fully dense, pore-free microstructure which is devoid of
any second phases. This is reflected in measured bulk densities
which routinely exceed 99.9% of theoretical density. The existence of pores or second phases in the volume of the grains or in
the grain boundaries is undesirable since both act to increase
light scattering and reduce optical transparency.

Optical Properties. The addition of lanthanum oxide to
PZT has a rather remarkable effect on the optical transparency,
especially when the amount of lanthanum exceeds seven atom percent. Thin polished plates characteristically transmit about
67% of the incident light. When broadband antireflection coatings are applied to the major surfaces, this transmission is increased to greater than 98%. Surface reflection losses are a
function of the index of refraction (n = 2.5) of the PLZT.
     Optical absorption in these materials is wavelength depen-
dent, becoming extremely high in the violet (short wavelength)
end of the spectrum near 0.37 microns. In the infrared portion
of the spectrum, transmittance remains high out to approximately
6.5 microns and then gradually decreases in a regular manner until 12 microns, where the material is full absorbing.
     The optical transmission characteristics of three PLZT comp-

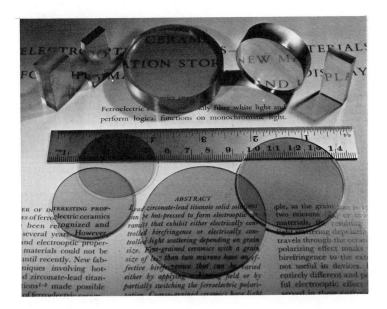

Figure 5. Examples of the optical transparency of quadratic PLZT ceramics

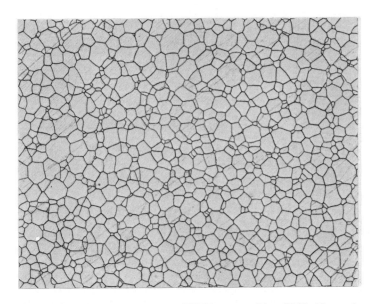

Figure 6. A typical microstructure of PLZT, composition 9565, illustrating the fully dense structure and uniform grain size

ositions are given in Figure 7. These compositions (see Figure 2)
were selected because they represent materials of distinctly different electrooptic behavior. Composition 9565 is substantially
more transparent than either of compositions 7065 or 12040. This
is most noticeable in the blue end of the spectrum where absorption and light scattering predominate. Both compositions 7065
and 12040 are ferroelectric and hence possess domain walls which
produce index of refraction discontinuities and light scattering
from within the material. The tetragonal phase composition 12040
is more transparent than the rhombohedral 7065 composition. All
samples were measured in the virgin state.

    Electrooptic Properties. The electrooptic properties of the
PLZT materials are intimately related to their ferroelectric
properties. Consequently, varying the ferroelectric polarization
with an electric field such as in a hysteresis loop, produces a
change in the optical properties of the ceramic. In addition, the
magnitude of the observed electrooptic effect is dependent on both
the strength and direction of the electric field.
    PLZT ceramics display optically uniaxial properties on a
microscopic scale, and also on a macroscopic scale when polarized
with an electric field. In uniaxial crystals there is one unique
symmetry axis, the optic axis (co-linear with the ferroelectric
polarization vector in ceramic PLZT), which possesses different
optical properties than the other two orthogonal axes. That is,
light traveling in a direction along the optic axis and vibrating
in a direction perpendicular to it encounters a different index of
refraction (n_o) than light traveling in a direction $90°$ to the
optic axis and vibrating parallel to it (n_e). The absolute difference between the two indices is defined as the birefringence;
i.e., $n_e - n_o = \Delta n$. In ceramic materials where a statistical
array of randomly oriented crystallites exist, the macroscopic or
effective birefringence is designated by $\overline{\Delta n}$. On a macroscopic
scale, $\overline{\Delta n}$ is equal to zero before electrical poling and has some
finite value after poling, depending on the composition and the
degree of polarization. The $\overline{\Delta n}$ value is a meaningful quantity
in that it is related to the optical phase retardation in the
material.
    Linearly polarized light, on entering the electrically ener-
gized ceramic, is resolved into two perpendicular components whose
vibration directions are defined by the crystallographic axes of
the crystallites acting as one optical entity. Because of the
different refractive indices, n_e and n_o, the propagation velocity
of the two components will be different within the material and
will result in a phase shift called retardation. The total re-
tardation Γ is a function of both $\overline{\Delta n}$ and the optical path length
t (generally, t is the plate thickness) according to the relation-
ship of $\Gamma = \overline{\Delta n} t$. When sufficient voltage is applied to the ceramic, a halfwave retardation is achieved for one component rel-
ative to the other. The net result is one of rotating the vibra-

tion direction of the linearly polarized light by 90°, thus allowing it to be transmitted by the second (crossed) polarizer in the
ON condition. Switching of the electrooptic ceramic from a state
of zero retardation to halfwave retardation will create an ON/OFF
light shutter. Selective color filtering of white light may be
achieved by extending the retardation beyond half wavelength.

Three common types of electrooptic effects are illustrated
in Figure 8; i.e., quadratic and linear birefringence and memory
scattering. Also included in the figure is a typical setup required for generating each effect along with the observed behavior shown in terms of light intensity output (I) as a function of
electric field (E).

The first and most widely applied of all of the electrooptic
responses is the quadratic (Kerr) effect. It is generally displayed by those materials which are essentially cubic phase (composition 1) but are located close to the ferroelectric rhombohedral or tetragonal phases. The designation for this effect is
derived from the quadratic dependence of Δn on electric field;
i.e., $\Delta n = kE^2$. These materials, by virtue of their natural
cubic symmetry, do not possess permanent polarization and are not
optically birefringent in their quiescent state. As such, they
contribute no optical retardation to an incoming polarized light
beam; however, when an electric field is applied to the material,
an electric polarization (and consequently, birefringence) is induced in the material and retardation is observed between crossed
polarizers (called an ON state). On removing the electric field,
the material relaxes again to its cubic state and is in the OFF
condition. Relaxation times to the OFF condition vary with composition but generally range from one to 100 microseconds. Turn
ON times are of the same magnitude and ON-OFF ratios as high as
5000 to one have been measured. Applications for the quadratic
effect include shutters, optical gates, displays, spectral filters, light modulators and variable density windows.

A second type of behavior existing in the PLZT's is the linear (Pockels) effect which is generally found in high coercive
field, tetragonal materials (composition 3). This effect is so
named because of the linear relationship between Δn and electric
field. The truly linear, nonhysteretic character of this effect
has been found to be intrinsic to the material and not due to
domain reorientation processes which occur in the quadratic and
memory materials. The linear materials possess permanent rem-
anent polarization; however, in this case the material is switched
to its saturation remanence, and it remains in that state. Optical information is extracted from the ceramic by the action of an
electric field which causes linear changes in the birefringence,
but in no case is there polarization reversal in the material.
The experimental setup for observing this effect, as seen in
Figure 8, is identical to that for the quadratic response, except
that the PLZT plate is prepoled to saturation remanence before
using. Applications include modulators and spectral filters;
however, no devices have yet emerged utilizing this effect.

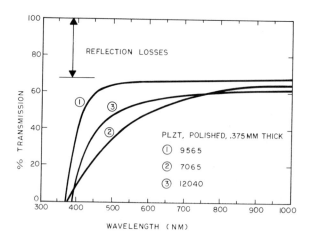

Figure 7. Optical transmission characteristics of three selected PLZT compositions

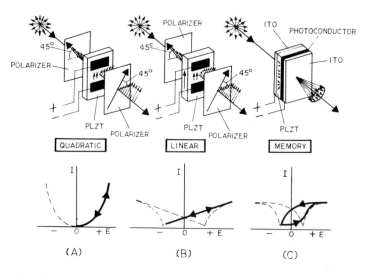

Figure 8. Operational configurations and typical light output responses of (A) quadratic (B) linear, and (C) memory PLZT materials; the heavy accented portions of the response curves indicate the usable range.

A third type of electrooptic behavior which is employed almost exclusively for displays is that of electrically controlled light scattering in a memory material. This effect, as observed in the Cerampic (ceramic picture) device, was first reported in 1972 by Smith and Land (17). The experimental arrangement involved in observing this effect is given in Figure 8. No polarizers are employed since it is predominantly due to light scattering from domains (areas of like polarization) within the material. The orientation of these domains are electrically alterable; and because light is preferentially scattered along the polar direction of the domains, the light transmitted by the PLZT plate is also electrically controllable. In addition, local areas can be polarized to different levels leading to an ability for storing images with a gray scale capability and a resolution of at least 30 line pairs per millimeter. Once a given local area is switched to a specific polarization state, it is permanently locked in until it is electrically switched to a new state or the material is heated above its Curie point (thermally depoled) which erases all of the polarization states. The means by which local areas are switched independently of each other is provided by the photoconductor layer sandwiched between one of the transparent ITO (indium-tin oxide) electrodes and the PLZT. When light impinges on the photoconductor layer, it reduces its resistivity by several orders of magnitude, electrons from the voltage source are transferred from the ITO electrode to the PLZT and the local polarization is switched to a new state. Erasure of the total image is performed by flooding the plate with light while the voltage is applied in the positive saturation direction. The maximum contrast ratio may be as high as 100 to 1.

In addition to the above three effects, there are two others; i.e., memory birefringence and depolarization scattering, which exist in the PLZT materials and have been proposed for device applications. These are described in reference 5.

Applications

Modes of Operation. Figure 8 also illustrates the two basic modes of operation used in electrooptic devices; i.e., the transverse and longitudinal modes. In the transverse mode, the electric field is applied in a direction normal to the light propagation direction while in the longitudinal mode, the field is applied along the light propagation direction. In general, the transverse mode of operation is most effective for variable birefringence devices, and the longitudinal mode is better suited for variable light scattering devices. Also, color effects can be produced with variable birefringence whereas they cannot with scattering. Variable birefringent devices always require the use of polarized light; however, scattering devices may or may not necessitate polarized light. It should be recognized that in order to produce polarized light from an incandescent white light source there is a substantial loss in light intensity. In the case of an ideal, linear polarizer, this loss amounts to 50% of the incident light; but this loss increases to approximately 70% with the use of plastic sheet polarizers such as Polaroid's HN32 material.

In transverse mode devices such as shutters or variable density filters, the electric field is generally applied by means of suitable electrode pattern on one or both major surfaces of a polished plate of material. Since viewing is accomplished through the gap between the positive and negative electrodes, it follows that the activating voltage can be reduced, for a given overall viewing area, by reducing the gap width and increasing the total number of gaps. This results in a number of narrow, interdigital electrodes on a given plate. By placing the device out of the focal plane of the optical system, the fine electrodes (~ 0.04mm wide) are virtually invisible, and image quality through the device is excellent. In contrast to the longitudinal mode, the transverse mode produces larger electrooptic effects; and in the activated or ON state, the material is optically clear with essentially no scattering. Devices utilizing this mode may or may not exhibit memory, depending on the composition.

In the longitudinal mode, voltage is applied through the thickness of the plate necessitating the use of transparent electrodes such as tin oxide or ITO. Since this mode generally aligns the macroscopic optic axis of the material parallel to the direction of viewing, optical birefringent effects are minimal. In this mode, the strength of the electrical switching field is dependent on the thickness of the plate and the specific composition selected, but is independent of the area.

Thermal/Flash Protective Device. In 1975 Sandia Laboratories of Albuquerque, New Mexico, began the design and development of PLZT goggles for the U.S. Air Force to provide protection for aircraft personnel from flashblindness caused by a nuclear explosion (18). At that time, the technology for producing such a device was in its infancy and many of the techniques required for its development and manufacture were non-existent. In the next three years, several new technologies such as PLZT polishing and electroding, high performance polarizers, lens bonding and the fabrication of specialized electronics were all developed and put into practice. The final product, officially designated as the EEU-2/P Flashblindness Flyers Goggles, is shown in Figure 9. It possesses several advantages over its predecessor, a liquid photochromic system, among which are included (1) smaller size, (2) less weight, (3) solid state, (4) faster response and (5) higher portability. It has been in production for the last two years and is the first PLZT device to reach this stage.

The flashblindness goggle is basically a transverse-mode shutter of the configuration shown in Figure 8(A). The shutter is

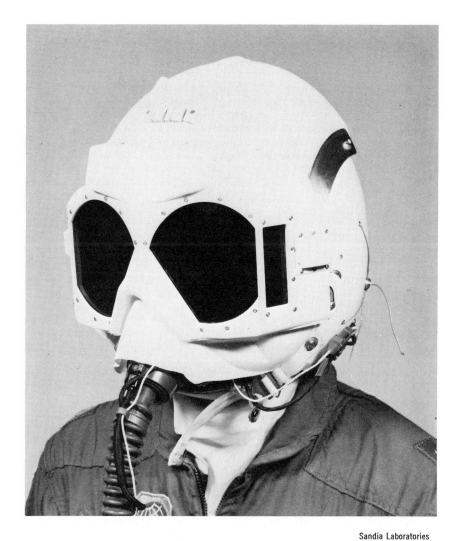

Sandia Laboratories

Figure 9.   PLZT Thermal/Flash Protective Goggle developed by Sandia Laboratories for the U.S. Air Force

operated in the fully open or energized state until a light haz-
ard is detected by means of sensors mounted behind the viewing
lens. When this occurs, the PLZT energizing voltage is rapidly
discharged causing the goggles to revert to the closed state.
When the threat is removed, the PLZT is re-energized and the open
state is restored. The open and closed states of the device have
typically 20% and 0.006% transmission respectively. Closure time
is less than 150 microseconds.

Data Recorder. The second PLZT device to reach the production state (1979) is a data display recorder manufactured by Bell
and Howell of Pasadena, California. This device is shown in Figure 10. The CEC HR-2000 Datagraph works on a principle not previously used in analog data recording; i.e., a digitally controlled electrooptic shutter using polarized light and a PLZT ceramic plate as the electrooptic material (19). By selectively
passing or blocking light through a linear array of hundreds of
tiny light gates or shutters, each of which is controlled by dri-
ver electronics, the input data signals are accurately reproduced.
Light which passes through the light gates impinges upon direct
print recording paper to record data waveforms with high fidelity
and accuracy. The operational setup of this transverse-mode device is the same as that described in Figure 8(A).

At the heart of the recorder is the array of light gates composed of a number of PLZT plates containing vacuum deposited electrodes spaced 0.0125 inches apart, thus providing high resolution.
By using this type of fixed, digitally controlled solid state
array, the data recorder has eliminated such problems as linear-
ity, beam deflection, tangential error, overshoot and inertia
which limit present galvanometer and CRT recording devices. The
instrument has a frequency response from dc to 5 kHz sine wave or
10 kHz square wave and a recording speed of 0.01 to 129 inches of
paper per second.

Stereo-Viewing Device. This device, now being sold under the
name of Megavision, has recently been developed by Megatek Corporation of San Diego, California. It makes possible true stereoscopic three-dimensional viewing of images on both vector refresh and
raster scan computer graphic displays. The device is shown in
Figure 11. It consists of a pair of lightweight (1.5 oz.) viewing
glasses, each lens of which is separately electronically controlled through a small cable to a belt-mounted backup unit. Each
lens is essentially an independently controlled transverse-mode
shutter of the type described in Figure 8(A). The shutters are
synchronized to an alternating pair of displayed images so that
only the left eye sees the left-eye view and the right eye the
right-eye view. The views are alternated at a rate more than 30
Hz for each lens, allowing the observer to perceive a single,
stereoscopic image with a life-like sensation of object depth.
Some applications of this device are flight simulators and train-

Figure 10.   Datagraph display recorder developed by Bell and Howell

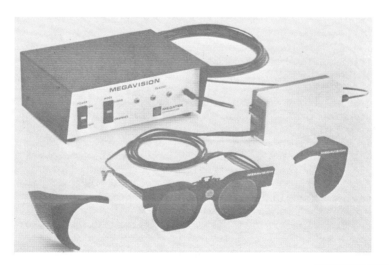

Megatek Corporation

Figure 11.   Stereo-viewing system developed by Megatek Corporation

ers, air traffic control, medical imaging, scientific modeling, radar and sonar displays and contour mapping.

Eye Safety Devices. Personnel eye safety devices such as the electronic welding helmet, inspection goggles and safety flip-down glasses mounted on a hard hat are some devices that are in the latter stages of development at the Ceramic Products department of Motorola, Inc. in Albuquerque, New Mexico. All of these devices operate in a manner very similar to that of the flashblindness goggles developed by Sandia Laboratories. They are transverse-mode shutter devices assembled in a configuration as described in Figure 8(A). An example of the electronic welding helmet is shown in Figure 12. The light sensors and power supply are mounted externally to the PLZT shutters which act as the variable density filter plate. When an arc is struck or some other similarly intense light source is activated, the sensors detect this change in light level and remove the voltage from the shutters, causing them to instantaneously darken to a shade previously set by the operator. When the arc is interrupted, the shutters quickly and automatically reactivate to their full ON condition. Since this automatic action eliminates the necessity of raising and lowering the helmet, the mask can be worn in the down position at all times, thus increasing productivity and preventing accidental eye burns from neighboring welding operations. A wide range of filter plates from shade 4 (5.2% transmittance) to shade 14 (0.0004%) are available.

Image Storage Devices. Research and development activities are continuing at Sandia Laboratories in Albuquerque, New Mexico, on image storage devices utilizing PLZT ceramics. The Cerampic device has received extensive study for the past several years and shows promise for image storage applications of the future. It is a longitudinal scattering mode device as described in Figure 8(C). Early designs utilized a photoconductor layer which provided the spatial variations of switching voltage when exposed to spatial variations of light intensity (usually through a contact negative) needed to produce the image in the ceramic. This photoconductor was subsequently eliminated by exposing the image with near UV light containing band gap (3.35 eV) or higher energy photons which produce a space charge field, thus aiding the domain switching process. Significant improvements in the sensitivity of the exposure and recording process were reported by Land and Peercy ([20]) through the use of ion implantation (hydrogen and helium) in the surface of the PLZT. Reductions in exposure energy by as much as 10,000 times have more recently been achieved through the co-implantation of argon and neon. Present exposure energy values of about 10 $\mu J/cm^2$ compare favorably with 100 $\mu J/cm^2$ required for fine-grained holographic film. An example of typical image quality is shown in Figure 13. The image in the ceramic (A) was obtained by contact exposure of a negative produced from the original photograph (B).

Motorola Incorporated

Figure 12.   Electronic welding helmet developed by Motorola Incorporated

Sandia Laboratories

Figure 13.   Example of image storage quality in memory PLZT 7065: (left) stored image and (right) original positive; ceramic device under development at Sandia Laboratories

Summary

The development of optical transparency in ferroelectric PLZT (lanthanum modified lead zirconate titanate) ceramics a decade ago has stimulated a considerable amount of interest in the nature of these materials, their electrooptic behavior and their application to electrooptic devices. Although some measure of optical transparency has now been achieved in other similar ferroelectric materials, rare-earth lanthanum oxide is unique in its ability to produce the highest quality material; and thus, it remains the standard of the industry. The ceramics are characterized by good electrical and optical properties, uniform grain size and microstructure, high electrooptic coefficients and excellent moisture resistance. Their unusual combination of properties have made them useful materials for such specific applications as nuclear flashblindness goggles, a data display recorder, a stereoviewing system, an electronic welding helmet and an image storage display device.

An estimate of the annual amount of lanthanum oxide presently being used in all PLZT applications is approximately 300Kg. This figure is conservatively projected to increase twenty-fold in the next five years as production volumes increase and new applications for these materials are realized.

Literature Cited

1. Haertling, G.H.; Land, C.E. J. Am. Ceram. Soc., 1971, 54, 1-11.
2. Okazaki, K.; Nagata, K. J. Am. Ceram. Soc., 1973, 56, 82-86.
3. Meitzler, A.H.; O'Bryan, H.M. Jr. Proc. IEEE, 1973, 61, 959-966.
4. Keve, E.T.; Annis, A.D. Ferroelectrics, 1973, 5, 77-89
5. Land, C.E.; Thacher, P.D.; Haertling, G.H., "Applied Solid State Science"; Academic Press, New York, 1974; p. 137-233.
6. Micheron, F.; Rouchon, J.M.; Vergnolle, M. Appl. Phys. Lett., 1974, 24, 605-607.
7. Drake, M.D. Applied Optics, 1974, 13, 347-352.
8. Maldonado, J.R.; Fraser, D.B.; Meitzler, A.H., "Advances in Image Pickup and Displays"; Academic Press, New York, 1975, p. 65-168.
9. Cutchen, J.T.; Harris, J.; Laguna, G. Applied Optics, 1975, 14, 1866-1873.
10. Roese, J.; Khalafalla, A. Ferroelectrics, 1976, 10, 47-51.
11. Land, C.E. Optical Engineering, 1978, 17, 317-326.
12. Samek, N.; Raymond, W. Proc. of the 25th Intl. Instr. Symp., 1979, 16, 485-500.
13. Hardtl, K.H.; Hennings, D. J. Am. Ceram. Soc., 1972, 55, 230-231.
14. Snow, G.S. J. Am. Ceram. Soc., 1973, 56, 91-96.
15. Haertling, G.H.; Land, C.E. Ferroelectrics, 1972, 3, 269-280.
16. Dungan, R.; Snow, G. Bull. Am. Ceram. Soc., 1977, 56, 781-782.
17. Smith, W.D.; Land, C.E. Appl. Phys. Lett., 1972, 20, 169-171.

18. Cutchen, J.T. Ferroelectrics, 1980, 27, 173-178.
19. Howes, P.A. Proc. of the 25th Intl. Instr. Symp., 1979, 16, 199-210.
20. Land, C.; Peercy, P. Appl. Phys. Lett., 1980, 37, 39-41.

RECEIVED December 19, 1980.

INDEX

INDEX

Jacket design by Carol Conway.
Production by Robin Giroux and Gabriele Glang.

Elements typeset by Service Composition Co., Baltimore, MD.
The book was printed and bound by The Maple Press Company, York, PA.